INDUSTRY AND
TECHNICAL PROGRESS

FACTORS GOVERNING THE SPEED OF
APPLICATION OF SCIENCE

BY

C. F. CARTER AND B. R. WILLIAMS

on behalf of the
Science and Industry Committee

LONDON
OXFORD UNIVERSITY PRESS
NEW YORK TORONTO
1957

Oxford University Press, Amen House, London E.C.4
GLASGOW NEW YORK TORONTO MELBOURNE WELLINGTON
BOMBAY CALCUTTA MADRAS KARACHI
CAPE TOWN IBADAN NAIROBI ACCRA SINGAPORE

Contents

Foreword

THIS book is written in the belief that the full and speedy application of science in industry is necessary to economic progress, and should indeed be one of the most important objectives of national policy. This being so, it is important to identify the hindrances to speedy application. Many people have already drawn attention to particular hindrances, but the three bodies which have sponsored this report did not consider that there was any up-to-date assessment of the problem which attempted to look at it as a whole, in all its variety and complexity. Hence the investigation which they undertook, and largely entrusted to us; an investigation which, through the great goodwill of many people in British industry, has yielded so much material that this book can only be a first impression and summary.

We did not expect to find any easy answers. No single measure like a remission of taxation, or a cutting of red tape, or an adoption of some particular form or size of industrial organization will suffice to open the way to a flood of new applications of science. We find that progressiveness in science and technology is not an optional extra which a firm can add to its existing qualities, but an expression of its general attitude and efficiency of management. Many applications of science require the coordinated advance of a whole chain of firms, and those which are indifferent to the need for technical progress may in fact delay far more than their own development. Behind all the factors affecting our study stands the question of the supply of able minds—managers, scientists, and technologists; and it will be seen that we are satisfied neither with the effectiveness of the British educational system in its work of selection and training, nor with the distribution of trained talent between industries and between firms.

To state these difficulties is not to be daunted by them, but they cannot be remedied unless they are first known and understood. We hope that this report will stimulate, not only the further examination of some of the difficulties, but the adoption of measures which offer a real hope of speeding up the rate of adoption of science. We are sure that there are many which could be devised; a national effort is needed, to which scientists, business men, and educationalists must all contribute.

The Science and Industry Committee was appointed by the Royal Society of Arts (whose full name is the Royal Society for the Encouragement of Arts, Manufactures and Commerce), by the British Association for the Advancement of Science, and by the Nuffield Foundation. It gratefully acknowledges that the preparation and publication of this book have been made possible by grants from the Board of Trade and the Department of Scientific and Industrial Research under the

Conditional Aid scheme for the use of counterpart funds derived from United States economic aid. The committee, as well as its staff, has taken an active part in the work, but it deputed the writing of this book to us as its Directors of Research, leaving to us the detailed responsibility, and regarding its own function as being to endorse the whole as worthy of publication. We in our turn acknowledge that without the constant help and support generously and freely given by our committee members, we should have made little progress.

C. F. CARTER
B. R. WILLIAMS

Belfast and Keele,
  September 1956

Chapter 1

THE NEED FOR THIS INQUIRY

WHY should there be any reason for concern about the speed of application of science in British industry? This is a question which deserves a more precise answer than it usually gets. The desirability of the fullest and speediest application of science is commonly regarded as self-evident, either because it is identified with Progress or because it is considered as a condition of fitness for survival in a competitive world. We begin by trying to define our own answer, and to relate it to the special problems of the United Kingdom.

A country becomes richer either by increasing the rate of exploitation, per head of population, of its natural resources (of materials and human labour), or by improving the manner of that exploitation so as to fulfil human needs better at less cost. The United Kingdom has to maintain a large population on small natural resources, and it does so by producing complex and advanced products, many of which can be exchanged overseas for the products which it lacks at home. The use of science and technology is, from one point of view, simply the exploitation of the natural resource of brains to make up the deficiency in other resources. In this sense it is the necessary condition for increasing prosperity in a 'mature' country which has no vacant land or large unexploited reserves of materials or labour.

It does not follow, of course, that science must be exploited 'at all costs'. It is all too easy in an inquiry such as ours to fall into the habit of regarding all applications of science and technology as good. Not all such applications multiply wealth, nor, of course, is the multiplication of wealth the sole aim of human existence. The removal of a hindrance to the application of science might make Britain richer, and yet the means of removal might be worse than forgoing the riches. Many people think, for instance, that freedom—even the freedom to be inefficient and unprogressive—is worth more than material progress; or that scientific advance can be too dearly won if it means the decay of the humanities. Such implications seem remote enough to be ignored when one is thinking of the installation of a particular new machine in a particular factory, but they may be very real when one views as a whole the broad advance of science and technology. This study, however, is concerned with facts, and not with policies—with the hindrances to scientific application, and not with the question whether some of those hindrances are justified or a 'lesser evil'; and we have in any case little doubt that great advantages can be obtained from the fuller exploitation of science without loss to other values of human existence.

A sense of urgency is often brought into discussions about the use of science in British industry by quoting examples of the way in which British industrial practice differs from that of the U.S.A. This preoccupation with a particular international comparison is not always healthy. For one thing (as we shall point out later, p. 11), the best industrial practice must be discovered after examining the circumstances of each country: the differences between a British and an American industry can often be explained by saying that each is doing the sensible thing in its own circumstances. Then, Britain is one of the richest countries in the world—over 90 per cent. of mankind live in countries with a lower average income—and it might be thought that there is ground for pride in her achievement, rather than for shame at her inability always to be top of the form. Finally, there are features of the abounding productivity of the U.S.A. which other nations should not copy even if they could—for instance, her profligate use of irreplaceable natural resources. Some people would add that the pace of United States technical advance goes side by side with a pace of living and a ruthlessness of competition which other nations ought not to copy—that, in fact, there is no evidence that the American is happier for his extra capacity to produce wealth. This argument is a further reminder of the possible importance of non-economic criteria.

On what solid ground, then, do we rest our belief that this book deals with an urgent and important problem? First, in the present situation of the U.K., increases in production are closely dependent on the application of scientific and technical knowledge. Second, a high rate of increase of production is desirable not only for its own sake, but also to give relief from the overstrain which has affected the British economy since the war. Third, the special position of Britain in international trade makes it dangerous for the country to fall behind the technical progress of its competitors. The cost of technical stagnation would not simply be stagnation in the standard of living : it would be a falling back, a mounting up of economic and political problems which would become worse the longer they were neglected. The United Kingdom's position has, and will continue to have, something of the nightmare quality of running up a descending escalator.

The dependence of increases of production on the application of science is partly a matter of the composition of final output, and partly of the way in which things are produced. The richer a country becomes, the more complex are the demands of its citizens. A desire to progress at six miles an hour can be satisfied by breeding a horse, and the care of horses is a matter of experience and tradition. To travel at sixty miles an hour needs the railway and the automobile—the first originally the product of engineering experience of a crude 'rule-of-thumb' kind, the second drawing on a good deal of more advanced scientific knowledge. But to travel at six hundred miles an hour requires an aeroplane whose development strains the resources of numerous complex sciences and technologies. The luxuries of yesterday which become the necessities of today are often goods of a high scientific content—nylon stockings, laminated plastics, television sets, soapless detergents, colour films, and so on.

Even without this advance of consumer demand, the application of science would still be necessary to provide for the fuller satisfaction of older needs. An outstanding example is fuel and power, where there is a prospect of avoiding the difficulty of mining enough coal by turning to the use of nuclear energy. As the easily-won resources of raw materials become exhausted or insufficient to meet expanding world needs, science must provide substitutes; and the 'ersatz' product, despised yesterday, becomes the equal or superior of its natural rival today—synthetic rubber is a good example. The relative scarcities of the factors of production vary from decade to decade, and technical progress is constantly needed to overcome the latest shortage. 'Automation', for instance, is sometimes the response to labour shortage, and sometimes to the need for full and flexible use of expensive capital equipment.

The other side of the dependence of increases of production on science is the rapid growth of industries with a strong scientific background. Over the period since 1948, for instance, the chemical industry has grown more than any other major manufacturing industry, and high rates of growth are also shown by industries such as electrical engineering and the manufacture of synthetic fibres. On the other hand, 'traditional' or 'craft' industries have for the most part had rates of growth much below the average. But although (as the previous two paragraphs show) there is a *general* presumption that increased production will require increased scientific application, there must at this stage be no judgement of cause and effect for particular industries. Stagnation in the cotton industry, for instance, may be the cause rather than the effect of a failure to show striking technical advance.

The overstrain of the British economy is not directly traceable to a failure to expand.[1] In 1956 the country was producing goods and services to a volume some 40 per cent. greater than in the 'good' year 1937—no bad record after a period which included six years of war. But the demands on the product had increased also, partly because of the less favourable position of the U.K. in international trade, and partly because of the great increase in peacetime defence expenditure; and the population to be supported had grown by four millions. The consequence of these factors was that the amount available per head for non-defence expenditure had grown, since 1937, by less than 20 per cent. Because of the higher level of investment and of communal spending,

---

[1] The overstrain is often traced to excessive haste in setting up the Welfare State, but this is a doubtful proposition; nor is the increase in the proportion of old people so far an important factor.

the volume of consumer goods and services bought per head ('consumer expenditure at constant prices') had increased by less again—perhaps no more than 10 per cent. The overall increase in the productivity of labour can be assessed at about 17 per cent., but this includes occupations, like teaching or hairdressing, whose 'productivity' cannot greatly change, and also manufacturing industries showing much greater changes.

It is natural, therefore, that people's hopes about their standard of living—based on a knowledge of increasing production and productivity—should show some contrast with the very modest increase in what their money will buy. The consequent dissatisfaction, fed by stories of the abundant wealth of the U.S.A., increases the intensity of the struggle for a larger share of the national income, which is part of the cause of inflation. Successive Governments have tried to slow down inflation by restricting the demands of one or another group of claimants on the national income. Every restrictive solution, however, has undesirable side-effects: by far the best way of lessening the strain is to speed up the rate of growth of production, so that the demands of exports, defence, and the rising population can all be met and still give an obvious and tangible reward for higher productivity. We have already pointed out relations between the growth of production and the application of science; but in the relief of the economy from excessive demands, science and technology have a special part in helping to save in the use of scarce resources.

In international trade the U.K. lives mainly by importing raw materials and food and exporting manufactures. She has long had to face a loss of markets for the simpler manufactured products (such as cotton cloth), since developing countries, wanting to share the benefits of industrialization, choose these simpler products for their first experiments in protected industrial growth. But the U.K. has so far managed to find developing markets in more complex or specialized products to replace some of those she has lost. This has been an uphill task, and in fact the troubles of British foreign trade (which can be traced back to the First World War and earlier) arise largely from the growing need for imports and the increasing difficulty of selling exports to countries in the process of industrialization. Manufactured exports must be sold against the competition of countries having good technical resources, and in some cases having also the advantage of lower labour costs and lower taxation.

The penalty for failure to meet this stern competition is either an inability to maintain the volume of imports, which would have to be cut back by regulation, or a need for a further devaluation of sterling. In either case the standard of living would have to be reduced—and only by its reduction could the foreign trade problem be solved. But the forces resisting that reduction are very powerful, and the failure of competitive power would create great internal economic and political stress, besides damaging the 'credit standing' of sterling in its international uses. There is no trick of Government policy which can painlessly keep British exports competitive. The only good solution is that they should be competitive on their own merits. This means first that productivity must rise so that export prices can be low enough despite a rising standard of living for those who produce the exports, and despite the expensive defence commitments of the U.K. Secondly, it means that the technical ingenuity of British exports must be such that they are, in some substantial lines, preferred to the products of competitors. Both these objectives depend on the speedy application of new scientific and technical knowledge, and it will be noted that it is necessary, not merely to run fast, but to run faster than one's competitors—a strenuous undertaking. It is true that the inability to buy American goods, due to the dollar shortage, gives some natural protection against the technical advance of the U.S.A.—no competitor can be outstandingly successful unless it is willing to be a great importer or a great lender. Nevertheless there can be few export industries in which the technological advance of competitors is not a matter of concern; and the aircraft industry gives, in the Viscount, a striking example of the prizes to be won by those who are ahead of the world.

For all these reasons, therefore, the hope of orderly progress to a higher standard of living depends on a rapid industrial application of science and technology. But if this is admitted, is there anything more to say? Are the hindrances to that application already known, so that the task is simply to find means of removing them, and to screw up the resolution of Governments to take the necessary measures? The Committee soon found that almost every member had friends who knew the real hindrances to the application of science, but that unfortunately the hindrances they named were not the same, and the measures they proposed for improving matters were diverse and sometimes inconsistent. The early inquiries yielded some impressive examples of the enthusiasm of the British for disparaging their own country; it was often taken for granted that British industry is backward, in relation not only to the U.S.A., but also to industry in Germany, Switzerland, and other countries. There was, however, no disposition to belittle British pure science—the popular view seemed to be that, as a matter of course, British scientists had big ideas and British manufacturers let the chance of exploiting them slip into foreign hands.

It seemed to us possible that we might here be facing some of those beliefs which, having a foundation in fact, are accepted as generally true without a search for further evidence. The twin beliefs that British manufacturers are less progressive than American, and British workers lazier, can be traced back for more than half a century, and they have gained in acceptance as the disparity in wealth between the two countries

has become more obvious. In 1902 Mr. Alfred Mosely took a 'productivity team' of twenty-three trade union officers to the U.S.A.[1] Mr.
Mosely's Commission was accompanied by a special correspondent from
The Times, and many of the comments of that newspaper might equally
have been taken from the productivity discussions of the last ten years:

'. . . a very large aggregate of smaller English businesses is carried on in
a stupidly conservative fashion, with antiquated machinery, traditional
modes of conduct, and methods which ignore the scientific advance of
recent years' (leading article, 28 November 1902).

'English manufacturers have been too prone to say in effect to those who
dealt with them, "If you don't like the articles turned out by our present
machines and processes you may go to some one else, for it is not worth
our while to alter them" ' (16 December 1902).

'The American manufacturer realises the supreme importance of order
and system in the factory, and accordingly sees not only that every operation is simplified and subdivided to the form in which it can be most
efficiently performed, but also that each worker is always fully supplied
with the kind of work which he or she can do best. . . . Probably he has
few, if any, machines that are utterly unknown in England, but he is more
determined and wholesale in his use of mechanical appliances generally,
and runs them for the utmost he can get out of them. Why, for instance,
are British ironmasters content with a weekly yield of, say, 900 tons from
each of their blast-furnaces, whereas the American, by using a blast of
twice the pressure general in England, together with other improvements
in design and operation, succeeds in getting 3,000 tons or more?' (26
December 1902).

The belief that 'Britain invents and foreigners apply' is also an old
one. Thus, in 1919 the great economist Alfred Marshall referred to two
recent reports as recording 'numerous cases in which members of the
small band of British scientific men have made revolutionary discoveries in science; but yet the chief fruits of their work have been
reaped by businesses in Germany and other countries, where industry
and science have been in close touch with one another'.[2] One such
case was referred to by Professor W. J. Pope, who then held the chair
of chemistry at Cambridge, in the following terms:

'It is interesting to enquire why this country, which had in its hands the
natural dyestuffs, which commanded cheaper raw materials than any
other nation, and whose chemists produced the first coal tar dyes both in
the laboratory and on a large scale, allowed these enormous assets to pass
into Continental hands. The answer is simple; during the past fifty years
hardly any English public man of affairs possessing any knowledge of
scientific principles has arisen, and no Government Department having
the faintest interest in scientific industry has existed. Developments of

---

[1] See E. H. Phelps Brown and S. J. Handfield-Jones in *Oxford Economic
Papers*, 1952, pp. 266–307.
[2] *Industry and Trade*, Macmillan, p. 102 n.

science, both theoretical and practical, have been greeted with a murmur of surprise, but no authoritative body has been deputed to watch them and to consider how they could be best utilised to the national advantage. Our Continental competitors, less wealthy and more necessitous, had either to seize upon and exploit this British weakness or to remain in penurious obscurity . . .'[1]

We do not know whether the complaints made earlier in the century were justified; but a seed of doubt about the wisdom of crude international comparisons may be planted by the observation that in 1900 American incomes were apparently greater than British by a large margin, just as they are today.

Then and now, discussions on technical progressiveness tend to speak with a fine generality of 'the American', 'the German', or 'the British' manufacturer, illustrating their judgements with examples from particular trades. The judgements may be correct, but they are in no way proved to be correct by the examples. Every country has backward industries; to find all industries equally progressive would be as odd as finding that all the pupils in a school form were 'equal first'. There is no ground for expecting the same industries to be progressive in different countries. Therefore it must be expected at all times that there will be some British industries which are technically behind their American counterparts, and there is no difficulty in finding some which are in advance. We early decided that at all costs we would be sparing in generalizations about British industry.

From the early discussions of the Committee, from the literature, and from personal contacts we soon confirmed our impression that there is a great variety of opinion about which hindrances to technical progress are important. Those mentioned included—

(a) The failure of pure scientists to communicate their ideas in a way in which industry can understand them.
(b) The crushing weight of taxation, either robbing firms of the money which they could have spent on technical advance, or fatally weakening the incentive to progress.
(c) The difficulty of raising new capital from private savers.
(d) The restraining, distorting, and time-wasting effect of Government controls.
(e) The enervating influence of security, full employment, and sellers' markets.
(f) The disturbing influence of insecurity, political or economic, making it hard to plan far ahead.
(g) The excess of small firms, technical progress being found more often in the larger units.

[1] *Science and the Nation*, ed. A. C. Seward, Cambridge University Press, 1917, pp. 11–12.

(*h*) The undue place of large firms, competitive inventiveness finding its true home in small firms.

(*i*) The smallness of the British home market.

(*j*) The inefficiency and lack of training of British management.

(*k*) The social approval which attaches to pure rather than to applied science.

Obviously these could not all be valid generalizations—even if we admitted *any* generalization to be valid: yet each is plausible enough in relation to some firm or trade. But is the list complete? One could think, *a priori*, of one or two other possible hindrances, and it might be that others had escaped the notice both of ourselves and of our informants. And if five or six of the influences were operating simultaneously on some firm, which, if any, would be found dominant? Only in Utopia would the course of scientific application run smoothly and swiftly, without hindrance; obviously one wants to know where the removal of an obstacle will yield the biggest and quickest results—to know (in the inelegant wartime phrase) the key bottleneck.

It seemed to us at this stage only honest to admit our double ignorance. First, we had not got the measure of the problem: we did not know how much variety lay behind the popular generalizations: the whole matter seemed to us still ill-defined and vague. Second, we were aware of no sufficient evidence enabling us to sort out the true causes of such failure to apply scientific knowledge as might appear. Furthermore, we had a strong suspicion that some of our informants were ignorant too—or, rather, that the validity of their knowledge was much more closely limited to the particular industries or areas of their experience than they were prepared to admit.

We could not therefore be satisfied merely to select, on *a priori* grounds, particular areas of the problem which deserve minute study. We felt it necessary to attempt to see the matter whole—to make an investigation not tied down by preconceived ideas, but designed to provide a general view of the whole vast and complex problem. We thought that the interrelation and relative importance of the different factors might be quite as significant as the study of each in isolation: and this has been confirmed by our experience. Some of the factors which might influence the rate of adoption of scientific knowledge have changed their nature greatly in the last few years—Government control is a good example. It is therefore likely that some assessments of the matter, fair and true enough when they were made, are still being accepted as valid in quite different circumstances; it was thus necessary for us to tie our work closely to current industrial realities. These are the reasons which led the Committee to rest its conclusions in part on industrial case-studies of a broad and general, rather than a narrow and intensive, type.

At the end of the road we are as impressed as we were at the beginning by the immense complexity of the forces impelling or hindering the application in the ordinary business of life of the products of man's scientific ingenuity. Any general statement is dangerous, because it can have only a partial and limited application even within a few firms, let alone within the heterogeneous mass called 'British industry'. Nevertheless, in all the complexity there is discernible a pattern, in which some factors linked together stand out as clearly important, while others often mentioned recede into a lesser importance. While discouraging, therefore, the easy and partial generalization, we do not regard the subject of this report as being so complex that it can never be reduced to order.

Chapter 2

THE BACKGROUND AND THE PROBLEM

THIS study was undertaken in a world which, by any past standard, has been prospering. It is a world in which the principal industrial countries have mostly been working at full stretch for a considerable period, and in which there have been impressive advances in productivity and wealth. It is, of course, a world in which most of the human race still live in great poverty, and the future is darkened by many problems and uncertainties. Nevertheless, the whole situation, not only in its material factors but in its 'feel' or psychology, is much more hopeful and expansive than in the 1930's. Our conclusions relate to this hopeful world of the 1950's. 'The spirit of industry is progressive, expansionist and free. . . .'[1] The crust that has been lying on this country for thirty or forty years is cracking and breaking up. . . .'[2] We found almost complete unanimity . . . that this country is embarked on a venture in economic expansion which has gone beyond the point of no return.'[3] It is difficult to imagine statements which contrast more with the pessimism of a world in economic depression. We have no doubt that many of our conclusions and much of our emphasis would have been quite different if this survey had been made twenty years earlier.

But (though scientists sometimes find it difficult to accept the tiresome fact) even under full employment all good ideas cannot be and should not be exploited. The fact that a product or a process is new and improved is no sufficient reason for adopting it. The male sex does not cast away its suits of clothes half-worn because the tailors have devised a new cut, and husbands sometimes feel justified in criticizing their wives for the wasteful following of fashion. Of course, the passion for trying something new is far from being wholly wasteful; it ensures that the good ideas are tried promptly and quickly appreciated. The willingness to give new things a trial may be a necessary condition of further advance.

The industrial equivalent of an unwillingness to cast away a half-worn suit is an unwillingness to adopt an innovation unless it yields a sufficient return on the costs of scrapping plant before it is worn out, disposing of outmoded stocks, and tooling up for the new product or process. This means that the application of new knowledge must, in many industries, take place discontinuously, and that in some the period between opportunities for change may be very long. Indeed, a wholly

[1] Sir Harry Pilkington. [2] Mr. R. H. Fry. [3] *Manchester Guardian* staff, all in *Manchester Guardian Survey of Industry, Trade and Finance*, 1956.

desirable technical improvement may *never* be worth adopting. It would, for instance, be technically advantageous to rebuild railways to a wider gauge, thus making it possible to use larger rolling-stock and bigger motive-power units, but it is almost inconceivable that the advantage could ever be sufficient to pay the cost of the alteration. Many people suppose that an automatic loom must necessarily be more advanced, 'modern', and efficient than a non-automatic loom; yet there are many kinds of work for which its advantage is so far too slight to justify the cost of displacing older methods.

If all developments are not to be exploited, how is a choice to be made? The answer is that the economic purpose of innovation is to make a better use of the limited resources available to mankind, and the value of a particular improvement depends on the scarcity, at the particular time and place, of the resources which it saves, compared with the scarcity of the resources which it uses. The generation of electricity from atomic power is more worth while in a country (like Ireland) with little coal or water-power, than in a country (like Britain) with plenty of coal; and is probably more worth while in Britain than in the U.S.A., which has easily worked coal and also oil and natural gas. The American farmer has dear labour and cheap land; to him, the most important kind of technical progress is the development of machines which save labour, and his best indicator of progress is production per man-year. The British farmer has much cheaper labour, but land is scarce; his object is appropriately the growing of a bigger crop on each acre of land, and his best indicator of progress is production per acre. British production of crops per acre is often higher than American, and production per man-year equal or lower; but it is impossible to say from this that one country is more efficient than the other—each is adapting itself to the relative scarcities of the factors of production.

This point is worth stressing, because the long-standing habit of bowing the knee to the technical superiority of the U.S.A. tends to make people assume that failure to copy that country is synonymous with backwardness. Britain has consequently taken over, in the course of its numerous comparisons with American practice, the idea that progress is measured by the productivity of labour—an idea which is a plausible first approximation in a country well endowed with land and raw materials. But it may be worth while to adopt an idea which *reduces* the apparent productivity of some workers, if thereby some even scarcer factor is saved.

The elusive ideas of 'efficiency' and 'technical progress' therefore imply the balanced use of the different factors of production—different kinds of labour, materials, machines, factory space, and so on. The right balance depends on the *relative* scarcities of the factors, and will vary with every change in the relative scarcities. Examples of the failure to obtain a right balance in the present conditions of the U.K. can be found in this report: for instance, the lack of attention to the science of using scientists (p. 104). The balance to be obtained should be, of course, the best possible within the framework of the institutions and values of society. Thus, a new machine may be worth using if there is continuous three-shift working, but the restrictions on work at night by women may (if the work is not suitable for men) prevent its adoption.

The rewards of technical change accrue over a period, and it is therefore necessary to ask not only 'Will this pay off?' but 'At what time will it pay off?' It is difficult to get men to do things which, however desirable they are, only yield their fruits very slowly and after a long time; this is why afforestation, for which one must think in centuries, is often a Government rather than a private function. A monopoly well placed to withstand public criticism (if any such exists) can perhaps lay plans for ten or twenty years ahead, and wait for their fruition. But even bodies like the Coal Board and the Transport Commission, which certainly undertake long-term planning, are in frequent difficulty because of the pressure for quick results. A small and hard-pressed firm in a highly competitive industry may be forced to use a time-horizon of a few months. If a change does not pay off at once, the existence of the firm may be in peril; it sees as far as the end of its order book, and little further.

The scope for change is limited if one demands quick results. Therefore it would be expected that an increase in security, making longer-term planning safer and easier, would open up fresh possibilities of technical advance. But the other side of this is that security may be soporific; and it would thus also be expected that any arrangements which (whatever their intentions) have as their part effect the protection of one producer from the new ideas of another would both lessen the incentive to adopt new products or processes, and slow down the spread of ideas from one firm to another. The soporific agent may be an agreement about prices and trade terms, or the division of markets; it may equally be the action of Governments—thus, the British motor manufacturers have the assistance both of a tariff and of restrictions on dollar imports in avoiding worry about German or American technical advance. They would claim, of course, that any effect this may have is outweighed by the advantages of security, and (as we shall see in Chapter 15) it is indeed difficult to know where the balance of advantage lies. A similar dilemma appears in considering the effects of prosperity; for prosperity is both the provider of the means for technical advance, and (if it is bounteous enough) the remover of the incentive for advance. If an order book for an antiquated product is full, why worry?—especially if one is used to looking only to the immediate future.

This book is written, not only about a period of prosperity, but about a particular country in that period, and it therefore takes for granted all the historically determined forms, institutions, and laws within which decisions about product or process development have to be made. The U.K. is a country which mixes public and private enterprise, but the incursion of the public corporation (or nationalized industry) has so far been into a limited number of basic activities. In what follows we are dealing mostly with private enterprise, organized in all its varied forms, from the individually-owned small business to the great company with hundreds of thousands of stockholders—firms large and small, public and private companies, family firms, director-dominated firms, and so on. One would expect to find that there are developments which can be handled only by the bigger firms, but that on the other hand large units may be sluggish to move. Chapter 11 confirms that it is difficult to generalize about the virtues or vices of size.

In the background which we take for granted there is the fact that the U.K. must meet (or considers that it must meet) heavy defence and welfare expenditure, and that in consequence it has a high level of taxation. Direct Government controls have varied a great deal over the post-war decade, but some of them must undoubtedly be taken as part of the 'institutional framework'—for instance, town-planning restrictions. It must also be assumed that the Government will accept a general responsibility for the equilibrium of the economy, and that in consequence its budgetary and credit policies will be active and not passive. As we must assume that an important element, whether stabilizing or soporific, is the trade association, so also we must take for granted a highly developed system of trade unions, whose actions are sometimes (as we shall see in Chapter 15) considered to be a major influence on technical progress.

In fact, we must take for granted the settled institutions and habits of a mature industrial country; and since our subject is concerned with technical change, it is not surprising that these institutions and habits appear frequently in the report, sometimes as hindrances to change and sometimes as influences guiding or deflecting its progress.

The examples of the application of science and technology to industry which come most easily to mind are the revolutionary changes, the basically new products—penicillin, nylon, Terylene, television sets, the gas turbine, the electronic computer. Changes in processes—high draft spinning, shell moulding, palletization—tend to be less well known, unless they are embodied in some notable machine. It is things, rather than processes, which catch the public eye. But for every radical innovation which thus rises to fame, there are tens of thousands of minor improvements in products and processes, which (though individually not a complete break with the past) may over a period of years create something quite new. Consider, for instance, the evolution of the piston-engined aircraft from the first small, slow and unsafe planes to the Super-Constellation, capable of maintaining regular and fast services over thousands of miles. Our discussion in this report is concerned with both small and large developments; and the closer one looks at industry, the more plain it becomes that many great changes are the product of countless steps of evolutionary development.

The hindrances to the application of science could be understood two ways, as relating to the *first* application or to the *general* application. If a research station brings out a new variety of barley, it will not be difficult to persuade half a dozen farmers to try it out. But (supposing it to be a radical improvement) how long will it be before other strains of barley are wholly displaced? An idea quickly adopted, but slow to spread, may have a lesser impact than one which has to fight for its first adoption, but is then quickly taken up by competing firms. The case-studies reveal instances where twenty or thirty years have elapsed between the first trial and the general acceptance by an industry. The committee therefore had no doubt that its investigations should cover both first adoption and general application.

In practice an 'innovation' is not easily identified. Capital equipment is constantly being altered, replaced, and extended, and products are constantly being modified, sometimes to introduce improvements, sometimes to make changes of fashion or to increase sales appeal. It is impossible to say how many millions of pounds are spent on developments of processes or products which are caused by the application of science or technology, for this expenditure (even within a single firm) is not usually identifiable as something separate from what is spent on replacements or extensions of plant. When a motorist replaces his old car with a new one, he is buying with the replacement a small increment of technical knowledge in the motor industry, embodied in the technical improvements in the new model, but not clearly separable from the other elements of cost.

This difficulty of 'sorting out' the effects of science requires us on occasion (as in Chapter 13) to examine the hindrances to the replacement or extension of plant in general, and not the particular hindrances to replacement or extension which embodies new knowledge. We have tried, however, to keep as close as possible to our subject, as it is delimited by the following definitions:

(a) *Science* we have taken to refer to the fundamental natural sciences, and we have not entered the very different field of the application of psychology or other social sciences. We do not deny their importance, but they require a different kind of study.

(b) *Technology* is 'the scientific study of the practical or industrial arts' (Oxford English Dictionary), and is therefore an extension of scientific method into direct industrial applications. Engineering is a technology, physics a science. The words 'science' or 'scientist', appearing alone, are to be taken to include 'technology' or 'technologist', except where the context shows that fundamental science only is intended. The line of division between science and technology is of course arbitrary.

(c) A *scientist* is one who applies scientific method in the fundamental natural sciences. For this it is neither necessary nor sufficient to work in a laboratory—a lab. assistant is not a scientist, but a technician, whereas an applied mathematician is a scientist. The training in the application of scientific method is essential to a scientist. A *technologist* is one who engages in scientific study of the industrial arts; he is therefore a kind of practical scientist. The definition in the Technical Education White Paper (Cmd. 9703), that a technologist 'has studied the fundamental principles of his chosen technology and should be able to use his knowledge and experience to initiate practical developments' and that he 'has the qualifications and experience required for membership of a professional institution', can serve as a rough working rule for identifying technologists. A technologist often brings together, in practical application, knowledge in a number of fields. An *inventor* does the same, but he may be successful by intuition or good luck, without having a full systematic knowledge of his technology.

(d) A *technician* is 'a person conversant with the technicalities of a particular subject' (Oxford English Dictionary): the White Paper offers the somewhat unsatisfactory definition that he 'is qualified to work under the general direction of a technologist'. The essential point seems to be that a technician is a practical man who can carry out assigned tasks in his technology, but that he need not be fitted to extend its borders by the application of scientific reasoning. But there are marginal cases where it is difficult to distinguish a junior technologist from a senior technician, and the distinction is then often a matter of habit or social prestige. Thus a draughtsman employed mainly on repetitive work, introducing minor variations into plans or drawings, is a technician: the same man, designing something with greater variations, so that he has to make a considerable use of his practical experience to create something essentially new, is a technologist. Because of this vagueness we have not hesitated to extend our inquiries to the senior ranks of technicians, when (in Chapter 9) we have to examine the supply of trained manpower. In that chapter 'technologist' includes 'senior technicians'.

(e) *Invention* we define as the creation and development of a new idea, whereas *innovation* is the act of bringing it into practical use. The dictionary definitions of these terms overlap, but we think that the distinction proposed is a convenient one.

(*f*) A *technically progressive* firm is one which, on a necessarily subjective judgement, is keeping within a reasonable distance of the best current practice in the application of science and technology. A *financially successful* firm is one which, on one of various criteria to be discussed, is increasing its assets or profits at a satisfactory rate (see p. 184).

(*g*) *Industry* is taken as including agriculture; but it does not include the financial and 'service' industries, such as banking or cinema ownership, nor does it include shops or merchants. 'Industry' is predominantly concerned with the manufacture or production of goods.

(*h*) *Research* is the activity of extending the bounds of knowledge; if it is *basic research* it is related to fundamental problems and has no necessary immediate application, while if it is *applied research* it is undertaken having in mind a particular application at a foreseeable time. The scale on which a piece of research is done is normally much smaller than the scale on which its results are later to be applied in production. Therefore, on the successful conclusion in the laboratory of a piece of applied research, the next step is often to set up a *pilot-plant*, which is a small productive unit in which the problems of full-scale production can be studied. The line between research and *development* is difficult to draw, but development may roughly be defined to begin when decisions to try to proceed to full-scale production have been taken. Development thus includes the pilot-plant stage. The terminology regarding the people employed in development is far from uniform. We use the terms *designer* and *development engineer* for those who do the pioneering work, the term 'designer' having the double use as meaning a highly original creator of a complex product (e.g. the designer of a new aircraft), and as meaning a draughtsman engaged on original work. A development engineer is capable, within the broad framework of a design, of dealing with the practical problems which arise during the process of development. He is a practical, but not necessarily an original, thinker; he must have good judgement and an idea of costs as well as of engineering possibilities. A *production engineer* is concerned with the practical problems of 'tooling up' for a particular model or run of production, and with the day-to-day responsibility for the engineering problems arising in production.

(*i*) University research can be either basic or applied, but most industrial research is applied, though the objective and the time-horizon may be distant. *Product-directed* or *process-directed* applied research is intended to yield a product or a process of given characteristics; *background* applied research is intended to increase the store of knowledge on which future applications can draw. Thus an oil company might engage in product-directed research, to produce a new fuel of defined characteristics; in process-directed research, to improve some particular section of a refinery; and in background research on the flow of liquids or the corrosion of materials, for general use in future refinery design. Background research is part of the work of research associations and universities as well as of firms.

The plan of this work is to cover the subject in two interlocking ways, like the warp and weft of a fabric. Chapters 3 to 8 deal with stages in the application of knowledge, from basic research to a decision to commit resources to full-scale production, and with the organizations concerned at these stages. Chapters 9 to 15 consider in turn some of the main conditions for the speedy adoption of new ideas in industry—the availability of men and money, appropriate organization, receptive management, a favourable market and environment. Chapter 16 sets out the results of an investigation of the relation between technical progressiveness and other characteristics of firms, and Chapter 17 summarizes our main conclusions. The appendices include material showing the scope and nature of the Committee's industrial case-studies.

Chapter 3

BASIC RESEARCH

THE purpose of this chapter is to give a partial answer to a question often asked: 'Does British industry neglect the opportunities provided by basic research?' We have defined basic research as being related to fundamental problems, and having no necessary immediate application, whereas applied research is undertaken having in mind a possible application at a foreseeable time. It is fortunate that the desire of men to understand the nature of the physical world remains strong, even though their research may seem to have no practical application, for there are many examples of discoveries which were first thought interesting but quite useless, but which much later have been the foundation of important applications.

In Britain, basic research takes place for the most part in the universities and major technical colleges. This has not always been true, for in the eighteenth and nineteenth centuries considerable advances were made by gifted amateurs working on their own account. Today certain important basic research projects take place in Government laboratories, in research associations, and in a few private firms in the chemical and electrical industries; but these are marginal cases of what we have called 'background applied research', and are undertaken with one eye to possible future applications, rather than as a pursuit of knowledge for its own sake. The academic scientist is more free than his opposite number in industry to follow interesting 'leads' occurring in the course of his research; the pursuit of knowledge for its own sake fits in with the traditions of university work; and the varied scientific and technological skills present in a university make for fruitful cross-fertilization.

In accordance with valued tradition and with the self-interest of scientists, the results of basic research are generally published. The basis of the tradition is quite simple—that secrecy impedes the advance of scientific knowledge; the boundaries of knowledge in science are extended by pushing forward from the limits of existing knowledge. The place of self-interest is equally obvious. University scientists get recognition, prestige, and promotion from publishing the results of research, while the employing body has no interest in impeding publication. In industrial research the employing body may not be anxious for publicity, but as industrial firms have come to employ more first-rate scientists, any interest they may have in impeding publication tends to be offset by the scientists' interest and belief in the value of free availability. The system by which results are made public is examined in the next chapter.

Despite the free international flow of knowledge there are national advantages in having a distinguished record in basic science; the speed of communication of ideas in the same language and within the same community is greater than it would be if national boundaries had to be crossed, and there are opportunities for basic and applied research to stimulate each other. Britain's record in basic research is undoubtedly distinguished, and it is often contrasted with the energy which the U.S.A. displays in applied research. It has even been claimed that the applied science of the U.S.A. is parasitic on British 'pure' science. This view, however, overlooks the steady growth of basic research in the U.S.A. since 1920.

It must not be supposed that the connexion between basic research and its final industrial application is a simple one; it is complex and indirect, so that it is not at all surprising that ideas conceived in one country should sometimes find their application in another. One cannot match each piece of basic research neatly with its applications, for a great part of scientific knowledge has no industrial application so far perceived. The ideas now being applied may have had their beginning a long time ago. Thus the new electronics industry depends ultimately on basic research on electrons started by J. J. Thomson and others at the end of the last century. In the early 1930's Lord Rutherford foresaw no practical application of his atom-splitting experiments, and neither Professor Kipping, nor anyone else, could see any industrial application of his laboratory work on silicones.

Even when an industrial application is seen to be possible, proving it may be far from easy. A long expensive process of applied research, which may incidentally necessitate further basic work, may be needed. For instance, the Badische Anilin-und-Soda Fabrik spent fifteen years of patient research and five million dollars in 'patient money' before they learned how to make synthetic indigo.[1] Penicillin is another good example. Applied research on possible applications does not, moreover, make sure that the application will occur. It is not possible to get useful statistics for the proportion of good ideas that are rejected after applied research—in industrial laboratories that we have visited it varies between 50 and 90 per cent.—but certainly the proportion is high.

Even when the possibility of application is proved, application will not be worth while unless investment in the new product or process seems likely to pay. Often this cannot be judged at the end of the applied research stage and a further process of development may be required. In this process there will be further expenditure on plant and materials, and this expenditure is in some cases five to ten times what is spent on the applied research. Once again no general rule can be given. We have found cases where the ratio of expenditure on research to that on

[1] T. A. Boyd, *Research, the Pathfinder of Science and Industry*, Appleton, 1935, p. 178.

development or 'pilot-plant' work is 1 to 10, the most-often-quoted relation; but others show very different ratios, such as 10 to 1, 1 to 1, and 1 to 200. There are great differences in the ratio of research to development not only between industries, as for example between the aircraft and the fine chemical industry, but also between different projects in the same industry. But the precise relation of the costs of research and development is not in this context important; what matters is that a development stage is often necessary, that it often involves a large expenditure on materials and equipment, and that many projects are rejected at this stage.

The application of basic research may also depend on the combination of the new scientific knowledge with technological knowledge or with old scientific knowledge, perhaps from a different field of science. Thus, in spite of persistent experiments with steam propulsion, the aeroplane became practicable only when a light-weight compact power unit was developed; the jet engine depended on the development of high-grade alloys; the soldering of aluminium depended on refinements in radio-frequency techniques.

Because application may depend on balanced advances in two fields of science, as well as on further extensive research and development devoted to application, the total scale of research effort in a country is important. With the specialization which is the necessary consequence of the increasing complexity of science, a country is not likely to be extending scientific knowledge in all fields at once. If important applications come from the combined results in two fields, a country advancing in only one of them will almost of necessity fall behind a country conducting research in both. Thus a country could be making a large contribution to basic science and yet not be in the best position to apply some of the new knowledge.

The uneasy feeling which led to the setting up of our Committee goes, however, beyond a recognition of these limitations. There have been complaints from scientists engaged in basic research that Britain was not putting as much effort into the application of basic science as she was into the extension of fundamental knowledge; that her effort was, in fact, ill-balanced. Alternatively, we have heard complaints that the genius of British fundamental research was being frustrated by the narrow conservatism of business men. We therefore made inquiries from a large number of university scientists, asking for examples of new ideas which were or are being neglected by British industry but developed abroad. It seemed to us that either a lack of balance in research effort, or the conservatism of British business men, would be likely to have as a symptom a tendency for British academic ideas to be taken up first in other countries.

Our informants, however, were unable to give any general evidence sufficient to support either complaint. This result is not conclusive, for academic scientists may not be aware of all the commercial applications of their ideas. But a number of old cases were quoted to us, and this suggests that either or both complaints may have been valid in the past, but may have been diminishing in validity. This proposition is consistent with the facts about the employment on industrial research and development, which has grown very rapidly since 1940. A second point made was that industry is quite quick off the mark if scientific developments are brought to its notice. It was said that several firms do not await publication, but show a keen interest in the course of university research that might be relevant to them; but in general United States industry was believed to keep a much closer watch on what is being done in universities. Third, our informants knew of no obviously bright ideas lying about *wholly* ignored by industry. Whether 'academic' ideas are used with sufficient rapidity or to a sufficient degree is another matter; for the use of academic work in industry is difficult to trace, since it often entails further basic as well as applied research. This was clearly put by Sir Lawrence Bragg when writing about the alleged neglect by industry of some great idea of a pure researcher: 'We all make these general statements lightly and then are hard put to it to justify them. The trouble is, I think, that it is generally impossible to trace the direct link between some piece of pure research and the industrial application. Pure research rather produces a protein of ideas which should be broken down into its amino-acids and then rebuilt into a new form of living matter.'

In the replies from academic scientists there is also quite commonly a suggestion that the 'financial heads' of industry are not sufficiently bold in their investment policies—that is to say, are not sufficiently prepared to risk failure. This suggestion carries the corollary that the discoveries which show a firm prospect of profit *are* developed quickly. This question of decisions to develop a new product or process is one to which we shall return in Chapter 8.

Despite the evidence from our academic informants that British industry is not now missing many commercially valuable ideas produced by universities, there remained a residue of examples of alleged neglect. One of these examples, Terylene, we rejected because inquiries showed that the significant early steps of development took place at much the same time here as in the U.S.A., and that the appearance of American supplies on the market before our own was due in part to the greater size of the American pilot-plant, but mainly to the much slower rate of plant construction in this country due to labour and material shortages and to the post-war system of Government control. The remaining significant examples were: transistors, new forms of valve, low loss transformer steels, penicillin, ion exchange resins, the synthetic production of vitamins B and C, and silicones.

An examination of some of these will illustrate the factors involved.

The transistor is a substitute for the radio valve. Its discovery was made possible by A. H. Wilson's theoretical work on the principles governing the behaviour of semi-conductors. The transistor was not, however, a simple industrial application of Wilson's work, nor did it result simply from a decision to apply these principles. The conception of the transistor arose out of fundamental work by scientists at the Bell Telephone Laboratories which had been in progress for a number of years.

The crystal rectifier or diode was known as an element of the original 'cats' whisker' wireless receivers (*circa* 1910) and had been developed empirically from the laboratory findings that certain crystals would conduct electricity in one direction only. Many crystals, such as impure lead sulphide, were found to possess these properties, but little was known about the proportions of impurity required in the salt and nothing could be predicted from theory. The crystal 'valve' was rapidly overtaken by the thermionic valve, which could not only detect or rectify voltages but by the addition of controlling grids could be made to amplify and fulfil the many functions characteristic of the present-day radio valve.

After Bloch, working in Germany in 1929, had developed a zone theory of metals, with general application to solids, A. H. Wilson put forward in 1931, in a paper to the Royal Society, a zone theory which analysed the fundamental principles governing the behaviour of semiconductors. Accounts of the theory were later published in his books, 'The Theory of Metals' (1936) and 'Semi-Conductors and Metals' (1939). The major practical interest at that time was in cuprous oxide semi-conductors which were used as rectifiers and photo-cells, but from the theoretical point of view silicon and germanium were simpler substances to investigate, and their behaviour followed closely the predictions of the theory.

The thread was next caught up by the Bell Telephone Laboratories of the U.S.A., where, before the Second World War, R. S. Ohl and J. H. Scaff initiated research into the perfection of silicon diodes for use as detectors at microwave-lengths (high frequencies). The war brought the development of radar, and work was immediately farmed out, to research establishments in both the U.S.A. and Britain, for the development of germanium or silicon diodes as point contact rectifiers. The British companies concerned were the British Thomson-Houston Co. Ltd. and the General Electric Co. Ltd., and research was also carried out at the Telecommunications Research Establishment (a Government station) and at Oxford University. In America most of this research was carried out by industry at the Bell Telephone Laboratories, the Westinghouse Research Laboratory, the General Electric Corporation of America, Sylvania Electric Products Inc., and the E. L. du Pont de Nemours and Co. The National Defense Research Committee was meanwhile directing work at the Radiation Laboratory of the Massachusetts Institute of

Technology and at Pennsylvania and Purdue Universities. A group working at Purdue under the direction of K. Lark-Horovitz were chiefly concerned with investigating the properties of germanium as a semi-conductor and as a rectifier.

Since the war research and development on both germanium and silicon rectifiers has been done in Britain and the U.S.A., especially by the leading electrical companies. The general programme of the Bell Telephone Laboratories, which led to the invention of the transistor in 1948, was directed by W. Shockley. Germanium and silicon were chosen for experiments because they were simpler to understand than most semi-conductors, although a considerable amount of work had to be done on the methods of purifying the samples. A series of concepts, proved by experiment, culminated in the discovery of the equivalent of the controlling grid in the thermionic valve. Thus a crystal triode was developed and called a transistor by Bardeen and Brattain.

The transistor has itself been modified considerably since 1948, the point-contact design being for some purposes superseded by the junction. Background research on the preparation of germanium and silicon has also been in progress in the metallurgical research laboratories of electrical companies and elsewhere. Many transistors have already been incorporated in hearing aids, guided weapon control units, and wireless equipment. The two principal advantages of using transistors instead of thermionic valves are a saving in weight and volume and a saving in electrical power. Much research has still to be done to increase the frequency range and to reduce 'noise'.

It can be seen from this that, although the fundamental characteristics of semi-conductors were known by 1931, the transistor was a far-from-obvious device and its conception required a high degree of creative imagination from Bardeen, Brattain, and Shockley. The setting in which they worked included a background of allied work on the materials themselves (stimulated by wartime defence research), Wilson's original theory on which to build their concepts, and the team work of many specialists. The probability that the discovery would be made in Britain was low because very few scientists were working in the field, even in the academic laboratories. During the 1930's solid state physics was unfashionable in academic circles, and, although there has been a revival of interest, America is still ahead of Britain in this branch of fundamental science.

The story of transformer steels begins from the discovery in Britain in 1900, by Barrett, Brown, and Hadfield, that the addition of silicon to iron improved its qualities in such a way as to reduce the loss of electrical energy in the sheets forming the iron core of a transformer when the core is magnetized by an alternating current. The 'iron loss' represents a waste of generated electrical energy. Production of hot-rolled silicon steel sheets began in Britain in 1903, and in the U.S.A. in

1907. Considerable improvements of performance were achieved during the inter-war period, but there were indications that these improvements could not be pushed much further within the bounds of the original process.[1] In 1930, however, Smith, Garnett, and Randall, working in the London research department of the Telegraph Construction and Maintenance Co. Ltd. (Telcon), were engaged on research into high-permeability alloys, and they paid particular attention to the cold processing of nickel irons. They took out a patent which related particularly to nickel irons, but incidentally they did a certain amount of work on silicon iron, and their patent was extended to cover this also. However, Telcon did not have any interests in the silicon–iron field, and the potentialities of this aspect of the patent were not apparent. Presumably some British iron and steel or electrical firms saw the patent at that time; but we find that none took any significant action about it.

In America there was a much greater interest in the cold-rolling of iron and steel, and close relations between steel and electrical firms; these were major causes of the American advantage in silicon steel. During the late 1920's, the Cold Metals Process Co. (C.M.P.) was formed to develop and exploit the Steckel mill for cold-rolling. In 1930, C.M.P. was asked by the President of the Allegheny Ludlum Steel Corporation to explore the possibility of cold-rolling silicon steels. C.M.P.'s research work on this during the next three years or so was sponsored jointly by C.M.P. and Allegheny, and was carried out under the leadership of N. P. Goss. No doubt Goss took note of the Smith–Randall patent, but it seems clear that his work would have been carried through even if their work had never been done. In 1933, Goss took out patents of a more advanced nature than those of Smith, Garnett, and Randall.

Also in 1933, Allegheny bought the Goss patent rights for the whole of North America, and they licensed the Armco Steel Corporation of Ohio to use them. Both Allegheny and Armco went ahead with development work, gradually perfecting cold-rolled silicon steel until the watts loss factor was reduced to just over half of that achieved by hot-rolling.

In Britain, little attention was given to the development until, in the late 1930's, news of American success began to drift into the country. There appears to have been no significant development work before the war forced attention elsewhere. However, interest sharpened during the war; by 1945, the British electrical industry was crying out for supplies of good transformer steel, and the steel industry started a development effort. This was possibly as successful as the American development work had been; but the fifteen-year American lead could not be overtaken at once, and it was not until the purchase, in 1953, of technical knowledge on licence from Armco that there was a prospect of high-

---

[1] For the history, see E. Marks, *Electrical Journal*, 11 May 1956, p. 1466.

quality production in Britain. We understand that during 1956 the material available from all British suppliers (10,000 tons) was little more than one-third of the demand. This material was mainly in sheet form; it was hoped during 1957 to install equipment to produce at a rate of 30,000 tons a year in coil form.

In assessing these facts one should remember the extremely costly and complex nature of development work in this field. It is necessarily costly, for this is a case where full-scale conditions cannot be reproduced in the laboratory. Moreover, practice outstrips theory, so that each advance springs from a success on a works scale; this can then be 'explained' by the theorists, and on the basis of their explanations the development staff can make inspired guesses as to the next step which needs to be taken. Since each experiment requires a new cast of steel, and since it is difficult—especially in a period of great scarcity of steel— to get a special cast of less than 100 tons, we can sympathize with the director who said: 'Every time I have an experiment done, I risk £5,000.' Moreover, one may be looking for a 5 per cent. variation in a process where there is a normal random variation of between 5 and 10 per cent., forcing multiple repetition of the experiment to get statistical 'certainty'.

Development is also a complex matter, for the composition of the steel, the methods of its manufacture, of its initial hot-rolling down to a size suitable for cold-rolling, of its cold-rolling, and its treatment after rolling can all vary. The heavy development cost was possibly a less serious impediment to the American work than to the British: the Americans could readily sell a development lot with a high watts loss factor, since no better was then available. By the time the British development effort was under way such steel was regarded by the users as of poor quality, and the costs could not so easily be reduced by selling the experimental products.

The American lead appears essentially to be a result of fruitful co-operation between suppliers and customers, and to be related to a general American lead in related technologies. In Britain, perhaps through lack of scientists and technologists of broad outlook in the key positions, the potentialities of the development were not realized in its early days, and co-operation did not come soon enough.

The story of penicillin is well known. The original observation of its bacteria-killing properties was made by Sir Alexander Fleming in 1928. Fleming's experiments, and others carried out by Raistrick and his colleagues at the London School of Hygiene in 1932, disclosed that penicillin was an unstable substance (and therefore difficult to manipulate chemically), and it was considered unlikely to have much practical value in medicine.

In 1938, Chain and Florey prepared a plan for the systematic study of some of the naturally produced anti-bacterial substances—one of

C

which was penicillin. In 1940 this team of specialists in the biological and chemical fields, using the earlier findings of Fleming and Raistrick, demonstrated that when circulating in the blood penicillin was a chemo-therapeutic agent of remarkable anti-bacterial potency and low toxicity. It is these characteristics which have made penicillin so important in medicine. In connexion with this stage of the work it should be re-membered that the idea of anti-bacterial chemotherapy had been much less familiar in 1928 than it became later, after the introduction of the sulphonamides.

The yield of the early methods of laboratory manufacture was low, and it was difficult to obtain enough penicillin for clinical trials. Owing to the serious war situation in 1940, it seemed unlikely that much progress could be made in getting large-scale production started in the U.K., and the prospects of early synthesis of penicillin were not con-sidered good. In June 1941 Florey and Heatley visited the U.S.A. to try to encourage larger-scale production, so that extensive clinical trials could be carried out. Florey was fortunate enough to obtain, at the North Regional Research Laboratory, Peoria, of the United States De-partment of Agriculture, the co-operation of experienced industrial microbiologists, who made the discoveries from which high-yield methods suitable for commercial exploitation could be developed. Dr. Heatley remained in the U.S.A., and none of the information which had been accumulated at Oxford was withheld. Research at Oxford con-tinued, and small-scale production by two British firms began in 1942. Penicillin was, however, in the main a war casualty as far as Britain was concerned, a possible subsidiary cause of the failure to complete the development being the lack of industrial microbiologists.

The case of ion-exchange resins shows on investigation little evidence to support the view that this country lags in applying basic research. These resins have a wide variety of uses in the extraction of elements from liquids, ranging from the complete purification of water to the recovery of residual uranium from gold-mining. The ion-exchange principle has a history going back to Thompson and Way, and papers were published by them a century ago. Further developments took place in the following eighty years, notably in Germany; but the most important development came in 1934, when Adams and Holmes, of the Chemical Research Laboratory, showed that ion-exchange materials could be built up on cross-linked synthetic resins.

The resins of Adams and Holmes were not suitable for immediate commercial application; a period of further research and development was necessary, and some six or seven years might be expected to elapse before this could be achieved. Only one British company appears to have done any significant development work, but there are no grounds to believe that it was sluggish before the outbreak of war.

During the war, research in Britain was limited in scope, and the

Americans undoubtedly went a few jumps ahead; but any British deficiencies in the technology appear to have been made up by the present time. There have been two main advances in the past decade. The first is the development of highly basic resins for anion exchange. The main work was done, and patents were taken out almost simultaneously (1949), in the U.S.A. by the Dow Chemical Co. and by the Rohm and Haas Co., and in the U.K. by the Chemical Research Laboratory.

Secondly, in the field of cation-exchange resins, sulphonated phenolic resins were used until about 1949, when cross-linked polystyrene resins came into use. This followed research and patenting by General Electric in the U.S.A.; the British patentees, the British Thomson-Houston Co. Ltd., granted an exclusive licence to the Permutit Co. Ltd. It was subsequently alleged [1] in a patent action 'that the potential demand for the material necessary for carrying out the patented process was not being met (by Permutit) and that the best material for carrying out the process was not being made available to the public'; but judgement went against this allegation. Additional evidence which we have collected, relating to the period since the judgement, does not substantiate the allegation.

At the present time we understand that there is considerable research on ion-exchange resins, sponsored by the British and American governments in connexion with developments in the atomic field. The nature of this research is, of course, secret; but our inquiries indicate that the technology is as advanced in this country as in America. Even though the situation may thus be quite satisfactory, there remains a possibility that it could be better. More manufacturers might have taken a lively interest in the development; but some feel that the British customer is too conservative. Greater publicity might also have led to more extensive application: there are very few articles in the British technical press describing ion-exchange processes of industrial importance.

The American advantages in the post-war period, then, can again be traced largely to the different impact of the war on the two economies. There is no reason to suspect that we lag significantly in the technology at the present time. On the other hand, four American companies are now devoting substantial efforts to research on this topic as compared with one British firm.

Silicones,[2] now a familiar ingredient of polishes and textile finishes (but having many other uses), are frequently cited as a typical example of the process whereby a British development in pure science goes abroad in the 'ideas' stage and comes back home (on licence) as a commercial product. The development originated from Kipping, who was

---

[1] 'In the matter of Colbourne Engineering Co. Ltd.'s application for a compulsory licence', *Reports of Patent Design and Trade Mark Cases*, Vol. LXXII, No. 9. The case was heard on 1 and 2 December 1954.

[2] See C. J. Baker, *Silicone Elastomers, Research*, 1953, pp. 458–64.

mainly concerned with studying the relationship of silicon with carbon, and his interest in stereo-chemistry naturally led him to attempt the preparation of an optically active silicon compound. This he achieved in 1907. During his work he obtained gummy products which he called silicones. At the time these silicones were fascinating laboratory curiosities of considerable scientific interest but of little practical value. Kipping, in an address to the Royal Society in 1937, stated that 'the prospect of any immediate and important advance in this section of organic chemistry does not seem to be very hopeful'.

The commercial production of silicones as we now know them arose from the search for heat-stable resins to be used in electrical insulation with glass products—that is to say, it arose from a new industrial possibility. In 1932, under the direction of Dr. E. C. Sullivan of the Corning Glass Works of America, J. F. Hyde studied Kipping's work and investigated the resinous, or gummy, by-products which had hampered Kipping's experiments. The assistance of the Dow Chemical Co. was sought towards the end of the 1930's in order to examine the possibilities of commercial production. At about the same time the General Electric Co. in the U.S.A. also became interested and E. G. Rochow began his work there. The commercial manufacture of silicones was hurried on by the entry of the U.S.A. into the war. The first practicable silicone was an ignition-sealing compound for aircraft engines. It was introduced in 1942, and was followed very shortly by a series of resins and fluids.

The development of silicones was thus set moving by entirely new needs, and it entailed research of a high order. It was Sullivan's genius which suggested an investigation of Kipping's silicon compounds when he started his search for heat-stable resins. It is clear from this example that Britain had no preliminary advantage in the development of silicones which she failed to exploit.

An examination of examples such as these—and note that they are chosen by academic scientists to illustrate not the British successes, but the British failures in the rapid industrial application of science—makes the proposition that Britain is pre-eminent in fundamental science, but backward in applying it to industry, appear rather meaningless. The industrial development of silicones and transistors required further fundamental work, and as this research took place in the U.S.A., it was highly probable that the industrial development would take place first there. America also had an advantage in silicon steel from her wider interest in cold-rolling processes. For penicillin the second research stage, involving both basic and applied work, but directed towards making something to be used, was carried out in Britain. This example is therefore different from those of silicones and transistors. The fact that the process for making penicillin on commercial scale was in considerable measure developed in the U.S.A. was mainly due to the impact of war and to the relative backwardness of Britain in industrial microbiology. The effects of war also account for the complaint of slowness over the development of ion-exchange resins.

The cases quoted help to emphasize the obvious fact that one cannot maintain scientific pre-eminence without scientists. There is a venerable example of this, more than a century old, in the work of Perkin on synthetic dyestuffs. In the 1860's Britain led the world in the application and development of his work; by the 1880's we had lost the leading position to Germany, whose production was five times our own. The basic reason was the absence of trained industrial chemists, caused by the backwardness of the British educational system. We shall see in Chapter 9 that the position is far from satisfactory today. Yet it would be unreasonable to suppose that we should always lead the world in every branch of science and technology, or that we should never have areas of knowledge which are temporarily neglected. It should be observed, too, that even where development has taken place overseas, the fruits of that development are normally still available (on licence) to British industry, and we have no evidence that the net payment to other countries of royalties is a serious burden on the balance of payments.

The evidence examined in this chapter is not sufficient to support a simple assertion that British basic and applied science is being frustrated by the conservatism of British business men. The facts appear to us to be more complex. Britain has a limited output of scientists, and cannot therefore avoid neglecting some parts of the long frontiers of science. In part because her output of scientists is small, and the realization of the need for research is recent, her applied research in industry is also patchy. For this and other reasons, industry does not reach out and pull in scientific knowledge as fully as it might. Because areas of both basic and applied science are neglected, the cross-fertilization of ideas is obstructed; because the objectives of many industrial research and development projects are not clearly related to the commercial objectives and financial position of their firms, industry does not make the best use of the small supply of scientists. These are themes to which we shall frequently recur in the later chapters of this book.

Chapter 4

COMMUNICATING THE RESULTS OF
BASIC RESEARCH

I F the results of basic research are to be used in industry they must cross various barriers to their communication, for often the industrial application of the research is not immediately apparent. The obvious essentials are to record the work done clearly, concisely, and in a form appropriate to those who will read it; and to make the record accessible by quick publication in an appropriate place. But these essentials are not as simple as they look, for research in different fields of science may have to meet in an industrial application, and (for instance) a discovery published in a journal of physics in a form intended for the reading of physicists may easily be missed by chemists, and be unintelligible to them even if they find it.

At the conclusion of a stage of his work the research worker may read a paper, in his own scientific language, at a meeting of members of a professional institution or a learned society appropriate to his field of research—such as the Institute of Physics—or at a meeting sponsored by a university. The reading is usually followed by discussion and the paper is subsequently published in a learned journal. Most learned journals are specialized, but there are a few (of which the most outstanding is the *Proceedings of the Royal Society*), which publish papers of common interest to scientists in a number of fields.

Since a worker in a field of basic research is often not able to foresee the applications of his discoveries, his sensible course is to direct his contribution to those bodies and journals which deal specifically with his science. The industrial scientist or educated business man knows which sciences have most bearing on his products and processes, and ought in principle to be able to read or to keep up with the headlines in the appropriate journals. For news of research work in other sciences he depends on 'discussion journals', or abstracts and indexes, which are discussed later.

The results of basic research conducted by research associations are published partly in journals, partly in research association bulletins and technical papers. The Department of Scientific and Industrial Research (D.S.I.R.) laboratories publish their results in a similar fashion. In both cases it is common practice to add to publication in the learned journals a report in a different form in the scientific and technical press. The results of basic research in industry are sometimes communicated to the learned journals, or, in a few cases, appear in the research journal of the firm concerned.

Conferences are another means of communication. National and international meetings held at universities, institutes, summer schools, and so on provide an opportunity for the discussion of a particular topic, perhaps from the differing viewpoints of various sciences. Papers read at such conferences are usually printed separately or published in a symposium. Conferences have proved to be useful in enabling scientists in different fields to keep in touch with each other and (if industry's viewpoint is represented by industrial scientists and technologists) in nurturing a better understanding of the potential industrial applications of science.

The research worker may also contribute the results of his work to the scientific and technical press, which can be divided into three main types. First, there are the 'discussion journals' covering a wide field and intended in part at least for general reading, such as *Science Progress*, *Endeavour*, *Discovery*, *Nature*, and *Research*. Second, there are a number of specialized journals covering specific fields, such as electronics, or process control or machinery. Third, there are many trade journals and reviews, such as *Dairy Industries*, the *Foundry Trade Journal*, and *Sheet Metal Industries*, which are concerned with the common technologies of a particular trade and which report on basic research results which provide technically useful information.

The style of an article in the scientific and technical press differs strikingly from the scientific exposition accepted by the journals of the professional and learned societies. The 'discussion journals' require the research worker to write an article about his work in a form understandable to its intelligent but non-specialist readers. In many cases the editorial staff rewrite the original article. To communicate his findings in the specialist press, the research worker must 'get inside' the particular field and write his article to appeal to the special interests of the readers. The trade journal is a rare medium for the original publication of basic research results; it translates scientific advance into the technical language of the industry concerned and relates it to its practical application in production. There is evidence that these trade journals are by far the most generally used source of technical information, especially in small firms.

There are, of course, other means of communication, such as books and monographs, exhibitions, films, and radio and television broadcasts. Special mention should be made of the national press, for there has been a growth of popular-science writing and many national newspapers have scientific correspondents on their staff. Apart from conditioning the popular mind to the possibilities of new discoveries, the national press may start the industrialist thinking that 'there might be something in this for us'. We have found several significant examples of this in our case-studies.

There are many scientists in the world, and there is little evidence that they are shy about going into print if their conditions of work allow them to do so. Consequently in most subjects a man who conscientiously reads all related papers would have no time for his own work. The problem is growing worse, as the output of papers and articles and the number of specialist journals increase. Hence the need for abstracts. The Royal Society lists 134 abstracting journals in Great Britain alone; the International Federation for Documentation lists some 1,500 for the world as a whole. The abstract is a shortened version of a scientific paper written either as an author's précis or by the abstracting journalist. It can be indicative or informative, the first acting only as a guide and index to the original work, the second making it possible for many purposes to dispense with the source altogether.

In case of need, appeal can be made to a scientific information service, such as is provided by D.S.I.R., by the Association of Special Libraries and Information Bureaux (A.S.L.I.B.), and by certain public libraries. In 1949 the Panel on Technical Information Services of the Committee on Industrial Productivity recommended that the Technical Information and Documents units of the Board of Trade be transferred to D.S.I.R. This was done, and D.S.I.R. now maintains a central library co-ordinating the libraries in its research establishments. It also runs a Records Bureau which acts as a central depository for all research reports from the various establishments, and an index of Russian scientific journals, with arrangements for the translation of selected articles from them. A.S.L.I.B. runs an Information Department, and maintains a Commonwealth Index of Translations and a panel of 135 translators capable of tackling specialized articles. The Commonwealth Agricultural Bureaux provide abstracts and an information service for agricultural science.

Despite these services, there remains a problem of communication—a double problem, both of the communication of ideas from scientist to scientist, and also of communication from scientist to layman, so that industry can quickly grasp the significance of basic research. The problem is an old one; in 1919 Professor A. F. C. Pollard was pressing for 'a national institute of scientific and technical information with librarians qualified in science' and in 1942, speaking to the British Society of International Bibliography, he still found it necessary to protest about 'the disordered state of bibliography and indications of its effect upon scientific and technical progress'.[1]

The question was discussed at the Royal Society Empire Scientific Conference, held in 1946, where papers were read on the dissemination of scientific information, and a working party, led by Sir Richard Gregory, dealt with the flow of such information to the general public. This was followed by a British Association and Royal Society Con-

[1] *Proceedings, British Society for International Bibliography*, Vol. IV, 1942, pp. 51–2.

ference dealing specifically with the dissemination of scientific know-ledge. It was agreed to set up an Institute of Scientific Information under the auspices of the British Association. This, in fact, came to nothing, mainly due to lack of funds, '. . . the main difficulties being the cost of staff, premises and equipment for carrying out the programme envisaged and some doubts as to the need for all the functions assigned to the Bureau'.[1] Later the same year the first post-war meeting of the International Federation for Documentation was held in Paris, and papers pressing for more complete documentation were read. The plans of the United Nations Educational, Scientific, and Cultural Organization (UNESCO) at one time included a centralized international bibliographical service, but later it was decided to encourage and co-ordinate the national services instead.

In June 1948 the Royal Society convened a conference in London to tackle the whole problem in a more thorough way than had been attempted before. Whereas the approach at the 1946 conference had stressed the point of view of the users, this conference stressed the point of view of scientists, and Professor J. D. Bernal paved the way with a survey of the needs of academic and industrial scientists. There were more than 160 delegates, and 300 observers, including sixteen working parties who, with the aid of technicians, examined problems of abstracting, coding, and indexing as well as the more general topics. The conference provided a valuable classification of the problems, but we have not been able to trace any major results.[2]

In June 1949 UNESCO held an international conference on Science Abstracting in Paris which led to the publishing of a new list of abstracting services or journals and the keeping of a card index of these by the International Federation for Documentation at the Hague. At an O.E.E.C. conference in 1954 at Nancy, part of the programme was devoted to the study of the dissemination of research results and their use in industry. The conference reached three conclusions: that the learning of foreign languages should be encouraged in the education of engineers, as it is in that of pure scientists: that it is of mutual benefit to universities and other research bodies to develop their communications more extensively: and that the needs of small and medium-sized firms with few or no technologists are not met by conventional documentation methods. It was recommended that the European Productivity Agency should encourage study of this last problem, to which we refer again below.

---

[1] Report of the Council to General Committee of the British Association, *Advancement of Science*, No. 16, January 1948, p. 370.

[2] The Royal Society Scientific Information Conference, 21 June–2 July 1948, *Report and Papers*. See also Vera Connell, *The Application of Results of Research*, Butterworth, 1954, which reviews the research services of the Commonwealth countries and the methods of making their work known.

UNESCO held a small conference in Madrid in October 1955 on the dissemination of scientific information. As an outcome UNESCO has been asked to consider the possibility of forming a consultative committee to further co-operation between various national associations for the advancement of science. The subject has been raised at many other conferences, including those of A.S.L.I.B., of the Federation of British Industries (e.g. the 1949 conference on Industrial Research), of the British Institute of Management, of the British Society for International Bibliography, and of the International Federation for Documentation.

There have been a number of surveys of the way in which scientific information is used, including Professor Bernal's questionnaire for the Royal Society Scientific Information Conference of 1948 and a survey of the reading requirements of borrowers from the Science Museum Library.[1] In October 1951 D.S.I.R. published the results of a survey, mainly of abstracting services.[2] It was concluded that subject indexes of abstracts could be improved, but abstracts are probably sufficiently comprehensive, and that there is a need for the systematic reporting and abstracting of experimental techniques. The rosy estimate, based on this survey, that 90 per cent. of the world's published scientific knowledge is abstracted at some time, is not generally accepted. J. E. Holmstrom suggests that 'about one-third of the worthwhile journal articles are abstracted several times over whilst two-thirds are missed altogether'.[3]

It is evident from this survey of recent work that the 'problem of communication' has had plenty of attention. Yet we think that perhaps the attention has been fixed too much on how scientists ought to write, what science librarians ought to provide, and what industrialists ought to read, and that the facts about the receptiveness of different kinds of firm have not been sufficiently considered. There is an important distinction, too, between the communication of ideas from one scientist to another, and the communication of ideas from basic scientists to laymen. It may be difficult for the layman to see the relevance of the basic research to industrial processes, for its use may involve an expensive process of industrial applied research and development. Hence the idea may become intelligible and interesting to the layman only when interpreted by the development work of others. This process of interpretation can be seen in the presentation of an idea in a learned journal, later in a technical journal, and finally in a trade journal which mentions developments which are ready-made for application. The time lag in the passage from the learned to the trade journal is often very long. This time lag, which is an important part of the problem of communication, is determined by

---

[1] D. J. Urquhart, *The Distribution and Use of Scientific and Technical Information, Journal of Documentation*, March 1948, pp. 223–31.

[2] *Unanswered Questions*, D.S.I.R., No. 5, October 1951.

[3] J. E. Holmstrom, *Scientific Information, Research*, 1948, p. 484.

the extent and effectiveness of industrial research and development, a subject which we study further in the next three chapters.

From our case-studies, it seems to us that the following classification of firms is important:

1. *Large firms with their own research departments* keep well abreast of research elsewhere through a skilled knowledge of the 'communication network' of science, and through informal personal contacts. Such firms often have staff of high professional status, who have a natural range of contacts with scientists and technologists elsewhere, and who have acquired the desire and the ability to keep themselves well-informed. The contact is especially easy if the firm is engaged in *basic* research, but we find that many firms carrying out *applied* research regard it as part of their programme to keep an eye on basic research being done elsewhere, since it may make their applied research quicker or cheaper. Such firms are usually well supplied with technical literature, though perhaps within a restricted field related to the subjects under investigation, and they often make good use of industrial research establishments.

2. *Firms with few scientists*, using them in production and sales departments, tend to have no one with much time to read scientific publications, and no one with much knowledge of the methodology of communication. In consequence such firms, and also firms which are progressive but employ no scientists, obtain their stimulus from research associations or from other firms or from informal personal contacts. This suggests that the 'gap' in *written* scientific communication is over-stressed: where firms employ scientists on research, there are men qualified to evaluate scientific literature: where there are few scientists employed, and where the technologists have 'come up the hard way' by experience within the firm, no improvement in abstracting services or in indexing and no amount of simplification of the language in scientific journals will be enough to ensure that management will grasp the significance of *basic* research. The real problem is the communication of the results of *development*.

3. *Firms with no scientists*, and no consciousness of the value of science, pose a different problem—not of 'documentation', but of propaganda. Some of the problems of 'selling' research are considered in later chapters. It involves such things as simplified and illustrated reports, 'open days' at laboratories with displays and demonstrations, and above all personal visits from people with the ability and technique of the good salesman.

We would suggest, therefore, that although there are no doubt excellent reasons for improving the efficiency of the 'communication network' for the results of basic research, such an improvement would not have far-reaching results on the application of science in industry. It would ease the work of the firms which are already receptive, and which do not miss much in any case, but it would not give sight to the firms which are blind to science. In particular, there is not much to be expected from persuading scientists to avoid jargon and write in 'plain English'. No doubt many scientists do perpetrate gobbledygook, and deserve censure for it; but the so-called jargon, 'the cant of a class, sect, trade, or profession', as the dictionary calls it, is often simply the easiest way of conveying a scientist's meaning to his fellow-scientists. If he wrote always with the object of making himself clear to the layman, he might sacrifice a vital condition of scientific advance, namely, that his work be in a form that can be tested and built on by his colleagues. Furthermore, a scientific advance can only be understood in full in its context, and by those with a training in science. The replacement of technical language by 'plain English' would slow down and obstruct communication with those firms which are already receptive, without necessarily reaching any of the unreceptive.

Our analysis also suggests that the scientific middleman is very important—the research association, the technical journalist, the salesman with a scientific background, the travelling advisory officer. Firms which do not receive knowledge direct through scientists on their staff are not necessarily rendered unreceptive; they may be highly receptive at the level of the technical journal. For instance, the Managing Director of one firm, having read in the technical press of the possibilities of isotopes, was able through the Institute of Physics to employ a consultant and make a striking advance in machine design. But not all the firms which do not employ scientists are as receptive as that. There are many firms in craft industries which have not even taken advantage of 'school textbook' scientific principles. Their real problem is not that scientific knowledge is too hard to come by, but that they have not begun to want it.

This classification of receptiveness, however, does not reflect the full complexity of the matter, and we should not wish to encourage the idea that the impulse to apply science in industry comes only from scientists. It is true that sometimes a scientist or an engineer may start a firm to apply new scientific knowledge or to bring into use neglected or partly neglected knowledge. Thus Perkin started a firm to apply the knowledge he had gained about aniline dyes; de Bruyne started a firm to bridge the gap between research (in particular Wagner's tension field analysis) and the development and manufacture of new structural materials for aircraft; the Government appointed scientists to start a new enterprise to apply and develop the knowledge of atomic fission.

But existing firms acquire the desire to draw knowledge from the great stores of basic science, and to make it ready for industrial application by applied research, in many and varied ways. Sometimes a general idea that scientific developments are likely leads to the institution of a research and development department; an example is a machine-tool firm which, following developments in control mechanisms, set up a research department to 'make ready' the new knowledge of electronics for machine-tool design, and to experiment with kinematic design as a prelude to computer control. Other firms have set up a research department because they think it wise to copy their competitors; others, misled by a too-simple idea of the way in which progress occurs, have attached a research department to their organization in the expectation that the mere presence of scientists will make them technically progressive. Where research and development departments already exist, or are thus created, there will be men in the firm whose job it is to keep track of scientific developments that have, or may have, application to the products or processes of the firm. But they are not the sole originators of such application; as we shall see, the impulse to undertake applied research and development may come from the sales department, with a consumer need to satisfy, or from a production department, with a technical problem to solve. Or the Board of Directors may decide on a new line of activity for which research and development work is essential.

Chapter 5

THE EXTENT OF RESEARCH ACTIVITY

IN the sense in which we have defined the terms in Chapter 2, the majority of research in industrial companies is *product-directed* or *process-directed*, that is to say directed to a specific practical objective. But it is impossible to make clear distinctions; in certain industries and certain firms there is much *'background' applied research*, that is research providing a general background of knowledge for future application, and even some that is *basic*, that is research undertaken to extend the bounds of knowledge of fundamental problems without regard to any special applications. Thus in the electrical, chemical, and pharmaceutical industries there are firms large enough to finance background and basic research, and they do so because they feel that they are close to the limits of existing fundamental knowledge. Research which is not closely tied to immediate application may (in a few large companies) be regarded as a general safeguard against future loss of earning power, or it may be regarded as a condition for winning a reputation in research which will attract able scientists.

But a great part of research in companies is subordinate to the immediate business policy of the company; that is to say, the research projects derive from the business policy. Of all the hundreds and hundreds of projects that might be tackled those few are chosen which are relevant (and, in an efficient firm, most relevant) to the business policy of the company. To some scientists this derivative nature of most industrial research is a sign that science is being frustrated by 'business men'. This is to misconceive the function of business men. It is not their function to encourage science *per se*, but to use science for a variety of purposes, such as to improve products or to create new ones, to improve processes and reduce costs, to reduce waste of existing materials, to find substitute materials. To use science for these objects business men must, simply because basic science seldom yields direct solutions to technical problems, employ scientists to find the applications. The use of science in industry would in fact be frustrated if applied research projects did not derive from business needs.

Research that is expected to pay for itself is sometimes put out on contract. The opportunity for this is not large in this country, though in the U.S.A. there are a number of research institutes which will undertake research on contract for industrial firms: the Mellon Institute for Industrial Research was founded in 1913 and the Battelle Memorial Institute in 1929. Both were started as a result of charitable bequests. Many other research institutes have been set up, particularly since 1945. In this country sponsored research institutes are a recent development, but their rate of growth suggests that they meet a real need, not only for industry but also for Government departments, which provide one institute with nearly half its income. The Sondes Place Research Institute has a staff of about eighty and covers a broad scientific field, with particular interests in applied chemistry and in chemical and mechanical engineering; it undertakes pilot-plant development as well as laboratory research, and also the design and construction of prototype machines. The Fulmer Research Institute, with a staff of a hundred, has a special interest in the field of metallurgy. There is also now a branch of the Battelle Institute in Britain.

But what of the company which is too small to undertake or sponsor applied research of its own, or which can do so only in a limited field? The results of academic basic research are not usually in a form suitable for immediate digestion. Fortunately there are many ways of meeting the needs of the smaller firms. We shall refer later (especially in Chapter 10) to the invigorating influence of larger firms which provide machinery or raw materials, or which are customers for the product. There are also many co-operative or government institutions which both help smaller firms and fill the needs which larger firms cannot meet from their own resources. The main types are as follows:

1. *'Trade promotion' associations.* These are prominent for certain raw materials, and exist to encourage the use of the material concerned. Consequently they are concerned in research to find new uses, or to remove difficulties in manufacture, and they maintain services for giving advice and information. They may sponsor research projects in universities or in member firms, using the results for the general benefit; or they may use the grant-aided research associations or private consultants. Thus the Lead Development Association is an advisory, non-profit-making body established for the furtherance of research and development work and the dissemination of technical information. One of its associate members, the Lead Sheet and Pipe Council, deals specifically with the uses of sheet and pipe. Both bodies are members of the British Non-Ferrous Metals Research Association, which carries out fundamental research on lead and its alloys. There are similar bodies for aluminium, tin, copper, and zinc, and for commodities as diverse as wool, iodine, plastics, road tar, concrete, timber, and bristles. Trade associations such as the Association of British Chemical Manufacturers and the Society of British Aircraft Constructors include in their functions the promotion of research and the spreading of technical knowledge.

2. *Grant-aided research associations.* These are bodies receiving grant from the Department of Scientific and Industrial Research, on condition that they obtain support from the industries they serve. The original purpose of the grant seems to have been to establish a sufficient scale of

operations quickly, after which the research association (having proved its value) would be supported entirely by the industry. The present position, however, is that grant-aid continues indefinitely, subject to review every five years. The size of the basic grant is fixed after considering the importance of the industry, its needs, and the nature of its productive units; it is linked to a minimum contribution from the industry, and additional grant up to a certain limit is paid in proportion to amounts raised by the industry in excess of the minimum. There is also power to grant additional funds for capital purposes. Government aid provides on average less than a third of total income. Full membership of a research association is open to any British firm engaged in the relevant industry, and associate membership is usually available to firms in other related industries.

There are at the time of writing forty-eight grant-aided bodies, of which thirty-nine are of full research association status, and seven are Research Councils or Committees. The remaining two are special cases: the National Institute of Industrial Psychology, and the Association of Special Libraries and Information Bureaux. Research Councils or Committees are usually set up for an experimental period, to enable a small industry, which could not support a full research association from the outset, to examine its requirements in the field of co-operative research: the intention being to set up a research association of the normal pattern in due course. In such circumstances it is found valuable to have a Research Council working closely with an established research association in a related field; thus the Cutlery and Files Research Councils are helped by the facilities of the British Iron and Steel Research Association. Most of the associations serve particular trades, though some serve common technologies such as packaging and production engineering. Their research must be justified by some expected application, but it is often concerned with long-term and fundamental problems, e.g. relating to the properties of materials. It is not 'profit-directed' in the same way as applied research done within firms, and many research associations have to meet criticism from member firms who complain that the work done is remote and 'academic'; though many operate in industries in which, before the research association was established, no research on materials or processes had been undertaken.

3. *Government research establishments*. There are fourteen laboratories under D.S.I.R.'s direct care, including some to deal with problems which are of interest in many industries (e.g. fire prevention, control of water pollution), and some to deal with industries whose structure makes them unsuitable for a research association (e.g. building, which is mainly organized in very small firms). There is a Chemical Research Laboratory dealing with selected fields of industrial chemistry of wide interest; a Food Investigation Organization, doing fundamental studies

of the properties of foodstuffs; a Hydraulics Research Station, whose work is of interest to bodies controlling waterways and docks or dealing with coast erosion; a Pest Infestation Laboratory, concerned with the protection of stored foodstuffs; a Road Research Laboratory, interested in road construction and maintenance and the problems of road safety and of traffic flow. The work of the National Physical Laboratory includes the testing and calibration of scientific apparatus as well as a wide range of fundamental and applied research in aerodynamics, metallurgy, radio, optics, mathematics, electronics, ship design, and electrical engineering.

It can be seen that these three classes of institution are in order of their distance from the motivation of research in private industry. The trade promotion associations are primarily interested in the profits of their members. The research associations have this interest in theory, but the link with profits is less strong, and the associations have often been persuaded and prodded into being (with the inducement of public subsidy) in industries which had failed to create adequate research facilities of their own. The Government establishments are free to follow lines of inquiry for their pure technical interest, or because of their importance for defence or for social policy; the link with profits is very tenuous.

A different function in the encouragement of research and of application is performed by the National Research Development Corporation (N.R.D.C.), a public body founded in 1949. It has two main functions. One is to deal with discoveries made in Government research establishments, holding the British patents and obtaining appropriate foreign protection. The other is to secure, if necessary by financial backing, the further development of unexploited new ideas coming to it, either from Government sources or from private inventors. In conformity with our discussion in Chapter 3, it has in fact found very few exploitable new ideas from private sources. It has hurried forward development work on some projects of importance, which would no doubt have been developed anyway, but perhaps too slowly; and it has in other cases confirmed that private industry was right to be cautious in taking up a new idea. By circulating details of the inventions in its care, it performs a useful service of communication. N.R.D.C. occasionally sponsors research or design work (for instance, in the kinematic design of machine tools) where this is needed to support development.

We finally look at the whole range of British research and development expenditure, and consider the motives determining each part, the size of the effort which results, and the way in which that effort has grown. As we have seen, industrial research in private industry is for the most part undertaken in the expectation that it will pay. A business firm when it invests money in laboratories, scientists, and supporting staff expects to get a return from the investment, either in the form of a

D

direct monetary reward from product or process improvements, or in the form of power to withstand a loss of earnings that would, or might in future, result from competition. Even where firms do not attempt to find the most profitable level of expenditure on research, this monetary basis of industrial research exists.

Expenditure on academic research, however, cannot be thought of in such definite monetary terms. Some academic research is closely connected with industrial application, but the greater part is not. Decisions about expenditure on academic research, which are made in this country by the Treasury through and in consultation with the University Grants Committee, and to a lesser extent by the Ministry of Supply, the Agricultural Research Council, and D.S.I.R., are doubtless affected by a judgement concerning the benefit to industry, but the decisions must be largely qualitative; they cannot be made on the basis of profit and loss accounting. Decisions about spending on defence research present much the same problems as decisions about academic research, even though the motives for the two forms of research differ. It is common to hear that in defence research 'money is no object', and although one hopes that this is not literally true, the essential basis of the statement is clear. The value of security cannot be expressed in money terms, 'defence is of much more importance than opulence', and the decision about research expenditure depends on an, often very uncertain, estimate of the hostile intent of others and on a (perhaps less uncertain) estimate of the others' development of new weapons. While it is expected that the research will produce new weapons of defence and offence, it is fervently hoped that they will never be used. Further, the Government has the power of taxation, and it is thus, in its expenditure on research, in a position quite different from that of a business firm. The final limit to its research budget is the limit to the taxable capacity of the community, after allowance for other necessary expenditure on administration, the Armed Forces, and the social services.

Government expenditure on defence research and development is more than one-half of Britain's total expenditure on research and development. Part of this work is carried on in Government establishments such as those of the Ministry of Supply and the Admiralty, but about half is done on contract by industry and the universities. In the universities such contracts are concerned with background or basic research work, but industry is concerned mainly with applied research and development. Some of this applied research may have no civil use, but much of it does serve civil purposes, particularly in the fields of aircraft, electronics, metallurgy, engines, and machine-tools. Indirectly, then, the Government subsidizes industrial research not only through D.S.I.R. and the research associations, but also through the Ministry of Supply and the Admiralty. Whether the full sum of defence research and development expenditure that has civil application would be spent on industrial research if it were not taken in taxation, or whether it would be better spent, cannot be known. What is known, however, is that the last two world wars did stimulate both the application of science to industry and direct spending on industrial research and development.

The Atomic Energy Authority also conducts basic as well as applied research, though as part of this is defence expenditure precise details are not known. That part which is concerned with lethal weapons is determined by non-pecuniary factors; that part which is concerned with the peaceful uses of atomic energy—such as power-stations, 'atomic' engines, and isotopes—has, or should have, an economic basis. This basis is not obvious at the moment: the development period involved is a long one, and the civil and defence research expenditure is not, at any rate publicly, always separable. At this stage there is often no clear distinction between basic and applied research, though the Atomic Energy Authority is likely to be an important centre of basic research. The entirely new type of research collaboration needed from mathematicians, physicists, chemists, metallurgists, and engineers make it practically essential to create a basic research centre unhampered by divisions into Departments and Faculties. Rapid development in atomic energy depends directly on basic research in such fields as neutron physics, radio-chemistry, and non-ferrous metallurgy, but basic research is likely to go beyond these foreseen needs; the potentialities of new discoveries are so great that the expenditure on basic research not connected directly with application is likely to be high.

There are direct estimates of spending on research by Government agencies and research associations. In 1954–5 the Government spent about £100 million in its own laboratories administered through D.S.I.R., the Agricultural Research Council, the Medical Research Council, the Ministry of Supply, and the Admiralty. In addition, Government agencies, mainly the Ministry of Supply in its defence work, spent £100 mn. on research and development contracts with industry and the universities. Research associations spent just over £3 mn. (in addition to grants by D.S.I.R. of £1·3 mn.), and universities and technical colleges spent perhaps £5 mn. in addition to Ministry of Supply research contracts.

Information about spending by industry is much less precise, for not enough attention has been given to the right rate of spending on industrial research. Most of the firms we have visited have been unable to give us a precise figure for their spending on research. If we run together expenditure on research and development we can make an estimate for Britain, though this estimate is subject to a considerable margin of error; for accounting procedures in research departments are generally sketchy, and there is no uniformity of treatment of what is and what is not research expenditure. In some firms research staff are called in by production or sales departments for 'trouble-shooting' jobs unconnected with development, or are engaged normally in some technical testing, while production staff or facilities are used on occasions for research and development work without any adjustment to the firm's calculated research expenditure. There is also difficulty about the treatment of pilot-plants which may be used to produce saleable output.

The Federation of British Industries made an inquiry in 1950–1, which showed 301 firms (who gave adequate replies to a questionnaire sent to firms thought likely to be carrying out research) as spending £24 mn., and employing on the work 31,000 persons, of whom 8,500 possessed a degree or equivalent qualification. The sample excluded the aircraft industry, but much work in that industry is financed by the Ministry of Supply. A similar survey in 1945–6 showed an expenditure of £22 mn. by 420 firms: and 107 comparable returns in the two surveys showed a doubling of expenditure in the intervening years. This suggests that the 1950–1 expenditure for the 420 firms might have been £44 mn., but since the 107 comparable returns included many large firms this is probably an over-estimate. On the other hand, there must be spending on research and development by more than 420 firms—though the F.B.I. survey appears to have caught the big fish. It would thus be a fair guess that 1950–1 expenditure was at least £40 mn.

In a paper read to Section F of the British Association in 1956, Mr. E. Rudd gave these preliminary results of a D.S.I.R. sample inquiry into research and development expenditure in 1955:

Government direct work . . .	£120 mn.
Government contracts	115
Universities, research associations, etc. .	16
Industry	74
Total expenditure in 1955:	£325 mn. (±80)

This would give total research and development expenditure as 2.0 per cent. of gross domestic product. This is a high proportion; as we shall see, the U.S.A. proportion in 1953 was about 1·5 per cent. It is possible to say with a fair degree of certainty that £110 mn. was spent on civil research and development, but what proportion of the remaining £215 mn. 'yields civil benefit' is (as we have noted) impossible to say. But it is a fair guess that in both the U.K. and the U.S.A. civil research and development was somewhat less than 1 per cent. of gross national product. This still means, of course, that there was vastly more work done in the U.S.A. because of her greater size and riches.

The U.S.A. figures mentioned above are based on a survey carried out by the Bureau of Labor Statistics for the National Science Foundation in 1954 and 1955.[1] This was a sample survey, carried out with great care and with precise definitions of the terms used. It showed a total research and development effort of more than 5 (U.S.A.) billion dollars in 1953, of which two-thirds was in private industry; over one-third of the work in private industry was done on Federal Government contracts. 1·5 billion dollars was spent by the electrical equipment and aircraft industries. More than 15,000 companies contributed to the nation's research and development effort; 85 per cent. of these had less than 500 employees, but these were responsible for only one-tenth of the work. Seventy per cent. of all industrial research and development was in the 375 largest companies with 5,000 or more employees. *Basic* research cost 150 million dollars, or 4 per cent. of the total cost of industrial research and development, and this work was notably large in the chemical and glass industries.

All this suggests a pattern which, apart from a greater concentration in private industry, is very similar to that in the U.K. It is therefore interesting to note that expenditure in the U.S.A. has been increasing rapidly. Unfortunately the latest data suggest that earlier estimates have been too low, and it is therefore safer to cast the results in the form of an index number, as follows:

Index (1952 = 100) of the proportion
of the U.S.A. gross national product
spent on research and development

1920	10
1940	60
1945	100
1948	85
1952	100

There are scattered data for the U.K. suggesting a similar, though later, growth. Thus the income of research associations was £0·5 mn. in 1939 and £4·4 mn. in 1953–4: D.S.I.R. expenditure has grown from £0·5 mn. in 1939 to £6·5 mn. in 1954–5. Allowing for price changes, these increases are of the order of three-fold and four-fold respectively. The F.B.I. surveys show expenditure on research and development as follows:

1930	.	.	.	£ 1·7 mn. by 422 firms
1935	.	.	.	£ 2·7 mn. by 484 firms
1938	.	.	.	£ 5·4 mn. by 566 firms
1945	.	.	.	£21·8 mn. by 420 firms
1950	.	.	.	£23·8 mn. by 301 firms

This is not a manageable series, but it suggests that expenditure after allowing for price changes more than doubled between 1930 and 1938, and doubled again between 1938 and 1950.

[1] *Science and Engineering in American Industry*, National Science Foundation, 1955.

We would like to stress the importance of the rapid and apparently continuing rate of growth of research and development expenditure. Some of the problems we have to consider, such as the shortage of scientists, are almost necessary accompaniments of rapid growth; and some of the inadequacies we observe may be overtaken by that growth before these words have been long in print.

Chapter 6

RESEARCH AND DEVELOPMENT AS A MANAGEMENT TECHNIQUE

IN this chapter we concern ourselves more narrowly with that part of research and development which is carried on in industrial firms and corporations, and we try to answer such questions as: What decides its scale? How are research projects selected? What are the particular functions of a development department? How should research and development be managed? Our special interest in this chapter, therefore, is in firms large enough to maintain their own research or development.

With the growth of research and development departments within firms, science has ceased to be external to business activity—product and process research and development have become a management technique. In firms with research and development departments, management neither ignores scientific advance nor waits passively for scientists to announce new discoveries of industrial significance, but makes direct provision for the creation and use of scientific discovery. It is thus misleading to speak of the research and business activities of the firm as though they were separate. Furthermore, a research and development department must be managed. Its task is not simply to solve scientific and technological problems, but to solve those problems which are most relevant to the changing position of the company concerned; that is to say, the successful research manager relates his actual programme to the market position of the firm—to such things as its competitive position, its selling policy, the size of project which the firm can competently undertake, its raw material problems and capital programmes. Unless this is done research projects that cannot or will not be used by the firm will be carried through, while others that could have been used will be ignored.

The growth of research and development as a management technique has not affected all firms equally. Some firms have not instituted a research department; others have not learned to use their research department efficiently. Such inefficiency may be due to the failure of senior management to realize that successful research is not an optional extra to the main structure of the firm, a coop containing a few well-fed scientific geese who will in due time lay golden eggs. To be successful, research and development must be related to the financial position and the commercial objectives of the firm, while the application of the results often entails a change in its management structure and methods. Sometimes senior management fails to give the research department information on the production and market problems of the firm, or fails to make provision for change throughout the firm; sometimes the research manager does not organize his department so as to create product and process development which will be profitable to the firm. In these conditions the department will be ineffective and the research workers will come to feel that research is something external to management, with a different set of objectives and a different outlook on life. This feeling can also be produced when a research manager or director fails to understand the particular requirements of scientific research and expects ideas to be produced to order, however short the time or unexpected the assignment.

The good management of research and development is thus of critical importance in the rapid application of science and technology. A good manager combines technical and managerial ability. For he must choose the projects most likely to profit the company, and he must increase or reduce the resources devoted to particular projects as the progress of the research shows that the result is likely to be commercially valuable or valueless. To maintain the enthusiasm of scientists under these conditions entails a capacity to understand and explain the role of research and development in the changing market position of the company.

A tension between research workers and management may also exist where there is a conflict of interests or traditions within a firm. Wherever there is more than one manager in a firm, the management may not be a consistent whole. There may, for example, be a Board decision to institute a research department, but if the managers of the production and sales departments are antipathetic, the research workers may come to feel that they are frustrated by an external force, 'the management', when in fact they are frustrated by a *part* of the management, or by a failure of management to create the conditions for the successful use of their department. A continuance of such frustration, we have found, is most likely where the research department does little to convince other departments of the value of its work, or where it fails to evaluate research in the light of the production, market, and investment problems of the firm.

The problems of conducting industrial research and development vary with the size of the firm and with the nature of the industry. The cost of conducting research is typically between £3,000 and £5,000 per qualified scientist (including his assistants and materials). Thus a small research department employing three qualified staff might cost £10,000 per annum, which is 2 per cent. of a turnover of £500,000. This sum would have to come out of trading profits, and be spent in the hope that a return would accrue from it at a later date. Now trading profit as a percentage of turnover varies widely, even the averages for industries covering (in recent years) a range from 3 to 16 per cent.; these figures relate to gross trading profit, before payments of tax and before providing for the depreciation or extension of capital equipment. Two per cent. of turnover may thus be a very big proportion of the available trading profits, and in fact in those industries in which research is not seen to be essential to production (for instance, pottery, cutlery, and cotton) small firms cannot afford a research department. But there are other industries—such as fine chemicals and electronics—in which small firms conduct research because there are good opportunities of creating new products; indeed, research may be a condition of production.

If we suppose that profit is 20 per cent. of turnover, and that the research expenditure is to be recouped from profits during the first three years of full-scale production, then a new product on which the small research team costing £10,000 per annum worked for a year would require an annual turnover of some £17,000. The chances of an innovation with such a yield vary considerably from industry to industry. We may expect to find the greatest attention to research and development in firms where a developed science has a close bearing on the firm's products or processes; for then an advance in the appropriate science is likely to affect—perhaps radically—the economy of the firm, and the time-lag is likely to be short. Thus an advance in organic chemistry is likely to have a more immediate effect on the chemical industry than an advance in electronics is likely to have on, say, machine tools. Firms in this close relation to a developed science will need to have a research department, if they possibly can, so that they may be in a position to foresee the advances which will affect them. They will find a vast amount of scientific data in existence, relevant to the firm's activities, and this makes it advisable to have staff competent to understand such data. Research is not only desirable, but rendered more possible by the existence of at least some supply of trained research scientists.

This explains why research, which in some industries is confined to the larger firms, is in others an activity of quite small units. The nature of research and development also varies considerably from industry to industry. We quoted in Chapter 3 ratios of research to development cost varying between 10 to 1 and 1 to 200. Such variations reflect differences between projects in a particular industry, and, more importantly, differences between industries. Thus in industries which have grown directly out of laboratory discoveries the form of development is different from that in the engineering industry in which improvements are still in large measure empirical. In the chemical industry it is appropriate to refer to research and development; in many parts of the engineering industry to design and development. The stage of development in the chemical industry does indeed involve engineering, but of a kind often different from that in the engineering industry because theory is more advanced in relation to practice, and it is possible to test the invention in a model or small-scale form. By contrast, in the development of a new aircraft engine it may be necessary to construct a number of full-scale engines, using research information about such things as combustion, the flow of gases, and the properties of metals, but proceeding thereafter by trial and error.

The variations in research and development expenditure with size of firm and with nature of industry have been analysed for American industry in 1953. The results show [1] that of 15,000 companies conducting research and development, 61 per cent. had less than 100 employees and 24 per cent. between 100 and 500, but this 85 per cent. of companies carried only 10 per cent. of the cost of research and development. More than one half of the spending of these small companies was by firms engaged in producing chemicals, machines, and electrical equipment. There are no comparable figures for this country, though there are the Federation of British Industries statistics for research expenditure as a percentage of turnover,[2] which show the effect of the type of industry on that expenditure. These show a range from over 5 per cent. in the case of light electrical engineering and scientific instruments to $\frac{1}{2}$ per cent. or less in textiles, food, drink, and tobacco, and ferrous metals. There is variation from industry to industry in accordance with the possibility of discoveries that will reduce costs and improve products; thus there is naturally a great difference between atomic energy and fine china table-ware. Where the industry is old and the processes involved have not been changed from a 'craft' to a 'scientific' basis, research effort may be limited by the human difficulties of getting the results applied to production. This is a subject to which we return later.

For 144 firms covered by our general case-studies, we have classified the approximate employment on research and development as a percentage of total employment. The industrial grouping closely follows that used by the Federation of British Industries, although certain ambiguities (such as including electronic equipment firms in the scientific instruments group and wires and cables in the light electrical group) may prevent a true comparison with the F.B.I. 'percentage of turnover' figures which are given in the final column.

Research and development as a percentage of turnover and as a percentage of employment varies not only between industries, but also between firms in the same size groups in an industry. We were not surprised at this, for there are so many imponderables, and such time-lags between the conduct of research and the possible profit yield from its application, that we did not expect firms similarly placed to reach the same conclusions about the optimum rate of research and development expenditure. In the majority of firms we visited, however, we felt certain that little thought had been given to the question of deciding

---

[1] *Science and Engineering in American Industry*, National Science Foundation, 1955.

[2] See also the recent D.S.I.R. statistics referred to on p. 44.

the level of research expenditure. We divided decisions on this matter into three kinds—'fully considered', 'elliptical', and 'Topsy'. In a *fully considered* decision a company examines the research and development tasks to be performed to maintain the products and processes of the company on a competitive basis or to achieve some chosen growth in turnover or profit. It then relates these tasks to the size of the research

	Percentages of total employment				F.B.I. Percentage-of-turnover figures
	Large firms	Medium firms	Small firms	Whole industry	
1. Chemicals . . .	4·2	5·4	10·9	6·0	2·4
2. Materials (all) . .	0·4	1·4	0·6	0·9	—
(*a*) Textile . .	0·3	2·6	—	1·8	0·5
(*b*) Clays . .	0·2	0·5	0·6	0·4	1·2
(*c*) Wood, paper .	0·7	1·3	—	1·0	1·2
(*d*) Other materials .	0·3	0·3	—	0·3	0·5
3. Metals (all) . .	2·0	3·3	—	3·0	—
(*a*) Ferrous . .	2·0	0·8	—	1·4	0·4
(*b*) Non-ferrous .	—	4·5	—	4·5	1·1
4. Food . . .	1·0	—	1·0	1·0	0·4
5. Electrical Engineering (all) . .	0·8	1·3	—	1·0	—
(*a*) Heavy . .	1·0	1·7	—	1·4	2·5
(*b*) Light . .	0·7	1·1	—	0·8	5·3
6. Mechanical Engineering (all) . .	5·2	1·7	10·0	5·4	—
(*a*) Heavy . .	10·2	1·3	14·2	7·7	0·7
(*b*) Light . .	0·8	2·5	6·5	2·8	1·1
7. Scientific Instruments .	2·5	7·7	31·4	11·9	5·1

(Large firms—over 2,000 employees; medium—500–2,000; small—under 500.)

No. of firms analysed: Large 52; medium 46; small 46 = 144.
Including firms without research or development staff: Large 2; medium 10; small 26 = 38.

department and its capacity for efficient growth, and the cost of performing these tasks to the finance available. This kind of consideration is rare: we found it in less than 10 per cent. of the companies we visited.

In an *elliptical* decision one or two factors thought to be critical are considered. The critical factor may be taken as the size of the research building, or the supply of scientists, or the availability of finance, or the rate at which research results can be used. In a few cases these 'elliptical' decisions give the same result as a fully considered decision—the choice of the key limiting factor avoids waste of effort. In most cases, however, we felt certain that the 'elliptical' decisions were not based on a limiting factor incapable of alteration, and that this method of decision-taking obscured the need to consider whether to try to overcome the obstacle. Such 'elliptical' decisions become hard to distinguish from *Topsy* decisions—that is to say, decisions to accept things which have 'just growed'. In several firms which replied that their level of expenditure on research and development has 'just grown, but seems to work', the maintenance of a conventional profit margin, or the absence of strong pressure from the research manager for more staff, were taken as evidence that 'it works'.

We have found that the lack of attention to the appropriate level of expenditure is due to three inter-related factors. The first is the absence of clear thought about the objectives of the company, about the role of research and development within these objectives, and therefore about the research outlay the company is to make to achieve these objectives. The second is that one of the major functions of research, as an investment in the future, is often obscured by making short-term survival the main objective of the research department. This may happen, for instance, if that department owes its existence to the pressure of competition, or if it has been created as an extension of technical service and testing. The third factor is that in most of the firms we visited the research department was of recent origin. Such departments have not had long to build up the experience of research and development work on which assessments of success with this or that type or scale of work can be based.

The object of industrial research is to make it possible to improve processes or products or to create new ones. Effective industrial research therefore depends not only on getting an able team of researchers and on bringing into use the worth while results, but also on effective management of the research department. One of the most important aspects of this effective management is the right choice of projects. This entails, not only scientific competence, but also a close knowledge of production and sales problems—and therefore a close liaison with the departments concerned with them. Apart from pressing demands from the production and sales departments that certain problems must be solved quickly, the choice of research projects is a matter of judgement which must take into account the chances of getting a solution within particular periods of time, and the commercial significance of the various lines of research if successful.

As we mentioned in the preceding chapter, very few firms undertake long-term basic research programmes in a new field of knowledge. The outcome of such work is unpredictable. Large firms may, however, do some exploratory research in a defined field. The outcome is also unpredictable, but it is possible to make a reasoned judgement about the wisdom of undertaking the work. Thus, assuming that on scientific grounds the research looks promising, judgement can be based on rough answers to such questions as: Is the potential product or process development of interest to the company? Does it fit in with the present operation of the company, or will it require a new organization? If the latter, is it likely to be too big or too small to be of interest to the company? Is there a good 'growth potential' in the field? Does the company possess special knowledge that makes success more likely than for any other company that might also be undertaking such research?[1] And, if there is a case for proceeding with the exploratory research, would part of the research facilities be better used for it than for less speculative work, such as product- or process-directed research?

In new-product research the questions to be answered are more definite and the answers to them less speculative. They relate to the size of the market, the likely growth in the market, the available substitutes and their prices and qualities relative to the possible prices and qualities of the proposed new product, the raw material position, and the patent complications. With new process research the relevant question may be very simple—how to reduce cost, or how to do what a competitor (who has either reduced price or improved quality) has done, or how to overcome a raw material or patent problem. Similar questions apply to research directed towards product and process improvement. An estimate can be made of the potential yield if the research is successful. This can be put alongside a guess (held with various possible degrees of confidence) about the potential yield from other forms of research, and a judgement made about the balance of research projects. The research director or manager may decide that, given the market position of the firm, the degree of competition, the cash position, and the potential levels of capital formation, he must use his existing resources on research which is likely to yield a quick benefit, without entailing a large capital expenditure. He may attempt to get additional resources for other research. If he fails, this will be because the company is not prepared or cannot afford to take a longer view. Once the issues are stated clearly, a sensible judgement can usually be made, for what in the abstract may appear to be an impossible choice between imponderables is often easy to make once the possible lines of action are stated explicitly.

This brief review of principles affecting the selection of research projects has been included to indicate once again the essential importance, in the successful use of research and development departments, of close linkage of the research policy to the production and sales problems and to the capital position of the firm. We have visited firms in which very little attention is given to the right choice of research projects; just as there are 'Topsy' decisions about the scale of expenditure, so, too, there are 'Topsy' decisions about the nature of research activity. There are other cases where the choice is inefficient because the research department is given (or acquires) insufficient information about the commercial or production problems of the firm—in other words, where the conditions of efficient choice are not satisfied. In other cases a conscious attempt is made to collect the appropriate information and to make a

[1] See J. A. Gardner, *The Evaluation of Research*, in *The Rational Organization of Research*, O.E.E.C., 1956 (E.P.A. Project No. 352).

wise choice, as, for instance, in the use of various types of research or development request forms which require information or estimates about such things as the objectives and cost of the project, its possible effect on the products or processes of the firm, and the capital requirements. Other firms make their decisions through committee systems comprising representatives of research, production, and sales departments. We have not found that any particular type of organization gives most promise of success, but rather that consciousness of the problem on the part of the Board and the chief executives is the matter of greatest importance. The Technical Assistance Missions of the O.E.E.C. reported after a study of industrial research in Europe and North America that 'outside the large industrial concerns . . . in most instances only a very superficial attempt is made either to assess the industrial need or to progress the research project on any economic or commercial basis.' [1] Our investigation in Britain confirms this judgement. The view of the Research Director in a large firm who wrote to us that 'at the moment we work on a programme partly determined by tradition, history, and personalities, and I am certain that some of the aspects of our programme are not well conceived' is a sign of a growing interest in the need to assess research priorities and the potential economic return of various research activities. There is a growing interest, and there is ample room for growth.

Waste of scarce scientific manpower results both from underestimating and from over-estimating the value of research in industry. 'Research' in some firms has not risen much above technical testing and 'trouble shooting'; in others it has been too academic—too little orientated towards commercial needs. The misconception underlying this latter waste of scarce scientific resources is that research is naturally a left-to-right process—that is, that fundamental research produces something which is communicated to the industrial scientist, who performs some applied research and communicates the results to someone else who takes matters a step further. We have not found any cases of successful industrial research where this left-to-right movement is not accompanied by a right-to-left movement, in which management in other departments suggests projects to the research department.

Several companies have made an analysis of the sources of research projects. Thus, for one British firm Dr. Lodge estimates that 45 per cent. of the topics arise from within the research organization, 26 per cent. from operating units, 16 per cent. from sales staff and 11 per cent. as a result of executive action.[2] Ogburn [3] presents for a typical American chemical company the research department as the source of 50 per cent.

[1] *The Organization of Applied Research in Europe, the United States and Canada*, O.E.E.C., 1954, Vol. I, p. 49.

[2] *The Rational Organization of Research*, O.E.E.C., 1956, p. 68.

[3] S. C. Ogburn, *Research Management, Industrial Laboratories*, Sept. 1951.

of the ideas (and 65 per cent. of those accepted), sales 25 per cent., and production 15 per cent. Furnas [1] and Rockwell [2] give similar figures.

Such statistics are difficult to interpret. If we are concerned with the sources of ideas, we must distinguish between the discernment of a need or a possibility and the formulation of the problem in a form suited to a research department investigation. If this latter sense is the correct one, the only surprising thing about the statistics is the lowness of the percentage of ideas coming from the research department. If it is the former sense, we cannot judge the significance of the figure apart from a knowledge of the formal and informal relations, or flow of information, between the research department on the one hand and the production and sales departments on the other. The closer the liaison, the less should be the need for a formal request from the latter two departments for an inquiry into this or that.

We have not ourselves found it possible to collect worthwhile general statistics on the sources of research projects. Many firms have not kept records, or would find it impossible to impute origins with any certainty, as, for instance, where there are technical committees for deciding on priorities. Further, an able research manager or director, when he finds that sales or production staff are not interested in discussing some proposition, may arrange for the proposition to be put to him from a different department.

We have, however, examined in some detail over 200 cases of product or process developments involving research and development departments. In most of these it is not possible to say whether the original impulse to undertake the research and development came from the research, or from the sales, or from the production, department. In sixty cases this is, however, possible. Twenty-five per cent. of the developments originated in a research or development department. Eighteen per cent. came from commercial foresight—that is to say, there was a forecast that, due to market developments, there would be the need for a particular new product or process, and the problem of meeting this need was thrown to the research staff for solution. A further 10 per cent. arose from shorter-term needs of the sales department. In 18 per cent. of the cases the origin was an overseas contact or an overseas example— in many cases related to currency restrictions; in 14 per cent. the origin was consumers' pressure—the consumer here being most frequently a Government agency such as a defence department or the Atomic Energy Authority; and 10 per cent. came from the production department.

In the other 150 cases, in which any attempts to impute precise origin would involve inaccuracies, it is nevertheless safe to say that substantially less than 25 per cent. appear to originate from the research

---

[1] *Research in Industry*, Van Nostrand, 1948.
[2] *Midwestern Engineer*, Sept. 1953, pp. 7-9.

or development department. This does not, of course, mean that research is unimportant in these cases, for these developments depend on industrial research. It simply means that the research and development department solves urgent problems supplied by other departments of the firm. We have not found much relation between technical progressiveness and a tendency for ideas to originate in the research department. The proportion so originating tends, however, to be higher in industries based on science and in firms in which research departments have been operating for some time.

If our conclusion that most projects originate outside research departments is valid, it is tempting to picture a queue of suitable projects forming up awaiting the attention of research staff, so that an expansion of that staff would yield a good return in new ideas well fitted to the production and sales needs of the company. But there are other points which must be watched. The productivity of research departments, as judged by the proportion of their output which is usable, varies greatly, and mere expansion of size may not be so important as an increase of productivity. Furthermore, the fact that a project has been suggested by a production or sales department is not a proof that it is worth attention. There has first to be an understanding of what research can achieve in the company's particular position; and that means a clear assessment of the likely lines of development and a judgement about the distance ahead that the firm should appropriately be looking. Without these, many projects (whatever their origin) will be ill-chosen.

We think that there is evidence of this bad choice, and we see it in the fact that some important advances have not been frustrated so much as never considered. The basic knowledge, the research staff, production facilities, and potential markets have all been there; what has been lacking has been the clear-thinking and imaginative individual or group who could see the appropriateness of the advance to the company's interests. While this lack is in part a sign of the general shortage of genius, it could also in part be made up by better routines of clear thinking about research policy.

We tended to assume at the beginning of this investigation that the use of research staff for 'trouble-shooting' frustrated the rapid application of science to industry, and that the existence of long-term research projects was a sign of a well-conceived and well-managed department. This view was humorously expressed in its extreme form by Mark Spade when he wrote: 'It is far better, if one needs a quick answer on some technical problem, to get a roughly approximate one from old Joe Binks the foreman, who hasn't the disadvantages of a scientific education. Give the Research Department only Big Long-Term Problems and leave the results in trust for your heirs.' [1] But this view ignored the existence of production troubles beyond the competence of the works

[1] M. Spade, *Business for Pleasure*, Hamish Hamilton, 1950, p. 22

staff, of pressing short-term research and development problems, which may have resulted from basic research elsewhere, of resistance within the firm to the use of research or development output, and of the shortage of resources to finance long-term research.

When research staff are first introduced to an established firm they are mistrusted by the 'old hands'. The process of acceptance is many-sided. It involves tact and understanding, but in gaining the confidence of the production department and the necessary understanding of production problems 'trouble-shooting' is a great help. Once the research department is accepted it is often inundated with requests to solve urgent problems. It may not be possible to employ other scientists to undertake less urgent work, but the successful solution of the urgent problem will often, by increasing turnover, make easier the employment of a larger research staff. The research department may then come to be less dominated by the immediate problems of the production and sales departments,[1] and may be able to work to longer time horizons, and to place rather more emphasis on creating big changes in products or processes.

There is also a limit to the rate of growth in research departments in any one time period. This limit is set by finance—for the use of the research department to increase turnover is often a pre-condition of an increase in research expenditure; it is set by the efficient rate of growth in the research team itself—newcomers must become familiar with the problems of the firm and new graduates with the ways of industrial research, projects must be formulated and planned, research leaders must be recruited and trained; it is set by the capacity of the production departments to absorb change, and this capacity is often dependent on draining scientists and technologists away from the research department itself. We have been able to trace in several firms the lengthening of the time horizon of the research department, and its gradual growth as a semi-independent agent of change in products and processes. Any suggestion that the research department should grow naturally through time into a quite independent agent of change is, however, misleading—if a firm is to make the greatest use of scientific developments there must continue to be close working relations between the various departments of the firm. The communication problem in basic scientific ideas may well be left to the research department, but not so with technology. In the development stage, technological 'know-how' is often the vital link between research and successful pilot-plant or full-scale work. This technological 'know-how' may be provided by the production department or by another firm. The sales force also often acts as an important

---

[1] Sales departments do not always take the short view—they do not do so if competitors have a research department which is making big changes, or if the sales force is technically competent and capable of seeing that a development in a field of science or technology creates a new possibility for their firm.

E

link in the communications chain, by providing information about technical developments elsewhere as well as about market possibilities. Furthermore, the vision to see from trends in technology and markets that there will probably be a need for this or that type of development may reside in a person outside the research department, so that if that department ceases to receive outside directions or suggestions it may miss important potential lines of development.

Thus far we have drawn no clear distinction between research and development. There are many cases where there is no clear distinction, as when, for instance, a research department is able to solve a problem in chemistry or metallurgy referred to it by the production department, which, in turn, is then able to use the result directly to change production methods. In design and development in engineering there is often nothing corresponding to research in the chemical industry. There are also many firms of a size which does not justify specialization between research and development or between development and production engineering. But development is conceptually a distinct activity, and we now turn to consider some of its special problems.

The first of these is that many firms *start* at the stage of development, using the published results of research in chemistry, physics, or metallurgy, to develop new products or processes. There is often, as we mentioned in Chapter 4, a considerable delay before the research results are published in a form that comes to the notice of, or can be absorbed by, the scientists and technicians in the firm with the development department. Even in a firm that also conducts research there is something of a transmission problem. A new research result may or may not have significance for production, and even when the researcher is at hand to explain what he has achieved and why his discoveries should be used, it may be difficult to catch the interest of the development or production engineers. This is of particular importance because not all research results can be taken to the development stage.

We have mentioned in Chapter 3 that there is no simple or uniform ratio of research to development and production expenditure. Nor is there any simple or uniform percentage of research results that go into development. That varies very largely from firm to firm with the origin of their research or development projects and with the ways in which potential projects are evaluated. Nevertheless many research results are not taken further, either because it seems fairly clear that it would be unprofitable to develop them, or because some must be excluded on cost grounds. The greater the cost of development, the greater the importance of exclusion. The less the attention of the research staff to the commercial significance of their projects, the greater the chance that research with great potentialities in industrial application will be excluded, if only because the man who is preoccupied with research as such will not be anxious to father his idea on to the development staff.

Various methods are used by firms anxious to avoid the loss of promising research ideas, but we have formed the view that organization is less important than attention to the evaluation of research and development.

Development work sometimes requires the services of scientists or engineers with training or competence in more than one field—for instance, the chemist with skill in engineering for process development in the chemical industry, or the engineer with competence in higher mathematics for the development of automatic control systems. Once the need for such 'hybrids' is recognized, training facilities are set up, but development in relatively new fields is frequently impeded by the absence of these 'hybrids'. Attention to special training facilities, such as we find in the Atomic Energy Authority, is beyond the capacity of most firms. In any case the general shortage of engineers sets an acute problem in development work.

In the process of development, reliance on persons or organizations outside the firm is generally greater than with research. Because of the need for special pieces of equipment, the interest and skill of outside firms can be vital to the speedy and successful conclusion of a development project. The dependence of the development on others also takes other forms. Thus a manufacturer of machinery for the tobacco trade may find that, due to the heavy duty on tobacco, testing in the development stage is feasible only if a potential customer undertakes it under workshop conditions. The manufacturer of diesel engines may find full-scale development work too costly without the co-operation of a friendly customer. At an earlier stage the development may depend on the willingness of the production department in the firm itself to co-operate in the work. This co-operation may be difficult to obtain except in odd hours and week-ends, simply because the use of production facilities for development purposes may disrupt planning and interrupt the flow of output. The provision of separate production facilities in the development department has led in a number of firms we have visited to a great increase in the efficiency of that department. This solution is not, however, possible in every firm. Further forms of inter-dependence that may impede development will be considered in the next chapter.

We have defined development in Chapter 2 as starting when decisions to try to proceed to full-scale production have been taken. This means that the development stage is properly concerned, not only with such things as scaling-up a process that works at laboratory scale, or building and testing an engine that looks fine in its paper design, but also with estimating the costs of running at full-scale and the potential demand for the product. In other words, the development stage is properly used, not only to establish technical probabilities, but also to establish market probabilities. It does not follow that all firms with a development department use it for both technical and economic assessment. They do not; firms that regard market survey work as part of their development process are rare. This weakness of approach to economic assessment is relevant to the question of whether firms are slow in getting through the development stage, though the effect of the weakness is complicated. Thus pilot-plant facilities may be used for testing the market for a new product. If the test is conducted by letting odd lots get into shops, the testing may be long and inconclusive. If other firms are given a chance to test what would for them be a process development, the testing may be shorter and more conclusive. We have found several examples, however, where success depends on a chain of reactions between firms and consumers, and where little effort was made to establish what this chain reaction was likely to be. This inadequacy of testing may lead to considerable delay in proceeding beyond the development stage. But a failure of testing at this stage may force the firm later to become much more aggressive or efficient in selling and production engineering than it had originally planned; we have found examples of this too.

Chapter 7

THE READINESS TO USE THE OUTFLOW
FROM RESEARCH AND DEVELOPMENT

THE burden of the preceding chapter was that industrial research is a management technique which for efficient use must be related to other management problems of the firm. We turn now to look at the other side of the matter by examining how the outflow from research and development comes into use. For even if research and development policy is based on a clear understanding of the financial strength, production problems, and market position of the firm, the output of the research and development department will not be properly used unless the other sections of management—finance, production, marketing—are ready to bring the potential new products or processes into use. The readiness, or even the capacity, to manage new products or processes cannot be taken for granted. Management is seldom a consistent whole, and there are firms where pressure from the research and development department to do new things is not matched by receptivity in other parts of the firm. In such firms a change in management structure and in the persons holding key positions in sales and production departments may be a prerequisite to the use of the output of research and development. This is a matter to which we give further attention below and in Chapter 12.

Decisions to use the output of the research and development department are influenced by three main things—the view taken on whether the new product or process would be worthwhile if it were introduced; the attitude to the problems which would be set by the introduction; and the preparedness, or the capacity, to find the financial resources for the innovation. On the face of it a new product would be worthwhile if it was likely to bring a significant reduction in costs of production, or improvement in quality. Whether the problems set by the introduction would be manageable or worth tackling raises different questions. There is a limit, in any period of time, to the amount of change that can be managed. A particular project may appear unmanageable because there are so many other changes on hand; or it may be judged unmanageable because its operation would entail the use of human skills which do not exist in the firm at the moment, and whose acquisition is not a simple matter of labour recruitment. There might, for instance, have to be a significant amount of retraining, or the appointment of new types of manager involving the demotion or retirement of existing managers, or the introduction of entirely new grades of staff at salaries which would disrupt the existing salary structure. Judgement on all these matters will be influenced by the degree of the external pressure to make changes, and by the personal attitudes of the people concerned. The preparedness to find financial resources for a project thought to be worthwhile and manageable depends on the quantity of financial resources available, on attitudes to risk and on alternative investment opportunities; but these 'investment decisions' we reserve for consideration in the next chapter. In this chapter we shall be specially concerned with judgements about whether research and development results are worth using and manageable in use. We shall deal in the first part of this chapter with a firm's use of its own research and development output, and in the second part with the use of the research and development output of research associations and private inventors.

The research and development staff of firms is properly regarded as yielding outputs that will be useful in so far as they are used in production; that is to say, useful in so far as they become production inputs. A large part of research and development output, however, does not become a production input. This does not prove that the research department is choosing the wrong projects, nor does it prove that the firm lacks the people or the organization capable of making use of the research and development output; for the outcome of both research and development is in some measure unpredictable.

As an illustration of a wise and planned wastage that follows from this unpredictability, the procedure in a successful medium-sized firm in the fine chemical industry is instructive. This firm attempts to produce two or three new products each year, an aim which is set in relation to the capital resources and the technical sales force of the firm. The relevant scientific literature is examined in a systematic way, leading throughout the year to 200–300 suggestions for research. These are reduced 'on paper' to the fifty that look most promising on scientific and commercial grounds. After preliminary laboratory investigations and further consideration of commercial factors—whether the market would be large enough to justify the venture, whether the field would be too strongly competitive, whether the cost of raw materials or the adequacy of their supply would be serious problems—a dozen ideas are selected for systematic laboratory investigation. Finally the two or three that look most promising on commercial grounds are chosen for actual development.

As this example shows, it may be quite natural for part of the output of the research department to remain unused. Similarly projects may, for a variety of reasons, fail to survive the development stage. The questions which should be posed at the research stage—such as the scale of capital investment involved, the cost of production, the likely market—are, in an efficient company, posed again; since more information will now be available, some previously doubtful projects will be rejected. In some cases rejection will be easy—for instance, if 'scaling-up' has produced insuperable problems, or has shown that the probable level of operating cost would be prohibitive. But for other projects the doubts will still not be resolved. The firm may think that the project, if taken into production, could be either a resounding success or a failure; to go forward may be costly, not to go forward may later prove to have been mistaken. In such a situation the *attitudes* of other departments to research and development results will be specially important.

Sometimes the choice of projects for continuance or rejection will be wrongly made. This may be due to an inescapable ignorance of the future; but it can be due to a variety of other reasons, which we must now examine. A wrong decision at the research stage may be due to lack of scientific insight. About this one can make the obvious remarks that the insight of some scientists is greater than that of others, and that if the average quality of industrial scientists were better, problems would be better chosen. Scientific insight is not, however, the only thing. An understanding of the key factors in the industrial application of science is important at the research stage. Lack of this understanding—a failure to think 'operationally' or in terms of inter-connected technical developments—may result in a failure to look at worthwhile problems.

There may be a choice of problems which does not fit the capital and market position of the firm. Research projects that, if successful, would involve a capital expenditure of some millions are obviously inappropriate in a firm that can only manage to invest a few thousands. Research projects that would not, even if found to be as successful as was supposed when starting the project, pay for themselves in savings of cost or in new revenue are also usually ill chosen. We have been impressed by the high proportion of companies that do not attempt an economic assessment before embarking on research projects, or choosing between alternative projects. The chance that projects will be foolishly chosen is reduced in those firms where a close liaison is maintained between the research, production, and sales departments; for then some sort of economic assessment, even if only rough and ready, is more likely to be made. Such an assessment is also important where the firm is in doubt whether or not to take a project into the development stage. A careful survey of economic trends will often enable a sensible decision to be reached, whereas otherwise the decision might depend on the moods or on the relative strength of personality of the persons involved in the decision. We have noted a number of cases in which a firm later regretted its failure to act on a project, but it had made no careful economic assessment at the time. The amount of attention given to market testing and research as an aid to decision taking of this type seems to be remarkably small.

Failure at the development stage may be due to a failure of technological insight. Some problems are taken to the development stage, though a good technologist would reject them; but equally some problems fail in the development stage because there are no good-quality technologists available. As we have seen the problem, the failure to carry through projects, or to carry them through quickly, is due more to the lack of technologists than to a wrong choice of problems. There is no point in taking into development more projects than the development staff can manage—in some firms we have noted an inefficient congestion in the development department.

A decision not to proceed from development to application may be due to a large number of factors. As in the earlier stages, there may be good reasons for rejection which have only just become apparent. Thus, it may be clear that the probable saving in process cost would not justify the expenditure on changing a process; or that a potential new product would not be of a quality or within a price range that would justify its introduction. Failure is not, however, always due to rejection on commercial grounds; it may be due to the inability of the research staff to convince others of the value of the development. Such inability may have its origin in a factor mentioned above, namely, the failure at the research or development stage to give adequate attention to the commercial objectives of the firm, the scale of production, the capital position of the firm, the time during which it looks for a return on capital invested, or the expected yield of capital that it regards as justifying investment in a new development. Where this attention is given, it is usual to find that results are presented in a form that is convincing and arresting to the production or sales or finance members of the management.

The possibility that the production or sales departments will not be anxious to apply what is handed on to them as a successful development is least where the development is something that they have themselves asked for. Where they have not themselves felt the lack of the new idea, receptivity will be lower and the departments may even have an interest in opposing the idea. Thus, the innovation might disturb smooth running in the production department. It may be necessary to disrupt output while new machines are installed, to retrain workers, and introduce new staff specialists. All this will increase the problems of the production managers and it may, where there are radical changes in techniques, make the managers doubt their capacity to manage. This type of situation is, in fact, almost certain to arise when science is applied in a former craft industry. (See Appendix III.) The opposition may not be due to a feeling of insecurity or to indolence, but to a genuine judgement that it is not in the interests of productive efficiency to interfere with existing arrangements. One of the most interesting attempted solutions to this is that adopted by a progressive engineering firm. Under boom conditions, when the actual or predicted order book is full for two years ahead, inventions produced by research and development are put into cold-storage. Production departments can, therefore, get on with the job of meeting orders and keeping to their schedules. But when the boom shows signs of breaking, when the order book shortens, the production department naturally changes its attitude and becomes willing, indeed anxious, to adopt innovations. At this point the fruits of research and development are brought out of cold-storage, and the firm is enabled to bring forward new products at a time when competition is most acute. It has been found that by adopting this policy the capacity to absorb change is increased rather than diminished.

This is a particular solution of the problem, appropriate to a particular firm. This firm had previously created the conditions for innovation, not only by setting up a design and development department, but also by appointing able and appropriately trained executives in the production, sales, and accounting sections of the firm. Such executives cannot function properly without an appropriate division of responsibility and without provision for co-ordination; that is to say, they cannot function without organization. The desirable form of organization is not unique, but varies with the size and pattern of activities of the firm, and the balance and strength of personalities in key positions; and since size, type of activity, and the occupiers of key positions change, the organization needs periodical revision if it is to remain efficient. Sometimes this revision is a matter of bringing the planned or paper form of organization into line with the actual organization that has grown up; sometimes it involves the planning of a new form of organization to accommodate new types of staff (e.g. research workers, works chemists, or electronics engineers), or an adaptation to new ways of production (e.g. on a change from batch to continuous flow production) or to new lines of activity.

We have examined many patterns of organization that have been evolved to facilitate change. Given a basic ability in the senior management, it is clear that consciousness of the problem and due attention to it are more important than a particular management structure. Attention to the problem is, however, commonly insufficient. This is sometimes due to preoccupation with pressing problems—often preoccupation with things that have already gone wrong—and sometimes due to a failure to conceive that there is a problem of organization. Often the simplest way to offset preoccupation with other problems is to call in a firm of consultants. This has a three-fold advantage—it adds a group of experts to the pay-roll of the firm, it gives an outside view of the problem, and it forces the Board when it considers the consultants' report to focus its attention on the problem. We have, of course, found several cases where the consultants have recommended what had already been urged from within—often an obvious change which the Board would have accepted if provision had been made to channel the recommendations to it and to focus attention on them. There were other cases where consultants had been called in because of a conflict of views in the company, or simply to get an outside and experienced view. In some of the most important cases the consultants had been brought in by a new managing director or by a new owner because of a desire or a need to make quite radical changes in the methods and managers in the firm— in other words, to overcome a past failure to see that there is a problem of organization for efficiency.

To a great extent the receptiveness of a firm to technical change must depend on the understanding and appreciation of science and technology to be found in the various ranks of management; and this, in turn, depends on the training and experience of individual managers. The significance of this may be judged from the great care which certain large and progressive firms in the chemical, electrical, and steel industries (for example) lavish on the selection and training of managers. In one firm, for instance, a large proportion of graduate entrants are given a comprehensive two-year course which includes training in research techniques, workshop and drawing-office experience, and work in production and sales departments, together with lectures and discussions on the structure and organization of the company. Towards the end of the course trainees are advised to take posts in departments— research, development, production, sales, etc.—for which their aptitudes, as revealed during the course, seem to fit them. Courses of this kind are usually under the direct control of senior management and are not a responsibility delegated to juniors, such as supervisors, foremen, and apprentice-masters. They are generally beyond the means of smaller firms unless organized on a co-operative basis.

The aim of such systematic training and selection is quite different from that of a course in a particular technique, such as may be provided by a local technical college. It is intended to give a general understanding of the firm's organization and work; applied to entrants who have already had a first-class scientific or technological education, it is likely to result in a management which is both receptive to change and knowledgeable from the first about the activities of all departments of the firm.

At the opposite end of the scale is the firm in a traditional industry which recruits potential managers at an early age, trains them solely in the technical knowledge of the firm and its industry, and prides itself on its 'practical' management, its independence, and its self-sufficiency. Such firms, as we shall see in Chapter 10, are often highly resistant to new ideas. This may be regarded as an example of the general proposition that the progressiveness of a firm or industry depends in some measure on the qualities and knowledge of the available professional labour supply. If we consider the chemical and electronic industries as, by and large, progressive, then surely this is not unrelated to the supply of highly trained chemists and physicists immediately available for recruitment? Men trained to a standard independent of specialized requirements may take with them into industry methods of thought and scientific attitudes different from those of men brought up in the established practices of an industry. This is not to say that scientific graduates know all the answers, but an infusion of men with independent views is beneficial to the firms and industries concerned, and industries without such an external supply are in more danger of a narrow parochialism.

The possibility that there has been inadequate attention to management structure and to the technical training of managers at various levels must be kept in mind when judging the output of a research and development department in relation to its use. On the face of it, it is reasonable to say that if a firm persistently carries through with success more research and development projects than it is able to exploit, then its research and development expenditure is excessive. Clearly there is some lack of balance or proportion in such a firm, but it does not follow that the correct action would be simply to reduce research expenditure. It may be that a transfer of scientists from research to production or sales would increase the rate of absorption of new developments, by improving the receptivity of management. It is not uncommon for progressive firms to recruit from research and development departments for production and sales posts—a policy which, so long as the scale of research can be maintained by new recruitment, is often popular with research departments because it gives them 'agents' or 'fifth columnists' in key positions.

The case-studies did not include comparisons with countries where the proportion of scientists employed in research and production differs from that in Britain, and we cannot speak with confidence of 'correct' ratios of employment of scientists in different parts of the firm. We have, however, formed the impression that there are too few scientists and engineers in production and sales relative to scientists in research; too few in the sense that the absorption rate for worthwhile developments could be increased by re-deploying the existing supply of scientists. We get some further indication of the possible importance of the problem by comparing the use of scientists in this country and in the U.S.A. The much higher output of scientists per head of population in the U.S.A. (see Chapter 9) does not lead there to the employment of a much higher percentage of the population in development or research. Most of the relatively greater number of scientists and technologists are used in non-research activities, including production and sales departments. As compared with this country, the U.S.A. has a smaller ratio of research scientists to production scientists.

The supervisory or foreman level of management needs further consideration. Foremen, upon whom so much in the last resort depends, have recently suffered a number of setbacks in status and prestige. In former years the foreman was able to fulfil his function through the disciplinary powers vested in him and through his own superior technical knowledge and gifts of character and leadership. Today, the advent of full employment and the growth of trade-union power have limited his disciplinary powers, while the development of joint consultation between senior management and the men on the shop floor has, to some extent, undermined his status. At the same time the elaboration of technical departments has diminished the importance of his technical knowledge.[1] Under modern wage conditions it is perfectly possible and, indeed, not uncommon, for ordinary operatives to earn more than the foreman, and this is not always compensated by a sense of superior responsibility or status. Many foremen have worked for years in one particular factory without having contact with, or knowledge of, people other than their immediate superiors and the members of their teams. Under these conditions it is scarcely surprising that some foremen do not take immediately to innovations: the sudden eruption into the production department of comparatively unknown sales, research, or development staff, with requirements and plans whose reasons are not known to the foremen and whose technical content is not understood by them, does not make for the best possible climate in which to launch an innovation.

Of course a great deal can be done towards solving this problem by fostering intelligent co-operation between departments and by cultivating the atmosphere of give and take. But a small number of large and very progressive firms have taken the matter a great deal further: they have instituted systematic and well-planned training courses for their foremen. The aim of these courses is not to impart technical information—that can be done by research associations, trade groups and associations, night schools, and so forth—but to enable the foreman to understand the operation of his firm and its various departments. He can thus be led to see that sales, research, and development departments have their own problems and that their demands are not arbitrary; and he can get to know other members of management, and also his fellow foremen. In brief, he is helped to fit his own job into the general picture of the activities of the firm. There seems little doubt that much more could and should be done for foremen along these lines.

One of the advantages of the management training schemes which we have mentioned is that, whatever his ultimate destination, the trainee must acquire an appreciation of the methods and problems of all the main departments of the firm. This is important because the interests and attitudes of research and development on the one hand and those of sales and production on the other may differ greatly. It is only natural that research and development staff should wish to see their brainchildren reach as near perfect a state as possible, while it is equally

---

[1] *The Foreman: A Study of Supervision in British Industry*, National Institute of Industrial Psychology, 1951, pp. 78, 83.

natural for sales staff to want to get any innovation on to the market as soon as possible. The production departments may be unenthusiastic about accommodating innovations which upset their steady flow, and may be unwilling to interrupt scheduled work in order to give the development staff facilities for pilot-plant or prototype work. In these ways tensions can, and in certain instances do, build up between departments.

It is evident that, if the purpose of the firm is to be fulfilled as efficiently as possible, these tensions must be kept to a minimum. We have not found that the differing interests or attitudes make co-operation between the departments very difficult, so long as the problem is recognized. Of eighty-four firms from which we gained useful evidence on this matter, only seventeen found these differences a continued impediment to the application of new ideas. In some of these firms, intermediate departments going by such varied names as 'model shop', 'methods department', and 'project unit' helped to provide bridges between the two sets of interests and attitudes. We did not usually find significant differences where research and development staff had transferred from production work, or vice versa; nor when the firm was likely to be staffed by people of similar attitude—as, for example, in many chemical firms, whose production, research, and development staff are largely chemistry graduates and where innovation is a normal and continuing activity. The difficulty does not exist when firms deal largely with unique products ('one-offs') and can claim that production and development are substantially the same thing; and it is not to be found when the usual practice of research and development staff is to 'follow an innovation through' until it is in full production.

In most of these cases the problem has existed, has been recognized, and has finally been successfully solved. It is remarkable that the great majority of firms which have solved the problem belong to the scientific and modern group of industries, whereas all but two of those in which, according to our evidence, it is recognized but still significant belong to more traditional or craft-based industries. Broadly speaking, there are three important ways in which differences of attitude have an effect in these cases. They are:

1. Hindrances arising through the reluctance of operatives, foremen, and managers to accept innovation from whatever source it may come. The attitude here is that of the old-fashioned craftsman with his dislike of innovation and his unwillingness to change his practices. This attitude may continue right up the tree to the manager who has 'come up the hard way'.
2. Cases where specific differences of view between research or development and production staff lead to hindrances which can be explained by the newness of research and development in

old-established firms operating in traditional industries; research
and development is still regarded with suspicion and distrust.

3. Cases of firms apparently anxious to innovate, but which, because
of the traditions of the industry and the training and experience
of the managers, lack the means of evaluating scientific information. There is a consequent scepticism about the help which they
can gain from research. In such firms one hears remarks of the
kind 'we don't need science in this firm; what we want are inventive men with practical experience. . . .'

Of these, the first, in which only three firms were involved, belongs
more properly to the general field of 'labour resistance' to innovations
(p. 172). It would be reasonable to say that the second hindrance is essentially a short-term affair which will disappear after production and sales
staff have got accustomed to the research and development activities;
that is to say, it is a 'growing pain' of research and development in an
old industry. These 'growing pains' may be dulled and shortened; we
have seen from the case-studies that firms in old-established industries
which deliberately set out, from the time research and development are
begun, to make the new department accepted by the rest of the firm
can often achieve a smooth and rapid transition. Hindrances of the third
type are of particular significance in long-established industries in
which research has been unimportant.

The second part of the general problem posed in this chapter was the
use of the research and development output of research associations and
private inventors. The work of the research associations includes basic
research into raw materials, applied research on technical problems of
the industry, and (less frequently) development work to pilot-plant
stage and comparative studies in operating efficiency. The balance of
these activities varies greatly in different associations. Co-operative research should give some economy of effort, and in traditional industries
where the predominant size of firm is small, as, for instance, in pottery,
cutlery, and jute, the research associations are the chief providers for
research. Industries in which research and development are concentrated
in the research associations present, however, special problems.

In most research associations the members who make greatest use of
the research output are the larger firms. This is easy to explain where a
large firm has a research or development department of its own; for then
it is able, through the technical committees of the association, to influence the association's programme and arrange its own to fit in.
There is, however, a more substantial reason. Much research association output, even when taken to pilot-plant stage, is unusable unless
the firm concerned has the scientific or engineering staff capable of
understanding it, scaling it up, and putting it in full working order.
Large firms are more likely to have such staff than small firms. Much re-

search and development output runs to waste because firms in the industry lack the technical staff able to comprehend and develop it. This waste presents research associations with a difficult problem of selection. Basic research into materials may seem a pre-condition of substantial changes in methods of production, yet, for the time being at least, this may increase the gap between research and application. Development work that fits an invention for shop-floor application often involves workshop trials and adjustments, yet development work of this kind may lead the research association (in an attempt to maintain equal treatment of its members) into a considerable amount of technical testing and consultancy, with a consequent reduction in basic research. There is no one solution to this problem and, quite rightly in view of their differing circumstances, research associations have taken differing views on the matter. Where facilities for technical training in the industry are little developed, and where the use of scientists and engineers in the industry is exceptional rather than common, the research association has a clear responsibility to place considerable emphasis on taking applied research results to the firms and on taking development to the stage at which it is ready for production use. Otherwise the research association, set up to facilitate the application of science to industry, will simply create a development gap.

The research and development output coming from within a firm is often not used unless it is 'sold' to the production department. The problem of the research association in getting its output used is necessarily greater because it is an outside organization. 'Selling research' is therefore still more significant to a research association than to a research department. Good selling often entails the use of scarce scientific staff as liaison officers, just as good selling by a company often entails the creation of a highly competent technical sales section. One of several good examples of this is provided by the Hosiery and Allied Trades Research Association. It has tried to concentrate its research and development work on instruments and devices that could be readily used in factories. When it made known the first instrument it produced, only 5 per cent. of members replied to an invitation to express interest on a business reply card, yet 85 per cent. of members ordered the device after liaison officers had visited the firm and demonstrated it.

But to invent a readily usable instrument and to appoint liaison officers is not always enough, even when (as in the textile industry) the nature of the processes makes it possible for the research association to produce simple machines and instruments that can be applied easily. The Shirley Institute has found it necessary to set up a special firm— Shirley Developments Ltd.—to manage its inventions for the cotton industry. After the Shirley Institute has built, modified, and tested a new machine, subjected it to normal workshop experience, and found it good, there are several stages of development before it gains or can gain a wide application. It cannot be sold unless it is produced, and produced at a price that will make it a potentially attractive proposition to textile firms. This may call for a re-design to facilitate economical production, and such re-design may delay market exploitation considerably. Finally, the machine must be made known in the industry by an active sales staff.

As the Shirley Institute is not a manufacturing organization it had to find a manufacturer who would produce each machine, not simply to oblige the Institute, but to do a good job and find a big market for the product. Textile machinery producers already have a sales organization to cover the trade, but they do not always possess facilities for the precision engineering required for the manufacture of the Shirley instruments or machinery. Precision engineering firms outside the trade, on the other hand, lack the trade connections and may not make effective selling efforts; or firms that could do the job may not be keen to take on a Shirley invention, as they have a sufficiency of their own requiring the attention of their scarce design and engineering staff; or (because of staff shortage) they may re-design for production efficiency without checking the re-design with the Shirley Institute—a procedure which, on occasions, has produced defects in Shirley instruments. These development difficulties have been so great as to induce the Institute to set up a separate organization with the specific job of overcoming them.

The critical nature of the relation between inventor and producer applies also with private inventors. We will take two cases. In the first, the Raper Autoleveller, the inventor found his own producer. In the second, the Packman potato harvester, the inventor worked through the National Research Development Corporation.

The Raper Autoleveller is a device used in the drawing of wool to produce a sliver of even thickness. This has made it possible to reduce the number of processes in the drawing operation from 8 or 9 to 3, to halve the amount of labour required, to reduce waste of wool in drawing, and save floor space. These annual savings come to more than one-third of the capital cost of the Autoleveller. As the device comes at the beginning of the process and entails very few alterations in the mill it is relatively simple to try out. Indeed, the industry was ready to try it out; despite the store it sets by traditional methods and the quality these seem to guarantee, there was a feeling in the industry that the drawing process was unnecessarily long. The Autoleveller has thus been adopted quickly; it was shown at a Manchester exhibition in October 1953, and large orders were taken from the beginning. Yet this desirable invention could easily have been frustrated or considerably delayed.

Mr. G. F. Raper, a Cambridge-trained engineer, left his family mill in 1948 to give his time to the invention of a shorter worsted drawing process. Throughout 1948 he worked alone, and in 1949 he had established the principle and constructed a 'mock-up' of the gill-box and draw-box Autolevellers, and of a 'pressure-drafter', a device which he patented in October 1949, but had then developed far less than the first two. Yet this pressure-drafter was ultimately to prove the key to success, for without it the advantages of the gill-box and draw-box might not have been enough to induce a manufacturer to tool up for their production.

After many attempts to get a sponsor both here and in the U.S.A., Raper approached the Wool Industries Research Association towards the end of 1948. He was given a consultant's fee and facilities for making an accurate and reliable prototype, but after gill-boxes and draw-boxes embodying several improvements had been made the Research Association suggested to Raper that he find an interested manufacturer for further development. At this stage a firm of textile machinery manufacturers took out a licence to produce the Autoleveller. The inventor was paid a retaining salary, and in 1951 two gill-boxes were made for mill trials. An associated company then re-designed the gill-box and prepared prototypes for further mill trials. Raper had informed this company of his pressure-drafter, but at that stage he did not envisage its use on an Autoleveller. Not until January 1953 did he perfect the pressure-drafter and realize that it could transform the efficiency of the draw-box Autoleveller; this in turn increased the advantage of the gill-box. (The gill-box is involved in the operation prior to the draw-box, and the operation of the pressure-drafter at the draw-box made it possible to use a higher speed gill-box, with a much larger package, to feed the draw-box.) Progress was made possible by assistance in January 1951 from a large company producing knitting wools and hosiery yarns, who gave Raper a salary, and provided a workshop and facilities for making a prototype. In January 1953 the pressure-drafter was put on the draw-box Autoleveller, and trials at a mill of the company producing knitting wools were so successful that in May 1953 Raper was able to demonstrate the nature of the improvement to the machinery manufacturer, who on the basis of these trials and its own trials with the new gill-box was ready to go forward. After intensive effort in the drawing-office, it produced two specially designed machines embodying the Raper inventions for the Manchester Textile Exhibition of October 1953. These machines, together with the jigs and tools for their production, were manufactured 'off the drawing-board'.

Success in this case was due to a variety of factors—first, of course, the talent and persistence of the inventor; second, the help given by the Research Association to bridge the gap between the mock-up and the prototype; third, the financial assistance, given by the three firms, which enabled Raper to keep working at his inventions; fourth, the workshop and testing facilities provided by the knitting-wool firm; and finally, the interest of a textile machinery firm which possessed the facilities for

F

precision engineering which production of the Raper invention required. This firm re-designed the gill-box for production purposes, produced a special machine to incorporate the Raper inventions, designed and produced (by 1955) a special Continental type of machine, and arranged working exhibitions in Australia and Canada. This combination of technical development and marketing drive played an important part in the commercial success of Raper's inventions.

The Packman potato harvester was tried out in prototype and gradually improved over a period of ten years by the inventor, who possessed a small factory, but lacked the resources to launch the machine on the market. The National Research Development Corporation (N.R.D.C.) arranged for further development work on it, particularly in the light of judgement on it at the Royal Agricultural Society's open competition for potato harvesters in 1952. In 1954 the harvester was, in the view of N.R.D.C., 'out of the development stage' and licensed for manufacture. To a manufacturer, however, the development stage may not be complete, for in development by an outside body the problems he faces may not (and often could not) have been foreseen. The machine may need to be re-designed to take account of the production methods of the firm concerned, or of the material that the manufacturer decides to use, or to fit in with the price at which the manufacturer judges it best to aim. All these difficulties have shown up in some degree in the commercial development of the Packman harvester, so that although to N.R.D.C. it was fully developed, to the firm it was not. To help a firm to cross this gap N.R.D.C. has been prepared to place development contracts and to reduce fears about the early stages of production by placing initial orders. 'In the case of the Packman harvester, Dr. Hallpike's Aural Microscope and Chick-sexer, the production of Hecogenin from Sisal and, most notably, Electronic Digital Computors, we have underwritten not only the development but the initial stages of production.' [1] In the case of the potato harvester, however, it was eventually found necessary for the developing firm to transfer its rights back to a special company formed with N.R.D.C. assistance.

There are thus substantial problems in the development of private inventions, but it should be remembered that the amount of private invention of industrial significance is small. The N.R.D.C. in eight years of operation has found few private inventions thought worthy of public support in overcoming the development gap. This does not mean that invention is so well catered for by the growth of industrial research and development as a management technique that the brilliant outsider no longer has any role. Fresh and imaginative minds with nothing of a particular technology to unlearn, or with a knowledge of other technologies which may have a creative application to a different industry, are still capable of making or suggesting significant inventions or

[1] N.R.D.C. *Report and Statement of Accounts, 1953/4*, H.M.S.O., 1955.

developments. Many striking advances indeed come when circumstances (such as wars) free men from one industry to apply their minds to another, as for instance in the development of marine turbines and nuclear energy. But in these cases the 'outsider' tends to turn into a 'newcomer' who works through the research and development facilities of the industry.

Chapter 8

THE DECISION TO COMMIT RESOURCES TO FULL-SCALE PRODUCTION

WE are concerned in this chapter with the crucial decision in the application of science and technology, namely the decision to commit resources to full-scale use of a new process or to full-scale output of a new product. This is usually, in the terminology of the economists, an 'investment decision'—that is to say, it involves capital expenditure. It is seldom an easy decision to make, for, however prolonged and careful the assessment of the chances of a new idea, there usually remains grave uncertainty about costs and markets and the actions of competitors. Even if the decision is easy, it may be risky; for instance, it may be easy to decide that it is essential for survival to copy some change made by a major competitor, and yet the long-run results of the change may be very uncertain. We have here, therefore, a particular case of the general problem of making business decisions in face of uncertainty.

It is important at this stage to get away from a conveyor-belt idea, that projects are periodically arriving ready for use on the Managing Director's desk from the firm's own research and development departments. The firm may neither have nor be able to have research of its own; as we shall suggest in more detail in Chapter 10, it may rely on other firms or bodies for its flow of new ideas. It is a convenient shorthand to distinguish the *invention*—the creation, and development to the point of practical use, of the new idea—from the *innovation*, which is the action of bringing the new idea into practical use. Where research and development is a management technique, the distinction is quite clear; the innovation occurs when management decides to commit resources to the use of the invention. The distinction is blurred in the development of a machine by the gradual improvement of successive models, but even then it can be discerned if tentative experiment on prototypes gives way to major capital expenditure for a 'run' of a particular model.

We have observed in previous chapters that the use of the management technique of research and development has grown much in recent years. A. N. Whitehead once referred to this as the invention of the art of invention. We have also noted that, although the object of this new management technique is to create profitable innovations, there is insufficient attention to the planning of research and development in relation to the production problems, the market opportunities and the capital position of the firm concerned. Because of this the step from invention to innovation may be insufficiently prepared; it may be made more difficult by failure to invent the right things. This affects the taking of investment decisions; for unless the development process is used to bridge the gap between the technically profitable and the economically profitable, the decision takers will often approach the investment decision with suspicion. The development stage cannot, however, be used to eliminate uncertainty altogether, for success in innovation often depends on the action of people outside the firm concerned. There is thus a basic uncertainty in decisions to innovate, and an analysis of the dependence on others will clear the way to an understanding of the nature of decisions to invest in new processes or the output of new products.

The carrying out of research or design and development may require the co-operation of several firms. There is a similar interdependence in innovation, though it may involve different firms which have taken no part in the invention. It is true of course that a firm may be able to carry through a process innovation without considering other firms, as when it builds or adapts a machine from stock parts. But more usually there is significant dependence on others. A new process may require a new raw material, or materials produced to closer specifications, or machines of new design, all of which must be bought outside. For instance, in 1946 J. A. Sargrove perfected a machine for the automatic production of radio circuits, but a high proportion of the assembled sets were defective because of faults in the electrical parts purchased from outside.[1] Here one of the main gaps between invention and innovation was the failure to give sufficiently close specifications for radio parts. Another example is the automatic transfer machine, which was invented between 1923 and 1925 by H. Taylor and F. G. Woollard in association with James Archdale and Co. Ltd. A machine was installed in the engines branch of Morris Motors Ltd. at Coventry, but it was ahead of its time; the possibilities of such machines were limited, for 'though they produced excellent work they were not to be relied on day in and day out because the ancillary equipment—electric, hydraulic and pneumatic—had not been sufficiently developed'.[2] Twenty years later the control mechanisms had been developed, and the use of automatic transfer machines was revived in the United States, adapted in France, and then in England. Again, the computer control of machine tools seems to have reached the stage of development and even of workshop test, but the bridging of the gap between invention and innovation is likely to require a re-design of machine tools. 'The design of machine tools has not changed radically for many years and is, in general, unsuitable for very accurate automatic control.'[3]

[1] J. Diebold, *Automation*, Van Nostrand, 1952, p. 40.
[2] F. G. Woollard, *Automation*, L.P.E. papers, May 1955, p. 8; see also F. G. Woollard, *Principles of Mass and Flow Production*, Iliffe, 1954, pp. 25–33.
[3] D. T. N. Williamson, *Computer controlled machine tools*, in *The Automatic Factory*, Institution of Production Engineers, 1955, p. 151.

The possibility of process innovation may depend, not only on the attitudes of the suppliers of parts or materials, but also on the actions of product users. The advantage of the new process may lie in a higher quality of product, which is worth providing only if it can command a higher price. Will the users, whether individual consumers or industrial firms, recognize that the quality improvement is worth the extra payment? An example of the kind of difficulty which can occur can be taken from shell moulding. One of the main advantages of this new foundry technique is in its ability to produce more accurate castings, thus saving machining time and scrap metal. But the machining is not usually done by the foundryman, who sells his output 'as cast'. The extra cost of the resin–sand mixture used in shell moulding means higher prices for the castings, and the user has to be persuaded that his savings in machining time will more than offset this higher price. This need for persuasion has delayed the spread of the new technique. Again, the savings from a new process (e.g. a transfer machine) may only be apparent if a great increase in output can be achieved, and the process improvement is thus dependent on an increase in demand as price falls.

Another case of interdependence arises when a process improvement is invented by a research association or other non-producing unit. The innovation then depends entirely on the actions of firms which did not participate in the invention. These firms may, as we pointed out in the previous chapter, be faced with additional problems of development to fit the development to their own production facilities, range of products, and natural markets.

These cases of interdependence all relate to improvements of *processes*, and it can be seen that their adoption may involve additional risk. Even in a simple case, where a firm has invented and developed a new process itself, and feels fairly confident (after a pilot-plant stage) that it can predict the costs of the new method, there remain awkward questions to be answered, such as:

(*a*) Will the new method be obsolete before it is paid for?

(*b*) Would the old plant last long enough to enable the firm to wait for a still better new method?

(*c*) Are the costs or expected return from the new method determined by some temporary distortion of markets? (The decision, during the sulphur shortage of 1950–51, to produce sulphuric acid from anhydrite must have been subject to such doubts.)

(*d*) Will the new process cause labour difficulties or new problems of management?

(*e*) How does the risk of innovating compare with the risk of *not* innovating?

These questions may in practice be evaded, or left for settlement by 'business instinct'; the straight comparison of costs for the new and old methods may yield so definite a result that the risks do not seem worth detailed consideration; the existing equipment may be worn out, so that its replacement cannot be avoided; or it may seem that the chance of survival in difficult and fluctuating markets is *bound* to be greater if processes are up to date.

Where the potential new process is not invented in the firm, but is some other firm's product, the risks may be either greater or less: greater if the selling firm is unable to prove its claim for performance, less if the new process has been used elsewhere and the results of its use are known. If a new process is invented in a firm in order to yield a new product, the process of development can be used for market research; for instance, the terylene pilot-plant was used in this way. In such a case the risks may be reduced, despite the fact that both process and product are new. Sometimes the marketing risks are absent—as where an innovation is known to be wanted by the Atomic Energy Authority or the Services—and the risks are those of failure in invention.

In *product* innovation dependence on others is always significant. There may, in fact, be two or more links of dependence; on the one side the new or improved product has to be sold, on the other its production may entail a process innovation which requires the help of others. A product innovation may be sold to final consumers (for instance, plastic raincoats or silicone polishes) or it may be sold to another firm as a process improvement. If it is to be sold to final consumers, there is a risk that, despite the arts of salesmanship which are further mentioned in Chapter 14, it will be found or believed impossible to overcome the conservatism of buyers. Thus it was long supposed, until a pioneer proved it untrue, that the British public would not buy paper-backed books; and there is more substance in the belief that the British public will not easily alter its methods of space-heating. But we have not come across other good examples of unnecessary consumer resistance to new products.

If the innovation is to be sold to another firm as a process improvement, the extent of sales will depend on the willingness of potential buying firms to change their methods of production. If firm A is offering a new product (say, a new machine or raw material) to firm B, then B may be expected to ask some of the following questions before buying the new product:

(*a*) Is the cost of change to the new product justified by the prospective demand for the products it makes?

(*b*) If it is a machine, will it pay for itself over its lifetime?

(*c*) Can we, in firm B, afford *not* to adopt the new product, if our competitors have done or may do so?

(*d*) Has firm A tried to ascertain the performance of the new product; and can it prove its claims for that performance?

(e) What are the likely repercussions in firm B of the change?

(f) Can we, in firm B, face the management problems arising from that change?

(g) Does the invention meet a serious need or solve a grave problem?

The last four of these questions require further illustration. The ascertainment of performance is of course an important part of selling policy; unless the potential buyer can be given details, not only of the cost price of a new product but also of its characteristics and performance, he will lack the information which he needs to judge it. We have found many signs of inadequacy on this matter. But it is not always possible to specify performance. Thus, as is shown in Appendix III, the development of tunnel ovens for the pottery industry was to some extent empirical, since it was not possible to deduce from laboratory trials what the performance of a scaled-up kiln would be. The builders of the ovens therefore had to experiment on their early customers, and they had to find these guinea-pig customers before they were able to give firm promises about performance. The development of the Raper Auto-leveller (see p. 72) illustrates the same point. At a crucial stage, a large wool firm gave facilities for the trial and further development of the invention, from which convincing data of its value were obtained. Commercial development and success were then rapid.

Some inventions entail little change in methods of production; they may, for instance, be devices to attach to a machine to simplify its operation or to improve quality. There are many electronic gadgets of this type. Often, however, the change is considerable. Thus the introduction of modern high-speed machines in an antiquated paper mill requires the recruitment of new grades of engineer and chemist (see Appendix III); the introduction of continuous tunnel ovens in pottery requires substantial rebuilding and a new layout of factory processes (see Appendix III); the use of the Shirley Institute's Auto-doffer saves on 'operatives' but requires maintenance engineers; the introduction of electronic information-processing equipment entails a substantial change in office procedure and numbers. The change may also strain the managerial capacity of the firm; thus a craft firm cannot manage a technique requiring engineers and chemists without recruiting them, but such recruitment may involve a prior change in the structure of management posts and in the persons holding them. Several firms we have visited which have been revived from a backward state have been forced to create a new management structure before innovation could go forward.

The new product may meet a minor or marginal need, or it may provide the key, the one missing part, in the solution of a grave problem. Thus the automatic transfer machine was very attractive to the automobile industry after the war because it made possible a rapid expansion of output while economizing skilled labour. In the same way automatic jute looms provided a way of escape from the shortage of weavers. But where there is not a known need or a naturally expanding market, the seller must create the desire for the new product, and this may be more difficult.

There are still other factors which affect the willingness of potential users to buy a new product; for instance (if it is a machine) the nature of their investment policy. Do they aim to spend a sum on improved machinery each year? Can they afford this? Is their costing system good enough to enable them to judge the value of the improvement? Enough has been said, however, to illustrate the very great complexity of the risks involved in innovation, and the way in which these risks are affected by interdependence. The risk to firm A, in the example above, depends on the (probably unknown) reactions of firm B to its own risks.

Despite all the risks and uncertainty, decisions have to be made. It is sometimes asserted that they are made in a way which is too timid; that the adoption of new scientific and technical knowledge is held back by the unwillingness of the 'financial heads' of industry to take bold investment decisions. Such a statement seems to imply either a comparison with a more successful country, or a judgement that business men are too timid to maximize production. Either way the statement is difficult to test. To make any progress we must try to give more precision to the meaning of the assertion. It may be taken to mean:

(a) that business men insist on a prospect of (say) a 20 per cent. return on capital, whereas American business men would go ahead on the prospects of 10 or 15 per cent.

(b) that to insist on (say) 20 per cent. prospective yield excludes projects that are in the national interest—that is to say, that there is or would be enough capital forthcoming to finance projects with prospective yields of less than 20 per cent.

(c) That business men are too cautious in their estimate of prospective yield—that is to say, that they assume something like the worst in estimating future revenues and future costs.

(d) That business men are too timid to back a project that may take two or three years before it yields profit. Such timidity may exclude some of the projects most likely to start a chain of developments. Timidity in backing these slow-maturing projects could also lead to a low investment in longer-term industrial research.

(e) That business men are insufficiently bold in creating new product and new process possibilities. This is related both to (c) and to the second part of (d).

(f) That business men are insufficiently bold in overcoming or attempting to overcome foreseen difficulties—in other words, insufficiently bold in exercising leadership.

When opened out in this way the possibility that conflicting meanings are given to the assertion is clear, and it can be seen that the apparent boldness or timidity of business men may simply reflect the environment in which they act. To require a high prospective yield as a condition of investment in a new product or process is not necessarily a sign of excessive caution. It may be a sign that new processes quite commonly become obsolete in a few years; a sign that industry is very progressive indeed. What evidence we have indicates that British producers do not set a higher standard of prospective yield than the Americans. The second possible meaning, that there would be capital available to finance projects with lower prospective yields, may have been true of the inter-war but not of the post-war years. If on the other hand it is true that industry is slow in taking up new methods in Britain but fast in the U.S.A., then it would, on the face of it, be entirely appropriate for a potential British innovator to take a less sanguine view of prospective surpluses of revenue over cost. Such an attitude would not be timid, but simply realistic. Further, there has been a great growth of expenditure on research. There is, as we have seen, a tendency to concentrate on the short-term projects, but in new organizations this may be the best way of helping the rapid industrial application of science and technology. As for the disposition of firms to accept the innovations of others and to change their own processes, there seems little doubt that costing and cost-consciousness is of considerable importance and that costing is not highly developed in the majority of British firms.

We have tried in the case-studies to get evidence that would enable us to make a direct answer to the various forms of the assertion that the 'financial heads' of business are too timid. On general grounds we expected to find in efficient firms (a) that decisions to invest would be based on a calculated or estimated relation between prospective revenues and costs—it is after all the responsibility of company directors to make a profit with the shareholders' capital, (b) that if the prospective surplus of revenue over cost expressed as a percentage of the estimated capital investment did not exceed some basic percentage (which would be different in different industries) there would be a decision not to invest and (c) that the projects with the highest prospective yields would be preferred.

In only thirteen of 150 firms in the general sample was an explicit financial criterion of this kind used in judging whether to go ahead with a product or process innovation on which they had done research or development work. The 150 firms include, however, twenty-six which do no development work at all, and twenty whose 'research and development' consists of routine testing and drawing office work. Excluding these, we have 13 per cent. of firms, engaged in some real development effort, which use an explicit financial criterion. In ten of the thirteen firms the minimum yield expected from an innovation, if it is to be adopted, is between 20 and 33⅓ per cent. per annum, though where there is thought to be no risk, or a strong national interest is involved, a lower yield is accepted. In the remaining three firms a 10 per cent. yield is regarded as satisfactory.

These thirteen firms are not the only efficient firms in the sample. The absence of a financial criterion in the other firms is in fact more apparent than real, since for many firms that criterion is implicit rather than explicit. In a further ten cases judgement is based on the potential turnover arising from the innovation. This can be regarded as equivalent to a rough and ready 'prospective yield' criterion. It means that the prospective market is thought to be big enough for the firm to include in the price a sum sufficient to enable it to write off the equipment in an appropriate number of years.

In other firms we found that 'a big saving' would be required for a process change, but we could not be certain what this meant in terms of prospective yield, or whether the judgement on this was consistent. In other cases we found that the firm used, in different situations, both a 'prospective yield' criterion and a 'size of market' criterion, but would not confess to any cut-and-dried procedure for judging whether to proceed with process and product innovations. They thought in fact that it would be misleading to do so; that the element of 'commercial acumen' cannot be reduced to rules or described in objective terms. In some of these firms, however, the commercial acumen is exercised on a list of projects which have already been through a prospective-yield sieve in the development departments, so that the claim of the final decision-takers to a kind of second sight is not important.

Sometimes, too, the commercial acumen or 'hunch' consists of isolating a special criterion for decision, of 'knowing what is important'. Thus a firm may consider an innovation in terms of one simple question—will it get costs down, or will the market be 'big enough' for a proposed new product? Here there must be at least an implicit estimate of the time before which the new process will become obsolete, or of the size of an unknown market.

This last instance serves to highlight the importance of uncertainty. Estimates which lead to an assumed yield from a new project do not ignore the uncertainty—they subsume it. The extent to which firms think in terms of these arithmetic sums rather than in terms of the key qualitative judgements seem to vary with three main factors:

(a) The size of the organization—the greater the size the greater the need to reduce the elements in the situation to arithmetic terms.

(b) The extent to which market research is used, with product innovations, to estimate the potential market.

(c) The extent to which the development department takes into account the market position and capital resources of the firm in its work. The development stage can be used to obtain relevant information and thus to reduce the uncertainty in committing resources to full-scale production.

Uncertainty cannot of course be avoided altogether. We dealt in the first part of this chapter with that network of relations between firms which influence decisions (and the desirability of decisions) to proceed from the invention stage to innovation. From this network of relations we can see that often the critical factors in an innovation are outside the control of the firm. This is the source of much of the uncertainty. But though it cannot be avoided, it can sometimes be safely ignored.

Thus a firm may ignore the uncertainty of profit from investment in a new process because it feels forced into innovation by competition. It may say in effect that the innovation is a condition of survival—without considering whether the invested sum might yield a greater return outside the firm. In other instances the firm might say that the potential reduction in process cost is so great that the innovation must be worthwhile. In other cases again the arithmetic calculation of the profitable yield may be based on the gloomiest conceivable assumptions, so that the firm concerned feels here, too, that it 'cannot miss'. In these situations, despite the uncertainty, the firm feels no doubt in making the decision to commit resources.

Where the uncertainty is not so easily dismissed the decision to commit resources, as we have seen it in the case-studies, depends on a number of personal and general factors. The best way to ensure that a project with great uncertainty attaching to it is carried through is to have a final decision-taker who believes in it. We have found several examples of this—in relation both to successful and to unsuccessful innovations. Apart from this personal element, the decision to proceed depends on obtaining a preponderance of favourable answers to the following questions:

(a) Can the project be financed from the resources of the firm?
(b) Can the project be managed by the present management or does it involve a new organization?
(c) Would it, if successful, make a contribution to the long-term stability of the company?
(d) Is it based on a significant technical innovation?
(e) Is technical progress in other fields likely to improve its prospects?
(f) Would it be sold to a receptive or to an unreceptive market?
(g) Is it a development in which complementary firms are interested?

In order to judge the dominant motives at work, we have examined the passage from invention to innovation in over 250 specific cases of product or process development supplied by 116 firms from the general and special samples (see Appendix II). In sixty-five cases (fifty-three involving the introduction of a new product differing markedly from the normal range) the firms were induced to proceed by the conviction that the potential market was large. In fifty-four cases improvement in quality of product was thought to improve the competitive position of the firm. In sixty-nine cases the expectation of a saving in process cost was a sufficient motive. In thirty-five cases the fact that there was a 'significant innovation' was thought to be in itself a sufficient reason for going ahead. In eighteen cases the innovation, by broadening the basis of the firm's operations, was thought to improve the prospects of long-term stability; in sixteen cases innovations were intended to guarantee supplies of materials; in ten cases 'government interest' made the project seem worthwhile. In thirteen cases the fact that the innovation 'increased output' was a sufficient incentive—a sign that profit margins on existing output were satisfactory.

There usually seemed to have been enough facts to give a reasonable basis for the decision to proceed. Thus, forty-three of the developments came from overseas contacts, and, even if further development work was needed—in some cases to acquire the 'knowhow'—the experience overseas gave confidence of success here. In twelve cases there was a situation of excess demand; in twenty a shortage of materials or labour was holding up production. In four cases innovations in other industries were adapted to the conditions of the firm. In six cases there was a government demand; in eight pressure from customers; in twelve pressure of competition to cut costs or to produce a new quality or design. In fact, in more than half the cases the element of uncertainty seemed small. Of the remainder about one-half seemed in prospect so productive that the element of uncertainty did not produce hesitation.

This inquiry does not enable us to give an answer to the assertion that our financial leaders are too timid in their investment policy. For that one would need a comparative study of the actions of British and foreign business men when faced with similar problems. What evidence we have from companies with American parents or children is that in comparable circumstances reactions are similar. The big difficulty is to find the comparable circumstances, both in the nature of the chain of relations and in the ways of creating innovation opportunities.

It must be remembered, too, that this inquiry has taken place at a time of full employment. If firms were prepared to wait longer for an innovation to pay, or if they were prepared to accept lower expected rates of return on capital investment, more projects would be acceptable on commercial grounds. But when resources are fully employed it is pointless to explain failures at the application stage in these terms; during the inter-war period they may have been important, but not since the war.

In looking for the critical factors in investment decisions, therefore, it would seem best to examine, not the boldness or timidity of financial leaders, but factors such as:

(a) The extent to which cost-consciousness permeates the production and research and development departments.

(b) The extent to which the organized development process is used not only to yield technological solutions but also to test market opportunities.

(c) The efficiency with which organized research and development is used to create big opportunities of innovation—this, of course, cannot be divorced from questions of scientific manpower (see Chapter 9).

(d) The chain of relations between firms and the possibility of weak links in that chain.

(e) The extent to which growth in the economy creates easy opportunities of combining expansion and innovation.

We hope to write more fully on these matters in a later report.

Chapter 9

TRAINED MEN AND WOMEN

IT is generally accepted that Britain is short of scientists and technologists. The existence of such a shortage is part of the gossip of industry: its visible signs are long and attractive advertisements in newspapers, and (in some lines, though not in all) the offer of relatively high pay. It is not only industry which is suffering from the shortage; the scientific Civil Service cannot attract enough recruits, school teaching is severely affected, and even the universities cannot (in some subjects) retain enough men for their research. There is not a universal shortage of scientists irrespective of their speciality, for certain kinds of biologist are in fair supply, and there are only a few openings at home for men trained in geology. Furthermore, any shortage of trained personnel is liable to be a little exaggerated, for employers do not readily distinguish between a scarcity of all grades within the given speciality, and their own difficulty in filling a particular job with a first-class man with relevant experience. Some employers advertise for an archangel, and grumble when they do not get any replies. Post-war experience with commodities, too, shows that only a narrow gap separates an apparently desperate shortage from abundance.

But, with all these qualifications, the shortage is real, and can be an important hindrance to the adoption of new scientific ideas. The following table shows, for 130 firms covered by the general case-studies, the proportions complaining of four types of scarcity, and the proportions for which the scarcity was *crucial*—i.e. in the opinion of our investigators the sole hindrance to fresh development, there being no significant financial or managerial hindrances or difficulties in the supply of materials.

Percentage complaining of—	Any shortage	Crucial shortage
Scientists	42	2
Engineers	38	8
Designers and Draughtsmen	49	15
Laboratory Assistants	33	2

These figures are, of course, related to what the firms *think* they need in scientific manpower. In many of the firms not complaining of shortage scientists are not employed at all, or are employed on a scale which (to judge from efficient firms in the industry) is too small. Any such backwardness gives the figures a downward bias. Further, there are other hindrances to development, such as a shortage or absence of machines or materials of an appropriate quality, which may be due to a lack of scientists or engineers in supplying firms. The need of a firm depends also on its industry: obviously firms in industries with a strong modern scientific basis are likely to think they need more scientists than traditional or craft industries. The breakdown by three types of industry was as follows:

| Type of industry * | Percentage complaining of any shortage (crucial shortage in brackets) of— | | | |
	Scientists	Engineers	Designers, Draughtsmen	Lab. Assistants
Traditional . .	23 (0)	13 (0)	20 (10)	13 (0)
Engineering . .	33 (2)	45 (10)	59 (20)	29 (2)
Modern . . .	61 (2)	45 (10)	55 (12)	50 (2)

* For an explanation of the classification, see p. 110.

This table shows that the 'modern industry' firms often complain of shortage of scientists, but it is rarely a *crucial* shortage; the firms affected by a shortage of engineers or designers and draughtsmen are somewhat less numerous, but the deficiency is more often crucial. The 'traditional' industries show much lower figures throughout. A breakdown by size of firm shows that smaller firms are less conscious of a shortage—perhaps because they are less conscious of a need for systematic scientific or technical development, or because they are too small to sustain research. In this connexion it should be noted that the 'under 500' group below contains a higher proportion of 'craft' firms.

| | Percentage complaining of any shortage of— | | | |
	Scientists	Engineers	Designers, Draughtsmen	Lab. Assistants
Large (over 2,000 employees)	61	54	58	52
Medium (500 to 2,000) .	49	39	60	37
Small (under 500) . .	13	19	27	10

As far as it goes, therefore, this evidence confirms the existence of a shortage, sometimes of a crucial shortage: and shows that the need for more trained staff is felt especially in the larger firms of the engineering and 'modern' industries.

An inquiry by the Committee on Scientific Manpower of the Advisory Council on Scientific Policy (published in the autumn of 1955) tells a similar story. Fifty larger firms in the engineering manufacturing industry were asked about their annual recruitment, particularly of graduates. The total number of graduates recruited was some 25 per cent. below the number required; but 'the general impression gained is that most firms, especially the big ones, look for men possessing both good honours degrees and good personal qualities, and that such men are very scarce'. Despite this, the committee concluded that the figure of a 25 per cent. shortage 'may well be an underestimate. The demand for such men is rising all the time with the increase in the general level of industrial activity and the increased awareness of firms of their need for trained technologists. The gap between supply and demand is thus bound to grow unless the steps now being taken to increase the volume and quality of engineering education become even more vigorous than they already are.' A further report[1] showed the requirements of qualified scientists and engineers for industry in 1959 as 37 per cent. higher than in 1956.

In the whole field, the most serious deficiencies appear to be of designers and draughtsmen, chemical engineers, metallurgists, mechanical and electrical engineers (and especially those capable of making original designs or original variations of a design), chemists, and certain types of physicist. The degree of shortage varies with fashion, and the less glamorous trades (like heavy electrical engineering and the manufacture of household equipment) complain that, at a given salary level, they are less attractive than 'new' trades like the application of atomic energy or electronics (see p. 102). People of double ability—for instance, engineers with a flair for assessing consumer preferences, or chemists who are skilled in financial matters—are naturally particularly rare. The deficiencies are at both graduate and non-graduate levels. The expected development of 'modern' industries and the increase in the scale of production will require greater numbers of trained people in the future. It is important, therefore, to find out how the flow of scientific and technical manpower is determined. Why does little Johnny go in for science?

This question at once suggests another. What qualities should little Johnny possess if he is to be a scientist or technologist? One would not expect to find a general answer covering the whole range from routine draughtsmen and laboratory assistants to chief aircraft designers and senior research chemists. But over a great part of this range it is necessary to be able to observe things accurately and to argue logically and precisely from what is found. For some scientific occupations there is a strong association with mathematical ability—a quality which is certainly far from universal even among highly intelligent people. But whereas a pure mathematician relies mainly on his ability for abstract reasoning, an engineer must have also qualities which, being undefined, are described in a variety of vague phrases. He must have 'a way with machines' or 'a practical sense' or 'a feeling for what can be done with his materials'. In the same way a successful chemist must usually have experimental ability, a quality which is again a 'flair', a 'sense', which can be recognized but is hard to define; and a draughtsman, if he is to advance beyond the merest routine, must combine with neatness and accuracy a strong practical sense. Many scientists and technologists will find themselves in charge of the work of craftsmen and labourers, and some will be administrators for most of their time. They must therefore possess an understanding of men and qualities of leadership. A firm in

[1] *Scientific and Engineering Manpower in Great Britain*, H.M.S.O., 1956.

G

the metallurgical industry wrote to the Committee on Scientific Manpower:

'We need scientists and engineers and other technologists as urgently
as anybody in the industry but we also want, as most other firms must do,
men with real qualities of leadership. Without sound human leadership
scientific prowess is obviously not going to get us very far. Yet the thing
which impresses us about the undergraduates and graduates whom we
interview each year is the very great proportion who lack any real leadership qualities.'

This list of recognizable but ill-defined qualities is not complete.
For instance, success to a scientist or engineer in industry is often a
matter of 'putting himself over' to his non-technical superiors. This is
something more than an ability to express an idea simply in plain English, though that is important and (we are told) all too rare. It is also a
question of personality, of an ability to 'win friends and influence
people'. The highest measure of success of the first-rate original
scientist rests on qualities still more difficult to define. The discoveries
of a genius often seem obvious, even trivial, to the discoverer. His power
to perceive logical connexions, and to imagine new possibilities, is in
some way less confined by previous teaching and experience; and he has
a 'flair' for avoiding dead-ends.

These considerations are important if we inquire whether the
shortage of scientists may not be an absolute shortage of people of the
requisite ability and qualities. If this were so—if the scarcity were simply
a matter of genetics—there would be no point in discussing this limiting
factor any further, save to inquire whether there was avoidable wastage
of ability through bad selection and training or diversion to unsuitable
work. The question raises another, namely the relative importance of
heredity and education in the development of scientific ability. But this
problem can be side-stepped, for we do not think that in the present
state of knowledge any firm answer can be given to the main question.
Since the specification of qualities needed by a particular kind of
scientist is ill-defined, we are not confident that any reliance can be
placed on the results of tests of intelligence or aptitude, as showing
what numbers of the population are suited for a scientific or technical
career.

There are, however, a few scraps of information from which a partial
answer can be guessed. The number of full-time students at British
universities is some 60 per cent. greater than before the war, and the
bounty of public authorities has undoubtedly opened the possibility
of university education to many previously denied it. 'Pass' degrees
have declined considerably in importance, and it is consequently not
surprising to find that the numbers obtaining second-class honours
degrees of any kind have increased by 120 per cent. But the numbers

obtaining *first*-class honours degrees have risen by only about 25 per cent. This is a small gain from a large improvement in methods of selection; if university examinations are accepted as consistent evidence of quality, it strongly suggests that a further scraping of the barrel will not yield many more first-class minds.

But the same evidence equally shows that it has been possible to obtain a large expansion in students of a slightly lower, but still high, ability. The evidence from educationists is that there are possibilities of further expansion, if only parents can be persuaded to keep their children at school to a later age. The able youth who enters apprenticeship at 16 is not of course lost to technology; industry (especially engineering) often prefers him to the graduate. But we are told by youth employment officers that there is still much wastage of talent through adolescents entering jobs which, though initially attractive, do not bring out their full ability. The Central Advisory Council for Education (England), in its report 'Early Leaving' (1954), suggested that for every two boys who stay on at school to take courses at the Advanced level of the General Certificate of Education, another boy of equal talent leaves. For English maintained and direct-grant grammar schools in 1953 'about 2,900 boys and 1,300 girls who could have taken advanced courses in mathematics and science were not doing so'. These figures are based on the schools' assessment that about 21 per cent. of their boys and 8 per cent. of their girls were suited to take two advanced level mathematics and science subjects: but one-third of these boys and 40 per cent. of the girls left too early to do so. It is possible that the numbers considered suitable for science, especially among girls, are unduly low. Whether this is so or not, we conclude that in the middle ranks of scientist and technologist—those recruited from the schools at age 17 or 18, or from the ordinary run of university students—there is no sufficient evidence that the potential supply of able minds is yet exhausted; and we reach this conclusion without reference to the question of whether other occupations are poaching talent which ought to go into science and technology.

If the raw material is there, is the scarcity due to wastage or misdirection in the educational system? This is a subject which could be developed into a major report on its own, and we refer only to selected points which seem to us of importance.

We would first of all direct attention to the importance of studying the way in which educational and career decisions are made. Take, for instance, the university trained scientist or engineer. He will normally obtain admission to his course by showing that he has reached a satisfactory standard in scientific or mathematical subjects in the General Certificate of Education or its equivalent. In other words, his chances of entering a science course are negligible if he has 'come up on the Arts side'; the main exception is that Imperial College and a few other colleges and universities now have small schemes for re-directing good Arts men into science and technology. A man's availability to become a graduate scientist is therefore usually determined at an early age, when his teachers and parents decide on the subjects he should offer in the General Certificate at its ordinary and higher levels.

We have tried to find out how this decision is reached, and what provision the schools have made for the proper guidance of pupils and for dealing with those who may wish to change their choice of subject or career. We sent questionnaires to one-sixth of the maintained and direct-grant grammar schools, and to one-third of the independent schools, in England and Wales, and to a small number of schools in Scotland. Three hundred and thirty-two questionnaires were sent out, and there was a 60 per cent. response; the possibility of bias due to non-response must therefore be remembered, but we think that the answers illustrate the main problems. We would like to express our gratitude for the trouble which schools have taken to give us information.

The age by which the crucial decision must be taken is shown in the following table:

	Percentage of number of schools		
Age of specialization	Boys	Girls	Mixed
13+	14	3	17
14+	17	54	51
15+	27	20	20
16+	36	12	10
Unknown, or effectively no science offered	6	11	2
	100	100	100

This shows that more than a third of the boys' schools make provision for the crucial decision to be taken as late as age 16; this is usually done by including compulsory science and Arts subjects in the curriculum for the Ordinary level of the General Certificate of Education, so that either may then be continued to the Advanced level. But most girls' and mixed schools, and a considerable proportion of boys' schools, require the decision to be taken at an earlier age.

Most schools have some provision for advice on the choice of careers, normally through a careers master or mistress in the independent schools and the headmaster or headmistress in the maintained schools. But although most schools claim to give advice at junior as well as senior levels, this appears to mean that they are willing to answer questions or to have discussions with far-sighted parents, not that there is any systematic attempt to relate the choice of subjects for specialization to the ultimate career of the boy or girl. We have a strong impression that the crucial decision is seldom the result of an adequate examination of alternative careers.

In girls' schools 'science' sometimes means biology only, and in general we are impressed by the special difficulties of staffing and laboratory accommodation in girls' schools, and by the small numbers wishing to take up scientific subjects. Independent schools are now receiving some help from industry for the improvement of laboratory accommodation; this is undoubtedly needed in many schools of all types. The shortage of teachers (which we discuss later in this chapter) is also certainly a serious barrier to any large expansion. In some schools—so we are told—the superior quality of teaching on the Arts side exerts an attraction on the best pupils. In some public (i.e. private) schools the tradition that classical studies have a higher status still lingers, though we believe that undue bias is shown, not by the greatest schools, but by their minor and snobbish imitators. Special complaint is made of the bias of some schools against an engineering career. It is also suggested to us that in public schools boys can move up the school quicker on the classical or Arts side and have a better chance of university scholarships; so that boys doing experimental science feel 'left behind'. The attitude of parents is influenced by the respectability and social prestige of different jobs, and technology is said to suffer from a prejudice against a career which smells of the workshop.

The casual influences would not matter, of course, if ability to learn scientific subjects could be precisely determined at an early age, and if the proportion specializing on the Arts and science sides were then decided by the capabilities of the students. But we are advised that there is a broad middle group for which no such decision can be made. The fact that nearly three times as many boys as girls do advanced work in science and mathematics at grammar schools, for instance, is not likely to be wholly due to differences in ability between the sexes. The 'Early Leaving' report, quoted above, remarks:

'Not long ago it would have been taken for granted that girls would show little interest in advanced courses in science and mathematics, and enough of this tradition survives to account for some general preference for arts courses among girls. At the same time the figures quoted (that nearly a third of "science sixths" in girls' schools have less than five pupils) suggest that in many girls' grammar schools there cannot be a full range of choice of mathematical and scientific subjects at sixth form level, and a girl wishing to specialise in, say, physics may be unable to do so for lack of facilities.'

Similar considerations apply to non-graduate scientists and technologists; the effective decision about a career is often made at an early age for reasons little related to the national need. There is a considerable wastage of able children from working-class homes who either never go to a grammar school, or leave prematurely. The proportion of grammar school places among all secondary places in local authority areas varied (in 1954, for England) from 10 to 44 per cent.: it is scarcely credible that suitability for grammar-school education shows such large geographical variations, and the differences in provision must have their greatest effect on children of poorer families who cannot pay for independent education. It is no doubt partly for this reason, and partly because of the effect of home background before the age of 11, that whereas on the basis of the population proportion about 9,300 children of unskilled workers might have been expected to enter English grammar schools in 1946, only some 4,350 did so, and of these only 1,500 reached a satisfactory point in the grammar-school course, and only 230 had obtained or were taking two subjects at the Advanced level.[1] About 44 per cent. of children from 'professional and managerial' class parents were staying for sixth-form work, against about 7 per cent. leaving before the fifth form: for children of unskilled workers these proportions were almost reversed—6½ and 40 per cent. The proportion of children from the professional and managerial classes proceeding to universities might be higher if the means tests for scholarships were more reasonable in their incidence.

The generation studied in the 'Early Leaving' report, which had its primary education mainly in wartime, may have shown these characteristics in an exaggerated form, but there is little doubt that there must still be considerable avoidable waste. The reasons for early leaving provide a complex problem in sociology; they are by no means entirely financial, though the desire for independence is important. Among boys and girls classified as capable of taking two advanced level subjects in mathematics and science, but leaving without doing so, about a half entered careers which might possibly afford scope for advancement in science and technology, and more than a quarter careers offering no such scope (the remainder being uncertain or unknown). But there is wastage even in the scientific careers: the Central Advisory Council comments (p. 51): 'There can be little doubt that when scientists are scarce it is wasteful to employ as laboratory technicians boys and girls who could stay at school to take advanced courses in science . . . this would appear to be as clear a case of genuine wastage as we are likely to find.'

Wastage may, of course, occur in another way, through inefficient selection at age 11 for technical schools. We have nothing to say on this difficult and controversial question, and it is too early to know how far the higher technical skills will be capable of development among school leavers from technical schools.

We conclude that there is probably a substantial loss of children suited to scientific and technological work, either through a failure to develop their talents or through their misdirection to careers in which those talents have insufficient scope. We believe that part of this loss is

[1] *Early Leaving*, H.M.S.O., 1954, p. 34.

avoidable, and that there is ample scope for ingenuity in checking the wastage of scientific talent in the school system. Comparison with other countries shows that familiar features of the British educational system are not elsewhere found necessary; for instance, both Russia and the U.S.A. manage to do without much specialization in their schools.

Next we must look at further education. The greater part of this lies in the technical colleges, with well over two million students, including 75,000 full-time and over 380,000 'day-release' students (released by employers during some working hours). Many of the students are, of course, doing commercial courses, continuing their general education or learning recreational handicrafts. But the contribution of the colleges to the education of scientists and technologists is considerable: it includes preparation for degrees and for the membership of professional institutions, courses for the ordinary and Higher National Certificates, and courses for special qualifications in particular crafts and trades. The contribution is especially important for student apprentices—that is to say, those recruited from the grammar schools at age 16 to 18, having usually passed the General Certificate of Education at ordinary or advanced level; they are to be distinguished from craft or trade apprentices, usually recruited at age 16 with a lower educational qualification. 'Day release' to attend a technical college is common for student apprentices, and there has been a considerable growth in 'sandwich courses', in which periods of full-time technical education are alternated with periods at the works. The alternating periods are commonly six months each.

We have made extensive inquiries from technical colleges in all parts of the country, in places both small and large. We have included National Colleges (which provide instruction, mainly full-time, for seven industries which require centralized and expensive teaching facilities); Polytechnics; institutions which act as technological sections of universities, such as the Colleges at Glasgow, Manchester, and Belfast; colleges with a strong connexion with a particular trade; and small general-purpose colleges. Our chief impression is of the lively variety in the provision made—as is natural in a service largely run by local authorities. There are institutions, such as the Polytechnics, which concentrate on advanced work (including research), and which can attract staff of some academic standing. There are others with hardly any advanced work, and with great difficulty in attracting staff to long hours of day and evening teaching. There are many places where the main limiting factor is the overcrowding of buildings; but there are also some which could take more students (particularly for advanced work), and where the real difficulty is to awaken interest in local employers and employees. There are areas (such as the North-East) in which sandwich courses are well supported, but other areas where principals have an uphill task to persuade firms (especially small firms) to support either sandwich or day-release courses. There are usually Advisory Committees which represent industrialists, but relations with local industry vary from cordial support to indifference.

Variety and vitality often go together, and the development of new ideas in technical education may well be quicker because of the independent experiment of different local authorities. But the system can cause a wastage of talent where local authorities are parsimonious or fail to achieve a balanced development of their service, or where the provision is small because the concentration of industry is low. The charge most frequently brought against the technical education system is that it has not done enough for the expansion of advanced work—that it has alleviated shortages of craftsmen and junior technicians more successfully than it has met the need for men of advanced training. The long discussion of what is usually called 'Higher Technological Education' has been confused by differences in answering the question 'How much higher?' Thus the Advisory Council on Scientific Policy stated in its second report (Cmd. 7755, 1949): 'Our concern throughout has been with higher education in applied science suitable for men capable of holding positions of the highest responsibility in industry. We have not been specially concerned with the more conventional training in technology, for which we believe suitable provision is being made.' The Advisory Council therefore concluded at that time that the problem was wholly one for the universities. But the report on 'the future development of higher technological education' submitted by the National Advisory Council on Education for Industry and Commerce in 1950 is concerned with the higher ranges of the work of the technical colleges.

There will no doubt continue to be controversy about the relative place of universities and technical colleges in such work. But our inquiries do not support a charge that the technical colleges are wholly failing in their duty to expand the output of technologists. The development since before the war has been impressive; in 1954, 7,000 higher national certificates and 250 higher national diplomas were awarded, both figures being more than six times the pre-war number. The Advisory Council on Scientific Policy itself observed in 1955 that in the engineering industry 'those who obtain Higher National Certificates . . . are considered eminently suitable for posts at all levels on the production and technical sides' and that a number of firms prefer them to graduates. Since 1937-8 the total load of work on the technical colleges has more than doubled, but full-time student-hours have trebled and part-time day-release students have increased eight-fold. There are some 10,000 advanced students taking university courses, practically all of whom are studying science or technology.

But despite this increase in the higher levels of technical college work, reason for disquiet remains. The staff of technical colleges is normally heavily engaged in teaching, with little time for research; its pay is often below university standards, and men capable of teaching at the highest levels are seldom attracted either for full-time or for part-time work. In consequence, the best students are not being trained by the men with the best combination of ability and practical experience. In a university, a scientist may well be trained by an F.R.S. with a world-wide reputation; similar opportunities for technologists are rare.

We would not, therefore, deny that there is a long way still to go; but we have not found evidence which suggests that the shortage of scientists can be blamed on an *unwillingness* to develop the technical college system. At a particular time and in a particular area the technical college may be a bottle-neck, but general national policy has favoured quick development, especially of advanced work. The Government's policy on higher technological education,[1] works at five levels:

(1) Encouragement, by 'earmarked' grants from the University Grants Committee, of technological development in selected institutions of university rank, e.g. Imperial College and the Glasgow Royal Technical College.

(2) The designation of a small number of colleges of advanced technology, concentrating entirely on advanced work.

(3) A large building programme to extend technical college facilities, particularly for day-release and 'sandwich' courses.

(4) The offer of a special 75 per cent. grant to local authorities for courses in advanced technology, provided that they are at technical colleges with a high standard of accommodation and equipment, a good proportion of advanced work, suitable facilities for teaching fundamental science as well as technology, opportunities for research, and a highly qualified staff with considerable freedom in planning courses.

(5) The establishment of a Council for Higher Technological Education, with Boards of Studies empowered to recognize existing courses in Technical Colleges as adequate for a new Diploma in Technology.

The fourth of these is a carrot dangled before the laggard local authority, and there is a high rate of refusal of grant on the grounds that the necessary standard is not being provided.

On the face of it, the charge of inadequate response to the need for trained scientists can more plausibly be brought against the universities. The numbers of first degrees and diplomas in pure science and in technology have both somewhat more than doubled since before the war. The total number of students (full-time and part-time) has increased from about 65,000 to around 100,000 and (after a post-war 'bulge') has

[1] See Cmd. 9703, H.M.S.O., 1956.

recently been stable. The universities have made plans for dealing with expected increases in the student age-groups, but the Government has urged a larger expansion, especially in science and technology. The proportion of full-time students taking Arts and allied courses has fallen only from 45 to 43 per cent., while the proportion taking pure science and technology has risen from 26 to $34\frac{1}{2}$ per cent. The proportion for technology alone (mainly engineering) has risen only from $10\frac{1}{2}$ to 13 per cent.: we have been turning out less than 1,500 people with honours degrees in technology a year, and less than 4,000 with first degrees or diplomas in technology of any kind. The U.S.A. produces about 22,000 engineering graduates a year, and the U.S.S.R. output of 'professional engineers' is said to be 60,000 a year. The U.K., however, relies much more heavily on part-time training for professional qualifications.

We have made a number of inquiries from University Appointments Boards, which confirm the fact that there is no relation between the supply of graduates and the demand for their talents. In a number of Arts subjects (such as history and English) graduates find considerable difficulty in obtaining posts, and must frequently face the fact that their material prospects would have been better if they had never come to the university. In technology the demand, coming mainly from large firms, appears to exceed the supply at least five-fold; though since firms make large offers of employment at many different universities, this demand is likely to be inflated. Within the sciences the rate of expansion is again not necessarily related to the national need for trained men: thus, despite the doubts expressed by the Fifth Report of the Advisory Council on Scientific Policy (Cmd. 8561, 1952) biology has increased by as large a proportion as chemistry, and geology proportionally more than any other pure science.

From the national point of view, therefore, it can be claimed that university expansion has been both inadequate and indiscriminate, and that the pace of expansion contrasts oddly with the urgency of the demands of science and technology. To this a double reply can be made. First, universities have a wider purpose than vocational training, and they have standards to maintain which would be threatened by further expansion. Second, the limits to the flow of scientists and technologists have been set, not by the universities themselves, but by the Government (which has not provided the money to pay for a greater expansion) or by the schools (which have not produced a larger flow of qualified entrants).

These arguments are not, of course, entirely consistent; either the universities are faced with too many possible students (in which case the size of buildings and staff may be limiting factors) or there is room for all qualified students. The Committee of Vice-Chancellors and Principals has recently made a survey which will give an authoritative view on this question. As far as we can tell from our inquiries, the fact is that (although there is great competition to enter certain universities and departments) it must be very rare for a qualified entrant to fail to obtain a place in some university, not necessarily that of his choice. The Institute of Physics recently reported that in that subject (which has quadrupled its student numbers since before the war) 'the number of additional students that could be accepted into the present university departments is about 170 a year, or roughly 25 per cent. . . . the intense competition for admission is largely illusory'. We think that the same is true of other scientific subjects.

If we are right in this, it follows that an expansion of student numbers can only come

(1) from increases in the numbers of births 17–20 years earlier (this will be an important ground for expansion in the 1960's),
(2) from improvements in the 'efficiency' of the school system in retaining good pupils up to the age of university entrance, or
(3) from a lowering of the standards of entrance.

The first of these is not unimportant: provided places are available, and provided the schools have been able to give the necessary preparation, it could lead to an increase of over 30 per cent. in students by 1965—followed, of course, by a decline. The second way of expansion might provide at most a further 30–40 per cent. if a majority of able 'early leavers' stayed at school. But if one thinks in terms of doubling or trebling the university population, it can only be by a complete change in what a university degree means. We incline to the view that the U.S.A. has a great advantage in having attached the social prestige of a first university degree to a level of attainment capable of being reached by greater numbers of students, and that the work of the graduate schools guards against a general fall in standards at the highest levels. The following table shows very approximately the contrast between the U.S.A. and U.K. 'educational pyramid'; the figures are roughly representative of recent years, though an exact comparison cannot be made because of the deficiencies of educational statistics and the difference in age-distribution between the countries.

	Great Britain. Actual numbers (thousands)	Corresponding numbers for G.B. if the 'propensity to enter higher education' (15 +) were the same as in the U.S.A.
At school, 5–14 . .	6,900	6,900
At school, 15 upwards .	360	1,500–1,750
At University, for first degree or diploma (full-time)	75	550–700
At University for higher degree . . .	10	60–65

An expansion of student numbers in science and technology can (apart from a general increase of numbers) be achieved by a diversion from other subjects. Within the sciences there appears to be room for some re-deployment in accordance with national needs—for instance, by diverting men to electrical or mechanical engineering. But a large change can come only from a change in the proportions studying Arts and science subjects. Our inquiries establish, as clearly as anything can be seen in the jungle of university entrance requirements, that there are few Arts students whose formal qualifications or previous education would allow them to enter courses in science or technology. Again, therefore, we find ourselves up against the question of standards at entrance. If a shift in proportions taking Arts and science is to occur, either the schools must produce more students qualified in mathematics and elementary science (which returns us to the question of the early choice of specialization, discussed above) or else the universities must accept unqualified entrants to science courses and themselves provide the necessary preliminary training—as, for instance, Imperial College, the Universities of Liverpool and Leeds, and the University College of North Staffordshire are doing on a small scale.

We conclude, therefore, that the slow response of the universities to the national need for highly trained scientists and technologists is mainly determined by the nature and standards of the universities and by the wastage or diversion in the schools. But we would not wish to minimize the subtle influence of snobbery. In some universities it is conventional to regard pure mathematics as 'better' than applied mathematics: the laboratory chemist looks down on the engineer, and the classical scholar thinks himself better than any scientist. If A thinks himself better than B, and B thinks himself better than A, not much harm is done; but if B is under pressure to conform to A's judgement, his chosen line of work will seem less attractive. Snobbery sets up a barrier of class distinction between the university and the technical college, and holds itself justified because of the difference in quality between them. It is odd that these nonsensical distinctions are not more frequently held up to the ridicule they deserve; but we have no doubt, from our inquiries, that they persist.

So far we have been looking at the inadequate supply of trained men and women as it is affected by the educational system. We now consider how that supply is influenced by industry itself.

The first and most obvious point is the offer of high salaries. We do not wish to embalm in this report salary figures which will be out of date before they are published; there is, of course, no doubt that a substantial salary differential in favour of scientific and technological occupations has occurred. But the attractive power of a profession depends not only on the starting salary, but also on what are believed to be the prospects. Starting salaries are easily ascertained, but it is much more difficult to find out what people ultimately earn. A survey made by the Royal Institute of Chemistry in 1953, based on a 67 per cent. response

from Fellows and Associates, showed 45 per cent. earning less than
£1,000, 44 per cent. earning £1,000–1,999, and 11 per cent. earning
more than £2,000. The modal salary was £600–649 in the age-group
21–25, rising to somewhere in the range £900–1,099 for all age-groups
from 31 to 55. The £1,000 level was therefore that at which substantial
numbers of qualified chemists were (in 1953) likely to stick in their promotion. But the higher ages showed substantial numbers attaining
higher salaries, so that the *average* pay rose to around £2,000 at age
61–65, with a third of the total number at this age getting more than
£2,000. The breakdown by industry shows, as one would expect, that
nearly all the big salaries were earned in manufacturing industry or
independent practice. The average salary in private industry was about
£100 more than that in universities, £300 more than that in Government, nationalized industries or technical colleges, £350 more than that
in local authority service or the research associations, and nearly £500
more than that in school teaching. The 'sticking point', for those of
moderate talent, in private industry was above the *best* that most school-
teachers could at that time hope to reach.

What this survey does not show is how far scientists of high earning
power were actually practising science. We have met a number of complaints that the highest posts are available only to those who desert the
laboratory bench for the desk, and that the ambitious and successful
man is early lost to research and transferred to management. This is a
matter which we discuss on p. 133, but it is worth asking at this point
whether the mere expectation that administration will provide a better
ladder of promotion than science acts as a discouragement to a scientific
career. We do not think this can be so in general—we have certainly
not heard of any competent scientist who has deserted his subject completely for this reason. But the point may be a serious one in particular
firms, perhaps especially in large firms or nationalized industries, where
well-marked ladders of promotion plainly extend less far on the scientific side. We are told also that it is difficult to get people to go to firms
where their talents will be obviously ancillary to the main business,
rather than in the direct line of that business; for instance, that chemical
firms find it difficult to recruit mechanical engineers.

Salaries and wages often contain a strong conventional or monopoly
element, and do not readily adjust themselves to shifts in supply or
demand. This is especially true at the senior level, where pay is often a
matter of individual negotiation; the organized pressure of trade unions
prevents the pay of junior technical staff from being too much out of
touch with current market conditions. At the senior level we have the
impression (though we can offer no statistics to support it) that engineers
are underpaid relative to laboratory scientists. This is perhaps because
most engineers 'start from the bottom' with a student apprenticeship,
and never escape the disadvantage of a lower starting pay.

Many firms seek to attract staff by offering good training schemes—whether in conjunction with technical colleges through day-release or sandwich courses, or (occasionally) in their own training schools; or for senior staff through a special training programme for graduates. It is very rare, however, for these schemes to add to the supply of trained manpower by accepting entrants with no previous technical background; the emphasis is on adapting the technical stream from schools or universities to the needs of the firm, rather than on re-training people of a different background. We understand that there has been a considerable extension of graduate training schemes in recent years, but that training schools for junior staff within a firm are naturally considered as an exceptional measure where local technical college facilities are inadequate. We think that the impact of some of the training schemes we have seen on the production of higher technologists is considerable.

The last few paragraphs suggest that the way in which technical staff are paid and treated has some effect—and not entirely a good effect—on the distribution of scientific manpower between occupations, but that its effect on the total number available is more remote, because the crucial educational decisions are often made much earlier than the selection of a particular job. There are other factors which influence and distort the distribution of trained people. Our evidence from University Appointments Boards stresses very strongly the importance of National Service deferment, which tends to give first pick of graduates to Government research, the aircraft industry, the production of equipment for guided missiles and similar work. This preference is of course in accordance with what are supposed to be national needs, but other industries consider that it goes too far. Despite the complaints of inadequate pay in the scientific Civil Service, we are assured that the precise status and known prospects in that service have some slight attractive force.

We are told also that the glamour and prospective development of an industry is most important in determining the flow to it of both graduate and non-graduate staff. Thus nuclear research has a great attractive power: in general new industries, especially those offering research prospects, do better than old. Electronics is more popular than heavy electrical engineering, the nationalized industries are often considered too rigid and uninteresting, and textile technology suffers from the poor prospects of the textile industries. Such preferences, though natural, may lead to the industries which are most in need of technical rejuvenation finding themselves starved of technologists.

There is no doubt that the great majority of technically trained graduates, and a high proportion of non-graduates, go initially to the large firms. The report of the Advisory Council on Scientific Policy on recruitment to the engineering industry (1955) shows that the fifty large engineering firms covered, together with the nationalized industries, take about half the whole output of graduate engineers, and that eight firms take a quarter. The large firms can afford a big recruiting effort; they provide good training facilities; and they are better able to use a man whose main interest is in research. The needs of small firms are provided for by men changing jobs when they are fully qualified and experienced, but (if the large firms continue to offer good prospects) those thus changing jobs might be expected to contain an undue proportion of the second-rate and of the misfits. The implications of this for the national interest should be seen in relation to our discussion of small and large firms in Chapter 11.

But the most harmful misdirection of scientific manpower is without doubt the starving of the schools (and to a lesser extent of the technical colleges). We have come across strong and repeated evidence that science teaching is usually regarded as a last resort for failures. There remain a few, of course, who (whatever the quality of their science) have a lively desire to learn the craft of teaching and to spend their lives in its practice. It is possible that the numbers of such people are increasing a little, but they are far too few for the demand. There has also been a recent increase due to a limited scheme of National Service deferment. The problem has been a subject of recent reports by the Federation of British Industries (1954), by the Advisory Council on Scientific Policy (1955), and by the Science Masters' Association (1954). The F.B.I. estimated that there would be an accumulated deficiency of 2,300 graduate science teachers by 1960, unless recruitment was increased; the grammar schools will, of course, have to provide for increased numbers during the next decade, because of the post-war rise in the birth rate. A recent article by Dr. B. V. Bowden (*Manchester Guardian*, 31 January 1956) shows how the age-distribution of science masters (especially those with good honours degrees) is weighted with older men; there will be a large number of retirements during the next twenty years, and these places must be filled as well as the posts required for expansion.

'Of 482 men who graduated in science in Oxford in 1953 only seventeen became schoolmasters. In a school not far from Manchester a senior physics master and a senior history master were appointed simultaneously in 1938. There were about 140 applicants for each vacancy, all of whom were reasonably well qualified. The same two vacancies were filled again last year. There were then 160 applications from historians but only four from physicists, three of whom had no adequate qualifications; the man who was appointed would never have been considered before the war . . . The teaching profession in the United States has already been almost denuded of science teachers because of the greater attraction of industry. . . . The number of students who are presenting themselves for courses in science and engineering in American universities is beginning to fall, for young Americans are not being exposed to the stimulus of adequate teaching in school.'

The suggestions made for dealing with this situation, however, are few and unconvincing. It is not much use suggesting (as the F.B.I. does) that the universities should produce more scientists, because the shortage of science teachers is serious enough to prevent a large increase in the intake of the universities (unless standards are lowered). To propose (as the Ministry of Education suggested to the Advisory Council) that Government and industry should reduce their intake of science graduates is about as practical as Canute rebuking the waves. An increase in salaries confined to scientists (beyond that already concealed in the allowances for advanced work) would cause bitterness in the educational profession; but a general increase in teachers' salaries involves paying several non-scientists for each scientist. There is no doubt (as we have shown above) that the science teacher's 'ceiling' salary is well below what he could hope for in industry. But many men like a gamble: and a certainty of rising to £1,500 (but never any more, except in a headship) might not be attractive against a bare chance of a dazzling £3,000 in industry or Government service. Furthermore, we do not know if even industry is paying scientists their full value: it may be that it would remain willing to outbid the schools.

A shortage of labour should lead to attention to the increase of its productivity. We have formed the view from our case-studies that efficiency in the use of scientists and technologists has not yet had the attention it needs. We find, for instance, that there is not enough labour-saving equipment in use: that tests of efficiency (such as comparisons of practice between successful and less successful research and development establishments) are rare: and that the problem of making the best choice of research projects has not had the attention it needs. But we realize, of course, that the efficient use of scientists is not an easy matter. A research team, for instance, requires both original and routine minds, in proper balance. Obviously one must avoid sterilizing originality by employing it on routine work. One cannot replace originality; the best which can be achieved by good planning and the use of mechanical and electronic aids is the replacement of numbers of junior staff by a few more highly trained people. But if the shortage becomes worse the higher the training required, this is very difficult to achieve. The most promising places for 'productivity study' are those in which there is an acute shortage of staff of lower qualifications. We think it remarkable that, despite the crucial importance of the shortage of draughtsmen and the great mass of routine work which often clutters up the drawing office, we have found only two firms which have put their best efforts into the task of increasing drawing office productivity. It is notable, too, that despite an acute shortage of science teachers, advanced classes in schools are often very small. Joint classes between neighbouring schools are becoming more usual, but we think they might be extended further without serious loss in the quality of teaching.

The statistics quoted at the beginning of this chapter show that the shortage of draughtsmen is more serious or crucial than that of scientists or engineers (apart, of course, from special groups such as the chemical engineers). The entry to this occupation is normally by an ordinary craft or student apprenticeship in the engineering industry, though some firms have special 'drawing-office' apprenticeships including practical experience in the workshops. A draughtsman must have practical experience:

'A sound training as, say, a fitter is one suitable background, since it provides opportunities for studying the construction of machines, seeing the effects of different machining and finishing processes, and studying the uses of different materials; similarly a tool-room apprentice is often well equipped to transfer to jig and tool drawing. The wider training of the "engineering" (i.e. student) apprentice is also most appropriate for a draughtsman.' [1]

But a fitter or a tool-room apprentice can sometimes, when his 'time' is up, stay in the shops and earn, by overtime or piece-work, more than a draughtsman: and an ambitious student apprentice will look to the bigger prizes on the managerial side. A draughtsman has prospects of more advanced work as a designer (though the distinction between draughtsman and designer is far from clear in the U.K.), but the greater part of drawing-office work is of a routine kind, and it can be broken down into relatively simple tasks. In consequence the prospect of further advance in status is considered poor. The *basic* rates of draughtsmen 'improvers' and fitters are the same at age 21, and at age 25 the draughtsman (then fully trained) has an advantage of over £3 a week. But this is in the basic rate: in actual earnings the position may be reversed.

In fact the drawing office is widely considered a dead end. Associated with this has been a fall in the social status of draughtsmen. Before the war a draughtsman was definitely part of the 'staff' or management: his status was marked by such things as longer holidays and better sickness payments. But now these advantages have been won by the 'workers' also, and the advance of union organization among the draughtsmen is believed by some to carry with it an identity of social status with the workers on the shop floor.

Some firms have attempted to circumvent the shortage by dilution— that is to say, by employing on elementary duties people with a pure drawing-office training, and no practical engineering experience. This is resisted by the unions, and is contrary to the traditions of engineering management, and consequently it has had little effect on the shortage. The root cause of that shortage is the immense expansion of engineering, and especially of the aircraft industry, bringing a more than proportionate

[1] Central Youth Employment Executive, *Careers Pamphlet no. 60*, H.M.S.O., 1954.

H

increase in the demand for draughtsmen. Employers were perhaps slow to see that it would take longer to produce the human requirements for their production than to obtain their machines, but (even if there had been much less competition from other jobs) it would have been hard to train draughtsmen fast enough to meet this buoyant demand.

The last point has a general application. The shortage of trained men and women is not in itself a ground for concern; it is the natural consequence of a rapidly increasing demand, and it provides the impulse to do something about it. What should be a ground for concern is the discovery that the impulse is not being followed by the necessary corrective action. The preceding pages suggest a number of factors limiting the increase in trained manpower which deserve fresh attention. First there is the influence on a later career of the choice of subjects at school—a choice which, we think, is too much a matter of chance. Then there is the limiting effect of the shortage of science teachers, and the wastage through able boys and girls leaving school too early and going to unsuitable jobs. We have drawn attention to the fact that Britain's poor showing in the training of graduates is largely due to our traditional interpretation of what constitutes a 'university standard': by setting a high standard, we put more responsibility on to the technical colleges, which (though showing a remarkable expansion) can offer neither the resources of a university nor the social prestige of a degree. We have shown various reasons why the supply and demand are not well adapted to each other; skills which are not scarce are developed more than those which are, and occupations in dire need of scientists are passed over in favour of others. One of these examples of misdirection, the avoidance of teaching, threatens the whole future expansion of scientific manpower. Finally, we have expressed doubts as to whether there has been enough development of the science of using scientists productively.

It would be a mistake to suppose that these problems can be disposed of by marginal changes in the country's methods of educating and using its manpower. Wherever the additional scientific and technical manpower is found, it will have to be taught, and the difficult problem of attracting more teachers will have to be faced. If wastage through a wrong choice of specialization at school is to be avoided, there will have to be a considerable change in methods of giving careers advice, in school curricula, and in the requirements of examining bodies. If a considerable part of the additional flow were to follow the route from grammar school to university, the entrance requirements of the universities would have to be easier and the whole conception of a first university degree would have to be altered. If the flow were to pass mainly through the technical colleges, great further measures of expansion would be needed, and the country would have to face the problem of making technical education sufficiently broad to develop the full powers of its pupils. Such changes would have to be planned to meet, not merely the difficulties of the present, but the greater problems of the future; for we see every reason to expect that the demand for scientists and technologists will go on rising for many years to come, and that new measures will constantly be needed to conserve the country's meagre supply of scientifically trained men and women.

Chapter 10

PUSHES AND PULLS

THERE can be no scientific progress without scientists, but it is not at all certain that, if more scientists are trained, unprogressive firms will leap into progressiveness. The various necessary conditions of progress—trained men, money, receptive management, favourable markets—are essential to each other, like the wheels of a clock. But what winds the clock or makes it tick? What are the stimulants of progressiveness? We turn next to this question, both because of its great intrinsic importance, and because it enables us to introduce some distinctions which are of use in the later chapters.

Some people suppose that the part of clock-winder is played by the inventor, the man of an original turn of mind, whose flow of new ideas and improvements keeps his firm constantly moving forward. This view is both out of date and inadequate. It is out of date because, in the larger firms of today, the flow of new ideas for product and process innovation results, not from the chance inspiration of exceptional individuals, but from a deliberate decision by management to spend money on research and development. There is still a great need for the inspiration of genius, but much routine discovery and improvement waits simply for the investment of sufficient resources. The view quoted above is inadequate because it is clearly possible for a firm to be highly progressive without showing much trace of originality. It may simply copy what is done elsewhere: it may be pushed into the stream of advance by its suppliers, or pulled there by its customers. If one looks at an industry of many units, like agriculture, it is nonsense to identify progressiveness with inventiveness. In fact in agriculture a great many of the new ideas come from outside, from research establishments, machinery suppliers, chemical firms, and so on; the progressive farmer is the one with the wits to select what is appropriate from the stream of ideas which impinge upon him.

This last remark is the key to the classification which we have found to be significant—a classification by the readiness to take and to give knowledge. At one extreme we have the firm which is self-satisfied in its isolation, which we call *parochial*. By a parochial firm we mean one which is confined within self-imposed and narrow limits; it is an object of its policy, or at least a result of that policy in practice, that it should not look outside itself for ideas. A typical firm of this kind might be found, for instance, making a traditional line of specialized machinery. Its managers have spent a lifetime in the firm, beginning as apprentices. Their view is that, whatever may be the case in other industries, in *their* industry it is experience which counts. They know all the reasons why it is impossible to strike out in new ways. Their product is marketed through long-established trade contacts, but their attitude to customers is 'take it or leave it'; their position in their speciality is strong enough to ensure that the customer usually takes it, and they make no real effort to join with their customers in planning the improvement of their product. They have no organized inflow of technical information from periodicals or research association bulletins, and no one capable of understanding the information (outside a narrow field) if it came. They have a useful term, 'academic', to describe what they believe to be the irrelevance to their industry of scientists working in laboratories. Research associations are 'academic': graduates in science and technology are liable to be 'too academic', and in consequence the firm finds it difficult to use graduates properly, since it cannot help regarding them as essentially inferior to those whose practical experience began at the minimum school-leaving age. The parochial firm believes itself to be different, believes that it has no need of outside help or stimulus; its failures are due to unkind fate or the wickedness of Governments; its ideal character is Old Sam, who has been in the workshops since he was twelve, and an ounce of whose practical instinct is considered to be worth a bushel of theory.

There are, of course, degrees of parochialism; not all the features of our composite description will be found in every firm. The common factor is the lack of interest in ideas developed outside the firm. The parochial attitude is not confined to traditional craft industries, though 'craftsmanship' is sometimes debased to mean a glorification of inherited knowledge which tends to exclude new ideas. It is also possible to find, in secluded corners of modern scientific industries, firms with a speciality which are now satisfied to be self-sufficient.

In a middle position we have firms which are receptive to new ideas, but which rely on some other firm or agency to provide them; these we call *adoptive*. Such firms are common, for instance, among sub-contractors to the aircraft industry; there is no unwillingness to tackle a new product or try a new process, but the specification must be devised, or the technical knowledge brought in, from outside. A small firm is frequently unable to finance a research and development department, and so has to rely on its suppliers of machinery or materials, or on its customers, for the information which leads to improvements in product or process. But we have found quite large firms which can certainly be classified as technically progressive, but which originate no ideas themselves—which, in fact, have decided not to attempt to provide the machinery of research and development, but to be parasitic on firms that do. Adoptive firms which could not develop their own ideas even if they wanted to we refer to as *involuntarily adoptive*; those which could support their own research and development, but have chosen not to, as *voluntarily adoptive*.

There remain those firms that are not parochial and not parasitic on the development work of others. These firms attempt to create new products or processes by the conduct of research and development and they stand ready to receive new knowledge from outside. Indeed, they are actively interested in pulling it in; they have a well-developed system of information, and their scientific, technical, and sales staff are encouraged to have wide interests and to keep their eyes and ears open for anything which may help their firm's progress. Some of these firms are truly creative—that is, highly successful in creating new products and processes; others are not so successful. We therefore refer to the whole group in our statistical classification as *non-parochial, non-adoptive*.

We were able to make a rough classification of 130 out of 152 firms covered by our general case-studies, in the manner suggested above, and we have related this to our classification by technical 'progressiveness', whose nature is discussed further in Chapter 16. The results, showing percentages in each category of progressiveness, speak for themselves:

	Progressive per cent.	Moderately progressive per cent.	Non-progressive per cent.
Parochial	—	—	32
Adoptive (involuntarily) .	2	17	9
Adoptive (voluntarily) . .	2	23	23
Non-parochial, non-adoptive	96	60	36
	100	100	100

These results depend, however, on the industrial distribution of the 130 firms, and firms or industries may be grouped in a number of ways. In the Manchester Joint Research Council report,[1] which was concerned with the Manchester area, where half the establishments make textiles, industries were grouped into Modern, Engineering, Textiles, and Miscellaneous. We have grouped firms into Traditional, Engineering, and Modern.

Under *traditional* we include extractive industries, baking, building and construction, cotton, wool, and jute processing, pottery, cutlery, paper, printing, furniture, and shoe-making. In *engineering* we include industries based on the engineering advances of the last century, associated mainly with prime movers—machine tools, pumps, motors, aircraft, heavy electrical equipment, and production machinery. In *modern* we include heavy and fine chemicals, radio, electronics, scientific instruments, man-made fibres, and nuclear products.

This method of grouping obscures important differences in production techniques—particularly in traditional industries where firms have transformed methods of production through research and development.

[1] *Industry and Science*, Manchester University Press, 1954.

We have regrouped firms to take account of this. Those firms which rely mainly on technicians to deal with their major production problems are put in a 'technician' group, those that mainly rely on engineers in an 'engineer' group, those that rely on scientists in a 'scientist' group. Most, but not all, 'traditional' firms are in the 'technician' group.

Percentages of Firms Classified as Parochial, Adoptive, or otherwise, by Industry and Technical Progressiveness Rating

	Traditional Progressiveness				Engineering Progressiveness				Modern Progressiveness			
	High	Med.	Low	Total	High	Med.	Low	Total	High	Med.	Low	Total
Parochial . .	0	0	75	18	0	4	30	7	0	0	0	0
Adoptive . .	22	35	25	28	8	31	20	20	5	50	100	17
Non-parochial, non-adoptive .	78	65	0	54	92	65	50	73	95	50	0	83
	100	100	100	100	100	100	100	100	100	100	100	100

Percentages of Firms in the Different Types of Industry

	Traditional	Engineering	Modern	Total
Parochial . . .	60	40	0	100
Adoptive . . .	35	45	20	100
Non-parochial, non-adoptive . .	20	55	25	100

Percentages of Firms Classified as Parochial, Adoptive, or otherwise, by Dominant Skill and Technical Progressiveness Rating

Dominant skill	Technician Progressiveness				Engineer Progressiveness				Scientist Progressiveness			
	High	Med.	Low	Total	High	Med.	Low	Total	High	Med.	Low	Total
Parochial . .	0	0	75	50	0	2	23	5	0	0	0	0
Adoptive . .	0	100	25	45	10	27	22	20	10	40	100	15
Non-parochial, non-adoptive .	100	0	0	5	90	71	55	75	90	60	0	85
	100	100	100	100	100	100	100	100	100	100	100	100

Percentages of Firms with the Different Types of Dominant Skill

Dominant skill	Technician	Engineer	Scientist	Total
Parochial . . .	70	30	0	100
Adoptive . . .	20	60	20	100
Non-parochial, non-adoptive . .	1	73	26	100

The concentration of parochial firms in the traditional industries and in the industries relying on technicians is significant. The case-studies in Appendix III indicate some of the reasons for this, and the difficulty of changing the situation.[1]

Our first conclusion is, therefore, that to understand the stimulants of progressiveness one must look, not merely within the firm, but at its relations with other firms and with other sources of ideas. These relations have a special importance because many substantial developments

[1] See also p. 117.

in products or processes require united action by a whole chain of firms. Thus an aircraft firm required, for an improvement in its product, a plastic moulding of special qualities and precision; it depended on a plastic moulding firm with experience of such work, and that firm in turn depended on chemical firms to supply the required materials and on the makers of precision dies. The gas turbine depends on new knowledge and new capacity in the metallurgical industries. Wherever a chain of firms is thus involved, progress can go no faster than the weakest link of the chain allows. The failures of 'weak-link' firms are of several kinds: they may fail to develop their own technology to match those of the industries to which they are related; they may (perhaps as a consequence of this) fail to produce goods of adequate quality; they may be unwilling to provide needed new capacity.

We have evidence on the 'chain effect' from 120 firms. In many cases there were complaints from fabricating industries about the failure of their suppliers of materials or machinery. These complaints came most strongly from the most progressive firms, which were naturally keenly aware of the disparity between their desired pace of development and that of their suppliers. As far as possible, we have visited the 'weak-link' firms, some of which appeared to be generally unprogressive; but these firms were often able to point to other weak links in the chain— for instance, in their own supply of materials—or were able to refer to difficulties general in industry such as the shortage of draughtsmen. In some cases the 'weak-link' firm was in general progressive, but its 'weak-link' activity was marginal to its main lines of interest.

No doubt because our inquiries were mainly in a period of high demand for capital equipment, the most numerous complaints were about the supply of steel. There were five references to difficulty in getting particular qualities, and twenty-seven to slowness of delivery. The 'delivery' problem has far-reaching effects. Not only does it affect the rapidity with which new plant and new equipment can be built, delaying projects for six months or more; it also in some cases involves duplication of drawing work, since companies which have prepared plans on the basis of the supposed current availability of steels may find that by the time they are able to execute these plans the supply position has altered, and the plans have to be amended. One highly progressive chemicals firm, severely hampered by the shortage of draughtsmen, estimates that 25 per cent. of its drawing-office effort has been wasted in this way. The steel shortage can also have an important cumulative effect when it delays first a pilot-plant and then a full-scale plant.

Many 'weak-link' complaints are made against the heavy engineering industry: against one small section of this industry, in which there are three (or possibly four) firms uniquely placed to provide equipment for a wide variety of other industries, we have seven complaints about deliveries and six about quality. The burden of the quality complaints is that the firms are not yet able to provide plant of a type already obsolescent (if not obsolete) in Germany and the U.S.A.—they are two or more steps behind the times. Comparable complaints (eighteen on delivery, nine on quality) were made against the machine-tool industry: seven on delivery and four on quality about the supply of chemicals; five on delivery and one on quality about the supply of chemical plant. Of sixty-five other complaints about 'weak links', eleven were about special components, five about special machinery, and two about the length of time taken in erecting buildings. No special significance should be attached to these figures, which are relative both to the industrial composition of our sample of firms (see Appendix II) and to the particular and changing circumstances of the time of inquiry; but they show that the problem of co-ordinated development in a chain of firms is widely felt to be difficult.

Some of the complaints, especially about long delivery times, are due to the natural pains of growth: the steel industry, for instance, cannot overnight create capacity to deal with an upsurge of capital investment as sudden as that which occurred between 1953 and 1955. But not all weak links are due to rapid growth; it can be seen how a chain is weakened if it contains any parochial firms. Such firms will only be slowly and dimly conscious of the need for adapting themselves to the requirements of other industries. They are not so much weak links as links which do not want to belong to a chain at all.

Our inquiries suggest that it is extremely difficult to persuade parochial firms to amend their standard of performance—the attitude of senior managers, the inability of parochial firms to realize that their business could be conducted in a radically different way, and the absence of technological skill or knowledge are strong barriers against change. It is also often difficult to outflank these firms, no doubt because the *surviving* parochial firms are those which have a strongly held position, and which can be displaced only after heavy expenditure on research and development and on new capital equipment. Nevertheless we have found cases in which combined Government Department and customer pressure has been used to induce progressive heavy engineering firms to broaden their basis of operations, and to start producing in 'weak-link' sections of the industry.

Some firms can advance more quickly by taking over the 'weak-link' functions themselves—we have come across a number which have opened up sections for making specialized machine tools—but this of course means the diversion of technical and managerial skills, which may be in short supply, to work which is not in the firm's main line of interest. Sometimes it is possible to overcome the difficulty by importing materials or machinery from more progressive firms overseas. Such action sometimes requires Government permission, but we find that this permission has normally been forthcoming when a firm has presented a well-documented case. Sometimes again it is possible to stimulate the necessary development by making firm contract arrangements with other firms, coupled with technical advice and assistance. An example of the stimulation of sub-contractors is provided by Messrs. Ferranti Ltd., who have a deliberate policy of technical assistance to small firms in the Edinburgh area in order to build up a body of firms with specialist knowledge in electronics. In the aircraft industry and its associated trades, in special branches of metallurgy, in the trades subsidiary to atomic physics, and elsewhere, the Government development contract has been an effective means of stimulating progress; this we discuss further in Chapter 15.

Since the problem of the 'weakest link' is often a problem of overcoming the isolation of parochial firms, something can be done by vigorous purchasing procedure. We have examples of development engineers repeatedly visiting suppliers' factories, impressing their management and operatives with the urgency of their order, making suggestions about production methods, and obtaining reasonably quick delivery. A more extreme example of direct action was that of a chemicals firm which was quoted two years for the erection of a plant when one year appeared to be adequate. It arranged to put its own staff in charge of progress and planning on the site, and considerably reduced the erection period.

Another weakness in the chain comes from the failure of a progressive firm to find customers willing to try out an improved product. It is difficult to distinguish, however, between justified complaints that a market is dominated by stupid or conservative customers, and excuses which hide a failure in selling policy or in market research. Better selling policy might have made the customers less stupid.

The 'chain effect' is the dependence of a single development on a number of firms. Complementary to it we have what we may call the 'gate effect', when the pioneering action of a firm or an industry opens the gate to a number of developments. A striking example was the wartime growth in the production of synthetic rubber in the U.S.A., which has led to development in the oil and chemicals industries, and thus in turn has helped forward work on petrochemicals. In the U.K. the production of a wide range of petrochemicals had to wait for the erection of large oil refineries with their associated cracking plant. The way to 'automation', in the sense of the automatic operation of machine tools and the automatic inspection of products, was opened by the developments of electronics, which again owed much to the special needs of war. War has been a great opener of gates; and so has labour shortage, which (for instance) has helped to induce considerable technical change in the jute and pottery industries.

There is another important aspect of relations between firms—namely, the willingness to be stimulated. A number of large progressive firms give technical help to suppliers and offer technical service with their products. Provided suppliers or customers are willing to take advantage of it, the offering of such service is good salesmanship, and in particular a new product sold to other industries needs to be backed by technical information and service. But from the national point of view this is much more than salesmanship: it is a means by which vital new knowledge can flow to places which otherwise it would never reach.

The necessary conditions of progress are further considered in the chapters which follow. To balance our discussion of external stimulants of progressiveness, however, we must here refer to the importance of dominant personalities in the firm. Important new developments frequently begin from the vision and drive of one man or of a small group of men. We find this both in small and in large firms. There are occasions too when, without a change in technical staff, market situation, or financial conditions, the arrival of a new man to a key position changes a firm from the unprogressive to the progressive class, or vice versa. This has led some observers to conclude that progressiveness depends on the qualities of the key personalities and that an unprogressive firm can be made progressive by changing the quality of the policy-makers. Such a conclusion is, in this context, either misleading or unhelpful. It is misleading if it gives the impression that the scale of research into the materials and processes of the industry, or the educational level of the industry, do not matter. It is unhelpful in that first-rate managing directors are in very limited supply.

Other things being equal, one might expect the talented key personalities to be randomly distributed. But clearly this is not so; in fact our evidence suggests that firms already under talented direction find it easiest to attract further talent, and firms which are in a rut find it difficult to attract the ability which could lift them out. We have made a special analysis covering 150 firms to enable us to identify the factors involved more clearly. They seem to us to be as follows:

1. *The Direct Attraction of Existing Talent.* A firm with able direction is attractive to talented men: a firm badly directed is likely to frustrate them, so that they are attracted elsewhere. Thus, in a particular progressive firm, the key personality is the Managing Director, who achieved his position through his outstanding pre-war and wartime record and through the impression he made on a famous financier. He has high scientific qualifications, an ability to plan ahead, and strong powers of leadership. The firm's progress is attributed to him: in the words of a subordinate, 'Our success comes from his building up of a good team, and committing us to do the impossible.' There are senior and junior management levels between the Managing Director and the shop-floor supervision, and the Managing Director has an active policy of recruiting good people to fill these positions. Once recruited, staff find the conditions stimulating. In a typical unprogressive firm, on the

other hand, the Managing Director took over the family firm, as did his father before him, on the death of the previous generation. He has no formal technical qualifications, and has been in the firm since he left school. His time is mainly filled with immediate problems of sales and production. There is no level of management between him and the shop-floor supervision, and no active policy of recruiting good people to provide for future management.

Research talent also attracts research talent. One firm, after setting up a research department, had seven years of difficulty in attracting worth-while research staff. Research results were, however, good, and now the firm has an excess of reasonable applications for vacancies. Another firm with a fine reputation for production engineering, but little reputation for research, has no difficulty in recruiting production engineers, but very great difficulty in recruiting research staff. Lack of knowledge of how to recruit is also important. We have been to firms that are quite anxious to employ graduates in engineering, but have been disappointed that none of them came to ask for a job; others have offered quite un-realistic salaries.

2. *The Nature of Ownership.* A tradition of family management restricts the field from which good people can be recruited, and offers a discouraging prospect to able outsiders who may be worthy of promotion. Unless the family breeds many sons and ensures that they have a training and an experience wider than that of learning the job in their own firm, the tradition of family management does not ensure talented direction. We have found a number of cases where the tradition has been broken by a member of the family who has been trained outside the industry.

3. *The Requirements of the Firm.* The proportion of administrative, technical, and clerical labour costs to total labour costs is much higher in some firms and industries than in others—higher, for instance, in modern than in craft industries. Where the proportion is low, there are few senior posts with the salary or the prestige to attract or retain good men. Where we have come across changes from craft to scientifically controlled methods (in pottery, paper, and engineering), we have found that there has been at the same time a creation of new openings in management for talented men. Firms founded on and growing with scientific developments have a much greater opportunity to use and attract talent. The nature of the productive process often entails the employment of men with, at least, sufficient talent to have acquired a formal training in science or technology. There is also an opportunity and a tendency for scientists to move from the research department, in the early-30 age group, to management positions elsewhere in the firm.

4. *The Rate of Expansion.* A high rate of growth leads to the creation of new posts, and improved prospects for those already in the firm. It is thus easier to retain good men in a growing industry. Sometimes ex-

pansion means that talent is too thinly spread, or that there is a difficult problem of altering the managerial structure and perhaps of losing the flexibility of small size. But if the firm is able to adapt itself at all, it will offer good prospects.

5. *The Conventions of Prestige and Salary.* We have found that in a number of craft firms using 'rule-of-thumb' methods of management, middle management is low in pay and prestige. The introduction of scientists or engineers would entail the payment of salaries which would disrupt the salary and prestige structure of the firm; it would not be worthwhile unless the craft basis of production was to be undermined.

6. *The Reputation of the Firm and the Popularity of the Industry.* Although we have in our sample very few of the nationally famous firms, there is clear evidence in our case-studies that the better a firm's reputation the less its difficulty in attracting talent. This is particularly so with scientists and technologists. The closer the links, both formal and informal, between a particular firm and the relevant universities or technical colleges, the greater the possibility of getting talented recruits. The training and recruitment of technicians are helped by proximity to a good technical college or university. Apart from the reputation of a particular firm, there are the intangible factors which determine the popularity of its industry: whether it is regarded as being 'new', 'advanced', 'progressive'. We have referred to this matter elsewhere (pp. 89, 102).

7. *The Encouragement of Outside Contacts.* A firm which encourages outside contacts (e.g. visits to other companies, attendances at learned societies, trade exhibitions, etc.) offers a good man a more stimulating prospect than one which believes in secrecy and isolation. There is, in our case-studies, a clear correlation between secrecy and unprogressiveness.

8. *The Progressiveness of Other Firms in the Industry.* The existence of other progressive firms may mean that there are good men (with the right technical background) to be bought. We have observed a case where a progressive American subsidiary in a backward industry has fertilized other firms, which have attracted away some of its executives. On the other hand, business ethics in the U.K. are somewhat unfavourable to the attraction of senior men from other firms with which one has relations.

The distribution of talent is thus not random. There is a process of selection which gives progressive industries a share of scarce talent out of proportion to their total employment. The industries most firmly stuck in the mud of unprogressiveness are thus less likely to secure the talented direction which might pull them out. We suspect that this is one of the most serious obstacles to the speeding up of the technical progress of backward industries.

Chapter 11

THE APPROPRIATE INDUSTRIAL
ORGANIZATION

THE way in which industry is organized—into small firms and large, private and public companies, nationalized corporations, and so on—obviously seems likely to affect the rate at which science is applied. Yet there are conflicting views about the nature and intensity of that influence. Research is an expensive activity, and development still more expensive, and it would therefore seem likely that scientific progress would move more swiftly in the large firms and public corporations, which can afford research and development departments of their own. Small firms must rely on co-operative research, or on the exploitation of an individual discovery, and the possibilities of both of these are circumscribed. But on the other hand the large unit, whether publicly or privately owned, may be sluggish; in a limiting case, the whole stream of development may be held up by the backwardness of one individual. Some people, therefore, see the best guarantee of progress in the lively competition of numerous small units, so that if new knowledge is dammed up in one place it may break through in another, and force itself upon the attention of backward firms by its success in the operations of their competitors.

There is some ambiguity about what is meant by a 'small' firm. There are some 80,000 manufacturing establishments in the U.K. with fewer than eleven employees, and they account for about 5 per cent. of the national output of manufactured goods, though of course for much more in certain trades. About 8 per cent. of the output is produced in establishments with less than twenty-five employees, and about a quarter in establishments with less than 100 employees. The repetition of the word 'establishment' is a reminder that these statistics apply to individual factories, and that it is very common for large firms or interlocking groups of firms to carry on production in many different establishments; there are no general data on the sizes of 'firms', defined as independent financial units. But since even on an 'establishment' basis about half of manufacturing production comes from units with 500 or more employees,[1] it can be seen that large *firms* are of predominant importance. The number of employees is a poor measure of size (the chemical industry, for instance, can show enormous plants run by a handful of men)—but if we divide firms into those with more than 500, 100 to 500, and less than 100 on their pay-roll, the contributions of the three classes

[1] About 35 per cent. of manufacturing output is produced in 1 per cent. of the establishments: more than 70 per cent. in 10 per cent. of the establishments.

can be estimated as roughly in the ratio 3 : 1 : 1. Within the large firms, the giants (some with more than 50,000 employees) are again of great importance.

The right emphasis, therefore, is to think of British manufacturing industry as mainly organized in big financial units, but with numerous small firms making a significant minority contribution. The public utilities, being mostly nationalized, are also dominated by large organizations. Building and contracting, on the other hand, is mainly organized in small firms, though even in that industry half the output comes from some 2,000 larger firms (with 100 or more employees). The unit of organization in farming is very small, though it is larger in Britain than in many continental countries.

The common idea that industry in the U.S.A. is organized in larger units, and consequently obtains the advantages of a larger scale of operations, needs closer examination. There is no information adequate for a comparison of the sizes of firms, but the great distances within the U.S.A. and the strength of sentiment against large combines would seem to make it unlikely that the number of establishments per firm is much greater than in the U.K. A comparison can be made of the sizes of establishments by numbers employed; where there is so much dispersion, a comparison of mean sizes or median sizes has little meaning, but we think that the following table gives a fair picture of the differences. It is based on data from the British Census of Production for 1948, and from the U.S.A. Census of Manufactures for 1947, these being the latest comparable years for which data were available.

Number of trades for which the U.S.A. has proportionally more big establishments, and fewer small establishments ('U.S.A. units bigger')	65
Number of trades for which the U.K. has proportionally more big establishments, and fewer small establishments ('U.K. units bigger') . .	35
Number of trades for which the U.S.A. has proportionally more big units *and* more small units, but fewer of intermediate size . . .	14
Number of trades for which the U.K. has proportionally more big units *and* more small units, but fewer of intermediate size . . .	6
Number of trades for which the difference in size-distribution is insignificant	2
	122

On the face of it, therefore, the assertion that the units of factory organization are larger in the U.S.A. was true in just over half the trades; and those for which the opposite was apparently true included important trades like building materials, coal-tar products, drugs, toilet preparations, soap, steel sheets, shipbuilding and marine engineering, machine tools, mechanical handling equipment, electric wires and cables, biscuits, milk products, confectionery, tobacco, and wallpaper. In the large Mechanical Engineering (General) trade there was little difference between the two countries. The broad picture was that the relative importance of big units was greater in the U.S.A. in the consumer goods trades, but that the trades which make capital goods or basic materials gave a very mixed answer.

But this comparison is based on employment; bearing in mind that labour productivity in the U.S.A. is usually substantially higher, it is clear that if we measured the size of factories by their output, there would be many more trades for which the U.S.A. would show (proportionately) more large units. The dependent generalization, that in consequence she obtains advantages from a larger scale of operations, is a matter for examination trade by trade in the light of the technique employed and the conditions of the market; there are certainly a number of trades for which the generalization would be unfounded.

We are not disposed to put much weight on the differences between countries in the sizes of factories as proof of the advantages of the large unit. There are many other explanations of the high productivity of U.S. industry. It is perhaps more relevant to observe that in both Britain and the U.S.A. small and large firms manage to exist, side by side in the same trade, over long periods. We shall therefore expect to find a balance of advantage and disadvantage in both small and large units.

There is, however, another line of argument which (using data from a single country) seeks to show that big-firm industries are likely to display more evidence of technical change than small-firm industries. Professor Almarin Phillips [1] has recently attempted to test a remark of Professor J. K. Galbraith: [2] 'A benign Providence . . . has made the modern industry of a few large firms an almost perfect instrument for inducing technical change.' Professor Phillips observes that partial and imperfect indices of technical change are provided by the productivity of labour and the amount of horsepower per employee. He compares these (for a sample of twenty-eight U.S.A. industries, and for the period 1899–1939) with indices of *concentration* (the percentage of output accounted for by the largest twenty establishments) and of *scale* (measured alternatively by capital per establishment and by the number of wage-earners per establishment). He finds that there is in fact evidence that industries with high concentration or large factories showed greater technical change, in the special sense defined above; and that this was not due to differences in the rate of increase of output. This does not, of course, prove that high concentration or large scale cause or facilitate technical change—the relation might be the other way round. But it does at least warrant the negative conclusion, that it yields no evidence to support 'the alternative hypothesis that industries with large numbers of small firms tend to be technologically more progressive'.

[1] *Journal of Industrial Economics*, June 1956.
[2] *American Capitalism*, Hamish Hamilton, 1952, p. 91.

We have attempted a small study on similar lines for the U.K., for the period 1907–48, but we have been able to use only a broad industry classification. For twelve industries there appears to be some correlation between the degree of concentration and the increase of output per employee-hour; the coefficient of correlation is 0·57. But the relation between the number of employees per establishment and the increase of output per employee-hour is much slighter, the correlation coefficient being only 0·34. For what it is worth, this evidence suggests that in Britain neither the virtues nor the vices of the small-firm industry have made much mark on the productivity of labour, which is an important indicator of the industrial change of the last half-century. But it might be that a further investigation by individual trades would yield a more positive result.

No conclusions can safely be drawn from the differences in net output per person employed in different sizes of establishment, as shown in the Census of Production. This quantity varies greatly from trade to trade, sometimes being much larger in big establishments than in small, sometimes showing irregular peaks at intermediate sizes. The overall result for all manufacturing industry in 1949 was that net output per employee was £522 for the smallest establishments, rising to £623 for those of size 2,500–2,999, and falling to £516 for those of size 10,000 and over. In building and contracting the smallest firms yielded £400 net output per employee, and the figure shows small and irregular variations up to size 3,000, followed by a sharp rise to £524 at size 5,000 and over. (The unit is in this case the firm, since an 'establishment' has an uncertain meaning in building.) There is no doubt that the main source of such variations is that firms of different sizes are making different things. The net output has to cover profits and depreciation as well as wages and salaries, and it thus reflects the great differences in the amounts of capital equipment used by firms, even in the same industry. Thus the small firm in building and contracting may be engaged on minor repair work, using hardly any capital equipment, while the biggest firms are civil engineering contractors using a great range of heavy equipment. We think that a similar lack of homogeneity will be found in most trades and industries. We note also that the Census classification of size by number of employees could give an impression quite different from a classification by size of net output.

To see the influence of industrial organization on the application of science more clearly, we will examine five different kinds of organization and look at the advantages and problems of each. These five are:

1. A very small owner-supervised business, with (say) from half a dozen to thirty employees:
2. A family business, organized as a company with members of the family as directors, and having (say) 100 employees:

I

3. A small public company with 500 employees, the directors and managers not being the principal shareholders.
4. A large public company, controlling subsidiaries with a total of 50,000 employees:
5. A large nationalized industry.

These are, of course, only selected possibilities from a great range of different sizes and types of organization.

1. In the small owner-supervised business, the application of science depends on the personality and ability of the owner. Such a business may indeed have come into existence to exploit some discovery which the owner has made, or some neglected process or product which he has revived. But it is a mistake to think of a typical invention as an improved mouse-trap, capable of being produced and marketed by the inventor from the shed at the end of his garden. The big improvements of product or process are usually the end of a long and expensive chain of research and development; the minor improvements are commonly applied to existing large-scale processes, and are not capable of being split off and exploited on a small scale by themselves. The small business, as we have met it, is not therefore typically the expression of the creative urge of an inventor. It is a producer of small components, or of 'tailor-made' goods, or of products which (like the services of repairers) must be available at a great many different places. Or it is the natural form of organization of a new industry; we have noted that in such industries as electronics and plastics many very small units spring up in the early stages, but that quite soon the growth of some, the merger of others, and the failure of a few, produces a more usual distribution of small and large firms.

But although the owner is not usually himself an inventor, and although his business is too small to support a research department, it does not follow that it is technologically backward. The stimulus to improvement comes from many sources: from the trade press, from research associations (and especially those which have officers continually visiting member firms), from the suppliers of machinery and materials, and from the customers for the finished product. The great agricultural shows are a striking example of the stimulation of improvement in an industry of small businesses; for the farmer is there subjected to the appeal of the equipment manufacturers, he sees the educational exhibits of the Ministry of Agriculture (whose advisory service is available to him at all times), and he also sees, if he is concerned with livestock, the finest products of his competitors on show.

We do not think, therefore, that the small size of an owner-supervised business is *necessarily* an obstacle to the speedy application of science. Such a business can be technically active and progressive provided it has access to sources of research information and is backed by a good service of technical education. The unprogressive small firm, which we have observed (for instance) in the brick and the pottery industries, is commonly one which has an obstinate self-sufficiency—which is, in fact, 'parochial' in the sense which we have discussed in Chapter 10. But a progressive small firm may make a living in competition with much larger firms, by virtue of its simplicity, and especially of the fact that the manager knows his men and can supervise every detail of the business. This advantage of simplicity may be lost if the business grows, and we have found cases of successful small businesses whose owners are not anxious that they should grow further, lest they should extend beyond the span of the owner's direct control. This is an example of a general difficulty in moving from one type of managerial structure to another, and the unwillingness to make this move occasionally means that a good new idea, not available for exploitation in other firms, is held back instead of being vigorously developed.

A small business must usually depend on the energy and credit of its owner for the capital needed both for its first creation and for its expansion. The difficulty of obtaining this capital is discussed in Chapter 13. It has been represented to us that, with the impoverishment of the rich through high taxation, it has become virtually impossible for private individuals to found new businesses or to obtain for them a sufficient rate of growth. We do not doubt the difficulty, and we are sure that there must be many failures. But even in our limited survey we have come across a number of examples of small and medium-sized businesses which have been built up from the ground in the past few years. There are nine such businesses in our sample of 152; three of these owe their continuance or further growth to help from other companies, and three to the stimulating effect of Government contracts. Perhaps it is only the lucky few that can survive and grow without such outside help, but we regard it as unproven that the difficulties of small businesses are any greater than they were fifty or a hundred years ago.

2. The business with 100 employees is still normally too small to support much research and development work of its own, though it may have more qualified staff and be better able to handle the information from research associations and trade journals. It is open to the same influences from suppliers and customers as smaller firms, and again there is nothing in its size which *necessarily* prevents it from being technologically progressive. A firm of any size but the largest may of course be held back because the next stage of technical improvement is too massive for its resources; but we do not think that this is a frequent problem in the kinds of specialist trade in which small firms flourish.

If, however, a company is organized as a family business, there may be additional hindrances to its technical progress. It is typical of such firms that the maintenance of family control takes a high place in

determining the actions of the directors. But, as we shall see in Chapter
13, the State, by the instrument of death duties, makes the maintenance
of family control difficult, and desirable technical progress may be prevented if it would soak up funds which are being reserved for the payment of estate duty. There is furthermore no certainty that the qualities
of vigorous personality and business acumen so essential to the founder
of a small business will be transmitted to his descendants. Marshall,
having observed the special advantages of the son of a man already
established in business, wrote:

'It would therefore at first sight seem likely that business men should
constitute a sort of caste; dividing out among their sons the chief posts of
command, and founding hereditary dynasties, which should rule certain
branches of trade for many generations together. But the actual state of
things is very different.

As a matter of fact when a man has got together a great business, his
descendants, in spite of all their great advantages, often fail to develop
the high abilities and the special turn of mind and temperament required
for carrying it on with equal success. . . . When a full generation has
passed, when the old traditions are no longer a safe guide, and when the
bonds that held together the old staff have been dissolved, then the business almost invariably falls to pieces unless it is practically handed over
to the management of new men who have meanwhile risen to partnership in the firm.' [1]

These words were published in 1890; the old saying, 'Clogs to clogs,
three generations', expresses the same point more tersely. During the
present century the importance of family business has greatly declined
(though this form of organization still dominates important trades), and
the appreciation of the dangers of managerial inbreeding is probably
more widespread. Nevertheless we think that there is some residual
harm done to technical progress by the special difficulties of the family
business. If a small firm adds to all its other problems the financial
difficulties of maintaining family control, and recruits its senior management mainly from the narrow circle of the founder's family, it requires
unusual luck to remain vigorous and progressive. It stands in special
danger of the parochialism which we discussed in Chapter 10.

3. The small public company with 500 employees, without family
control, is free from these special difficulties, though it may find it
difficult to raise the capital it needs. It can be subject to all the stimulants which affect smaller firms, and in addition with increasing size it
becomes more able to support research and development work of its
own, or (by having more technical staff) to increase the range and
usefulness of its contacts with outside research bodies. It is free to buy
managerial skill in the open market, and (if the shareholding is well

[1] *Principles of Economics*, Macmillan, IV, xii, 6.

spread) the owners of the business commonly exercise only the lightest of control over the actions of management.

4. Many of the opportunities of progressiveness grow with the size of firm. The large organization can afford extensive research and development, and can attract staff of the first quality to do them; it can balance risky with safe enterprises; when it is frustrated by the backwardness of suppliers, it may be strong enough to take over their functions. The capital needs of development can be met more cheaply and with greater certainty as the company becomes larger. But there are, of course, countervailing disadvantages of great size. Because the span of management is limited, the number of layers of management or control increases, and the problem of obtaining decisions at the right time becomes greater. This is not a problem capable of resolution by ingenuities of organization, though a bad organization can add further frustrations. By the time one reaches the giant combine, commonly organized as a holding company with semi-autonomous subsidiaries, which are themselves further subdivided into divisions or plants, there is a constant tension between the desire to decentralize (at the cost of losing the sense of control at the centre) and the desire to co-ordinate (at the cost of slowing down decision). The histories of I.C.I., of the National Coal Board, of Unilever, of the British Transport Commission all illustrate this difficulty. Its outward expression is often the tension between the functional director—controlling (say) personnel matters in all divisions—and the divisional director, who wants undisputed control of his own division without meddling from functional departments at Head Office.

The existence of these tensions in large organizations may lead to committee government of an unsatisfactory kind. Disagreements on policy, which threaten to divide management, are met by a decision to do nothing, or delay, where an undivided management would have seized an opportunity quickly. There is a danger of botched-up compromise action, which misses the virtues of the proposals of both sides. Sometimes these dangers are avoided because the firm is dominated by a person of exceptional strength and ability—a William Lever or a Morris—but it is too much to expect that such abilities will appear in all generations of management.

5. To the disadvantages of size, the nationalized industries add the special problems of working under constant public comment, often malicious and ill-informed, and of working to rules of conduct which are in most cases not clearly laid down nor understood by the public. If a highly centralized organization is adopted, a nationalized industry is open to a special danger of monopoly—namely, that a technical decision for the whole country may depend on one man, who may be removable only by his retirement. Alternatively, technical decisions may be subjected to delays and unsatisfactory compromises in committee

government, perhaps even by a multiplicity of committees. The Report of the Committee of Inquiry into the Electricity Supply Industry (Cmd. 9672, 1956) has this to say about research and development:

'All industries must have on the inside men who can scan the horizon of knowledge and take note of what they see and interpret it for the guidance of their own enterprise. The industry that has to have scientific knowledge pushed at it is never as strong as the industry which is organised to pull it in. We have carefully examined the organisation set up by the (Central Electricity) Authority and we are not altogether satisfied with what we find. The responsibilities for research and development inside the Authority are considerably diffused.'

The report goes on to say that there was an Electricity Supply Research Council, but with limited responsibilities; a Research Liaison Committee; a committee dealing with research in universities and technical colleges; a Utilisation Research Committee; and a Technical Development and Contracts Committee: while responsibility for engineering research came under the Chief Engineer, to whom reported the Director of Laboratories and the Engineer in charge of Electro-Technical Research, the post of Deputy Chief Engineer (Research) having been vacant for four years. This proliferation of committees and confusion of lines of responsibility often occur, we think, in giant organizations.

But these difficulties of large, and especially of nationalized, organizations have to be seen against the considerable advantages which come with great resources, and with the possibility of massive research and development programmes directed to particular productive ends. The giant firms can command such research resources that they are almost sure to obtain some successes. In some industries the advantages of size will, given reasonable managerial skill, outweigh its frustrations; in other industries technical advance could equally well be planned and carried out in smaller firms, without the hampering effect of unwieldy administration.

We conclude therefore—and this conclusion is confirmed by our case-studies—that there is no general and systematic connexion between the size of firms or form of industrial organization and the *possibility* of technical progressiveness. This possibility exists at all sizes and in all forms of organization, but each has its own balance of advantages and disadvantages whose outcome depends on the circumstances of the time and industry. Apart from noting the special handicap of family firms, we do not find it possible to assert that the *possibility* of technical progressiveness is translated into the reality more in one type of firm than in another. The answer varies with the techniques of the industry, with past history and present environment, and with the personalities of management.

This conclusion may be compared with the results of a special investigation which was kindly made for us by the Board of Trade. They extracted for us from the returns of the 1951 Census of Production details of capital expenditure analysed by sizes of establishments within each trade. For technical reasons these details are confined to what are known as 'non-combined returns', but we do not consider that this limitation makes a serious difference to the results. Now the adoption of new scientific and technical ideas usually involves capital expenditure, and it could reasonably be expected that, if this adoption was occurring more freely in large firms, these firms would show a significantly greater capital expenditure per employee. This would occur either if large firms were (owing to their greater resources) more *able* to adopt new ideas, or if (resources being the same) large firms were more *willing* to do so.

We would not wish to put too much weight on the conclusions of a single year, but it seems to us significant that, outside two industries, there is little evidence of a general relation between capital expenditure per employee and the size of establishment. The two exceptions are the chemical trades and the food, drink, and tobacco trades, in which there seemed on the whole to be a tendency (though by no means a strong one) for larger firms to undertake more capital expenditure per employee. Outside these two industries there were fifty-five trades showing a positive association and forty-eight showing a zero or negative association, the balance being fairly even in most industries and the degree of association being often small and irregular. Using another measure, the ratio of capital expenditure per employee in establishments with more and with less than 300 employees was less than one in fifty-seven trades, and greater than one in eighty trades, the distribution being practically symmetrical with the exception of eighteen trades, which form a group by themselves with ratios between two and four. If we exclude building and contracting (which is even less homogeneous than most Census divisions) 45 per cent. of the employment is in trades with a ratio less than 1, 46 per cent. in trades with a ratio from 1 to 2, and 9 per cent. in the eighteen exceptional trades with high ratios. The only large trades among these eighteen are iron and steel melting and rolling and cotton-spinning and doubling. While these data support the hypothesis of a weak association between size and intensity of capital expenditure, it seems to us fair to say that they also support our own unwillingness to generalize.

Finally, we suggest that the technical opportunities open to industry react, though no doubt slowly and imperfectly, on its organization. The replacement of the old type of tinplate mill by the strip mill necessarily meant the substitution of large for small organizations. The joint-stock company itself grew up in response to the need for the means of financing and organizing larger units. The partnership of groups of firms, which, without losing their identity, co-operate in some project too large or varied for any to attempt alone, is a form of organization which is gaining ground—for instance in atomic-power projects. A method of organization which appears likely to frustrate technical progress may therefore prove on closer examination to be in process of adaptation to meet the needs of that progress.

Chapter 12

RECEPTIVE AND EFFICIENT MANAGEMENT

IF a firm is to make rapid and effective use of scientific developments it must include people capable of evaluating scientific ideas and of developing or interpreting these ideas in accordance with the needs of the firm. It is natural, or at least it is common practice, to infer from this that if a firm is to make rapid and effective use of science it must have scientists on the Board: 'the scientist is needed in the board rooms as well as in the laboratories of modern industry'. Sir Alexander Todd, F.R.S. (*Progress*, Summer 1955), has gone beyond such inference to the proposition that 'the decline in pioneer spirit (in British industry) was associated with a decline in the participation of the scientist in policy matters'.

To test the proposition that 'progressiveness' depends on the presence of scientists on the Board is difficult. We must find a reasonable standard of progressiveness, and a way of identifying 'scientists'. We must also clarify the meaning of 'participation in policy matters'.

When we are concerned with the industrial application of science and technology it is reasonable to define a progressive company as one which has a good record in applying science to production problems. It is possible, for the firms included in the case-studies, to make a judgement about the degree of progressiveness from a study of policy and achievement in invention and innovation. To test the proposition from a wider sample of firms we have used another definition of progressiveness, namely, the growth of profits. This was one of three alternative criteria of financial success which we used in a study (referred to in Chapter 16) of the relation between financial success and technical progressiveness. Our investigations showed that the growth of profits was the criterion most closely associated with other measures of technical progressiveness; the precise criterion was the ratio between profits for financial years ending in 1952–5 to those for financial years ending in 1948–51. The averaging of years avoids some of the peculiar influences which may affect the profits of a single year. Using this criterion, we selected the best fifty and the worst fifty from a sample of 500 public companies quoted on the London Stock Exchange. This particular study is therefore one of medium and large firms only.

Identifying 'scientists' is not always easy. In the F.B.I. questionnaire on research and development in British industry qualified scientists were those who possessed 'university degree or other qualifications which are generally accepted by professional bodies as equivalent'. Thus a Higher National Certificate was taken as equivalent to a university degree in Engineering. Where information about the scientific or engineering qualifications of directors is gained directly or by questionnaire the difficulty, if we except the difficulty of extracting the information, is not great. To collect such information from (say) a company report is, however, an unsatisfactory proceeding in that H.N.C. is not customarily put after a man's name; and a title such as M.A. may be a qualification in either Arts or Science. We have none the less made a sample count of Directors' stated qualifications to put alongside the statistical tests of progressiveness such as the rate of growth of profits. These qualifications have been sorted out into professional qualifications which appear to be relevant to the technique of the business: degrees in science; other degrees; and other qualifications (mainly accounting or secretarial).

The greatest difficulty, however, is to clarify and render unambiguous the phrase 'participation in policy matters'. Must a scientist be on the Board to participate in policy matters? There are two further questions relevant to the answer. First, where is policy decided—is it or is it not decided on the Board? Second, how is policy decided; if there are scientists in the firm—say as heads of the production department and of the research department—but not on the Board, do they have ample opportunity to brief and persuade the Board on matters pertaining to the application of science? The answer to these questions varies between companies. We will, however, assume to begin with that 'participation in policy' does entail membership of the Board.

The statistical tests that we have applied give a limited confirmation to the proposition. After correcting for differences in industrial distribution and size distribution, the fifty firms with the worst profit record have directors with known qualifications in numbers below the average for the whole 500; but the fifty firms with the best profit record have more directors with professional qualifications than would be expected, on the basis of that average. The contrast between the two samples is quite marked.

From the general case-studies we have excluded those firms in which the progressiveness of the firms or the qualifications of directors are marginal or uncertain. This exclusion leaves 110 firms. Of these, fifty-five are progressive and possess one or more scientists on the Board; fifteen are unprogressive and have no scientists on the Board. Of the remaining forty, nineteen had scientists on the Board but were unprogressive, or did not have a scientist on the Board but were progressive. The other twenty-one have directors who claim 'qualifications by experience' in technical operations.

Qualifications by experience in technical matters should not be ignored. Those men who have risen from a technical job, in contrast to those qualified by experience (or formal qualification) in sales or finance, must have some competence in technical matters. But there is a world of difference between a director qualified by experience in one or several parochial firms and a director qualified by experience in progressive firms. If the former he may simply solidify the traditional outlook of the firm. If the latter, he may, if transferred to a less progressive firm, help to transform its outlook and practice. There are also within the 'qualified by experience' category those qualified by talent. In nine of the progressive firms there are such directors, and they are renowned for their technical innovations. The remaining twelve progressive firms with directors qualified by experience but not conspicuously by talent in technical matters are almost counterbalanced by non-progressive firms with similarly qualified directors.

The positive correlation between progressiveness and the use of scientists on Boards is most marked in the scientific and modern industries. The scientific content of production in such industries is high, and where research and development are well established most grades of management are staffed by men with high technical qualifications. High technical qualifications are, however, not the same as high scientific qualifications—there is a considerable difference between the H.N.C. and the D.Sc.; a man with the former may be quite incapable of evaluating recent advances in, say, chemistry and physics. The positive correlation mentioned is therefore significantly higher than it would be if we restricted 'scientists' to those capable of evaluating and interpreting scientific developments.

How should we interpret this evidence? Should we conclude that there is a causal relation between progressiveness and the appointment of scientists to the Board? The most significant evidence to take into account here is, first, the cases in the general sample that suggest the opposite relation and, second, the cases of firms in the industry samples which have made a significant attempt to move away from traditional methods of production.

Cases in the general sample which refute the proposition that there is a causal relation between progressiveness and the presence of scientists on the Board amount to almost one-fifth of the sample. These cases are of two kinds—unprogressive companies which do have a scientist or technologist on the Board, and progressive companies which do not. Firms in the industry sample which have made a significant move away from traditional methods of production have in most cases done so without appointing scientists to the Board. They have employed scientists and engineers; they have encouraged the formation or used the output of research associations; they have, in some cases, used consultants, both technical and managerial. In some of these firms, which had to face extensive changes in employment and in management structure, there has been a change in senior management. But this has not been so in all cases—we have examined several where an unchanged Board has changed its outlook and policy under the pressure of a new set of conditions provided by the post-war period of labour shortage and high profits. We have also studied cases where the technical members of the Board would have rejected a particular technical innovation but for the capacity of 'lay' members of the Board to see its value. It is simple-minded to suggest that any firm can become progressive merely by drafting a scientist on to the Board.

Personal qualities of character and leadership are clearly important, though they cannot easily be catalogued and classified like technical qualifications. A man trained in science may lack the vision or the interest to provide a drive to progressiveness. A man not trained in science may have such qualities, and, so long as he has an appreciation of the potentialities of applied science, he may provide the drive, recruit the appropriate scientists and engineers, and create the administrative machinery and financial policy appropriate to continuing technical innovation. As technical progress goes on, the importance of scientists and engineers is obvious, but it is by no means obvious that they need to be on the Board. It is, however, natural that they should be. For unless a training in science drives out the capacity for judgement, initiative, and leadership, or unless only those without the judgement, initiative, and leadership go in for science (and we have no evidence that either is true) it is natural to expect that scientists of ability will be recruited to the Board. It would be frustrating if this were not so. We have found cases where scientists have suffered such a frustration and lost efficiency, even in research activities, in consequence.

We have found that companies which have no scientists on the Board fall into four classes. First, those that employ no scientists. Second, those that employ scientists but regard them purely as backroom boys. Third, those that employ scientists but restrict the Board to members of the controlling family. Fourth, companies that have only recently gone in for the employment of scientists. The first two types of company are not efficient in applying science to industry. Firms in the first class lack the capacity to use scientific developments other than those embodied in marketed machines or easily applied production techniques; firms in the second class lack the capacity to produce commercially valuable developments. In the third class the companies are not progressive unless some members of the family on the Board have had a training in science, or unless the status of top executives not on the Board is high, and they are given ample opportunity to make or to influence decisions. In the fourth class we may expect to see scientists on the Board in due course. During the conduct of our case-studies we have noticed several examples of scientists being appointed to the Board after they had proved their worth in research or production. This fourth class has a bearing on the question raised earlier—namely, whether 'participation in policy' entails membership of the Board. It is only in small companies that all policy is made by the Board, and even then the extent of consultation may be great. In larger companies the Board cannot make all policy. For the research and development staff the real test of 'participation in policy' is to be found in two things: in the extent to which, and the way in which, the Board discusses research and development policy, and in the extent to which the research and development department has an effective liaison with the production and sales departments. Where the Board has a periodical review of the progress of research and development, and brings the research chief in to take part in this review, he will to some extent participate in policy matters. Where there is an effective liaison between research, production, and sales departments the research chief will, through this liaison, participate in policy—otherwise the co-ordination of activities could not be achieved. However, the more effective the participation in policy, the more likely is it that scientists (from research or from production) will be found on the Board.

The employment of scientists in jobs not directly concerned with research and development has led to some complaints about the 'loss of scientists to administration'. These complaints contradict the ones about inadequate representation in senior management. In general they rest on two major misconceptions. In the first place, the nature of scientific industry is such that scientifically qualified people are indispensable in departments other than research and development: for example, only a person with the understanding of the technical principles involved could sell process-control equipment to firms engaged in such highly technical industries as steel, petroleum, etc. In the second place, research and development is an instrument of management, and as such should be integrated with other activities in the firm. There is ground for complaint only if scientists are used in jobs that could equally well be done by people with skills that are not scarce. This may perhaps occur if the prizes to be won on the production or sales sides are demonstrably much larger than those in research and development, so that scientists are attracted by the prospect of high salaries to work which does not necessarily employ their special talents. We have not been able to make a firm judgement on the extent to which this happens. Undoubtedly it does happen—in some firms we found the attitude that if a scientist does not find his way out of the research department, then that is *all* he is good for—but we should not assume that the special talents of scientists are not employed outside research. It is, as we have pointed out (p. 67), doubtful whether there is a sufficient employment of scientists and technologists in production relative to employment in research.

To bring new process or product developments into full-scale production, we need not only receptive but efficient management. Can we say, however, that attention to management efficiency creates a favourable climate for the introduction or extension of research and development? Is there a possible conflict between the receptivity and the efficiency of management?

Product and process research and development is now treated, at any rate by bodies such as the British Institute of Management and the British Productivity Council, as an aspect of efficient management. The 'art of using scientists', however, is not a highly developed one, and it is conceivable that a set of techniques developed for and used in other departments of the firm would be found quite inappropriate for a research and development department. Research activity cannot be organized after the fashion of an assembly line. Even development work is unpredictable—if it were not, it would be an unnecessary activity. Is it then not possible that attention to management efficiency will lead to a bias against so unmanageable a thing as research and development; or at least that there will be a bias against the least predictable research and development activity—the long-term or the quite new?

Let us start from the standpoint of scientists determined to apply science in industry. Will not these scientists bring about the maximum possible rate of investment in research? There are three firms in our sample in which policy was determined by such scientists. These firms have been so keen to develop and apply science that they have invested in research and development to an extent, and for a length of waiting period, that is (or was) beyond their resources. In these cases, revenue from sales was insufficient to cover the cost of salaries, equipment, work in progress, and stocks. The management of these firms was receptive but inefficient. Attention had to be given to the problem of balanced growth throughout the firm as a pre-condition of further research activity. By paying more attention to this, and by *reducing* research and development as a percentage of turnover, the firms concerned will be able in the course of time to increase their research effort.

These cases further reinforce the statement that the function of industrial research and development is not simply to advance knowledge or to follow the imaginative urges of designers, but to create new products or methods of production that are commercially sound. Accordingly we analysed the attitude to and organization of research in the seventy-seven firms from which we obtained clear information. Seventy-three of them confirm the proposition that 'cost and profit mindedness' on the part of those conducting research is a necessary condition of effective work. It might be objected that this controlled nature of industrial research negates the essential conditions for scientific work: that is, freedom from outside authority, and absence of anything that might hamper or restrict work. This objection is misplaced—from the earliest times to the present day, all but a handful of British scientists and technologists have been accustomed to working within strictly limited budgets. Scientists are, moreover, capable of working within specified time limits—were this not the case, the entire system of post-graduate research degrees would be impracticable.

There were, in our general sample, six firms which were led by a conscious attention to management efficiency to a policy decision to introduce research and development. Here attention to management efficiency induced receptivity to invention. We have found, in general, that efficient management is receptive management; that inefficient management is unreceptive. Only in three cases did we identify a clear disharmony between attention to management efficiency and receptivity. In these three cases there was such a close attention to costing and calculating prospective yields from investment, that research and development were rejected as unmanageable. If others succeeded in developing something that could be bought with profit it would then be bought. These firms were extreme examples of the 'voluntarily adoptive' (p. 109).

Perhaps the most interesting of the case-studies relevant to the relation between management efficiency and research activity are those which 'catch' a change in management. In several cases, as the result of this change, modern management techniques such as production planning and control, materials control, work study, standard costing, and budgetary control have been introduced; then research and development have been instituted or extended. What at first sight is a case of pursuit of management efficiency calling forth research activity, however, generally turned out to be a case of step-by-step change that followed a key decision to modernize, to become 'progressive'.

Chapter 13

MONEY TO FINANCE AND ENCOURAGE DEVELOPMENT

THE idea that action seen to be good is prevented by shortage of money comes very easily to the mind, for it fits in with one's private belief that one could make good use of a larger pay cheque. But there are few subjects more difficult to analyse with clarity and accuracy. Money is sometimes seen as of secondary importance, a mere symbol of the underlying reality of usable goods and services; as Adam Smith said, like a highway, which, while it circulates and carries to market all the grass and corn of the country, produces itself not a single pile of either. But the symbol affects the reality, and the production of real goods and services is significantly influenced by monetary policy and by the working of the institutions which deal in money. There is confusion, too, because statements which are true for each individual or firm are not necessarily true for the sum of all individuals or firms. Thus every Board of Directors in the country might feel that, given a tax remission, they would spend more on research. Yet if the true limiting factor were a shortage of scientists, the tax remission might achieve no net result whatever in the encouragement of research. It is difficult to remember that what seems obviously possible to one firm—which can always hope to attract scientists from its competitors—may be quite impossible if all firms are considered together.

To make the discussion coherent, let us first put three questions:

1. Is there evidence that the adoption of new scientific and technical ideas is being impeded by lack of finance?
2. In particular, is it impeded by the action of high taxation in draining away money which is needed for the finance of technical advance?
3. Is it impeded by difficulty in raising capital from outside sources?

To these we can add two more which are concerned, not with the availability of money, but with attitudes to advance:

4. Is the adoption of new ideas discouraged because high taxation leaves insufficient incentive for advance?
5. Are there special features of the British tax system which discourage the adoption of new ideas?

The first three questions are relevant only if the adoption of a new idea 'costs money'—that is to say, if it involves laying out money which would not otherwise have been spent. This is true of most major developments, involving an interruption to the process of production and frequently also the replacement of a simple machine by a more complex one; or (if the product is entirely new) involving new construction and tooling. But there are many minor improvements which are introduced in the natural process of replacement, and which involve no extra cost—or at any rate none that can be identified and assessed. And occasionally the scientists or technologists can offer a method or a product which fulfil their purpose not only better, but at a lower initial outlay. The automatic transfer machines installed in the Austin factory of British Motor Corporation, for instance, are said to cost less than the individual non-automatic machine tools which they replace.

The first group of questions needs to be related to a particular background. There are three quite different situations to be considered. In the first there is a deficiency of some physical goods essential to the adoption of new scientific knowledge and not capable of being easily released from other uses. For instance, there may be a steel shortage, and there are few big innovations which do not use steel. In this situation what appears to each firm as a shortage of money may simply be a form of control, designed to prevent people bidding for supplies which are not there. The release of more money would not help the adoption of new ideas, unless it were selectively released to support this kind of investment at the expense of others. Although each firm may think it can spend more, to allow all to try to do so might actually impede progress by producing queues. In a queue-bound economy, any progress involving a combination of components becomes difficult: one firm finds it can get structural steel but no cement, while somewhere else a firm can get cement but no structural steel—and so both are held up.

The second situation is one in which there are no serious specific shortages impeding investment, but the economy in general is fully employed. More money will not buy more output, taking the country as a whole, save that one can hope for a slow year-to-year rise in the total product. More money can perhaps achieve a diversion of resources from one use to another, but usually only at the cost of partial frustration through the forcing up of prices. In this situation, difficulty in obtaining finance for a new product or process is a form of control imposed, not by physical shortages, but by the unwillingness of people to release resources from other uses. The consumer is spending too much (and saving too little), or the Government is spending too much, or firms are spending too much on non-scientific forms of investment: the words 'too much' meaning simply 'too much to allow room for the new product or process', which is left out like a suit which no ingenuity of packing will get into the suitcase.

In the third situation there are no serious specific shortages, and there are unemployed men and machines which could produce more. Lack of finance then deserves to be considered as probably due to a fault in

K

economic institutions; if the new product or process is desirable, and the men and materials which could make it are idle, it is foolish if the lack of money holds things up. In this situation the real problem is the meaning of 'desirable', for if business expectations are generally gloomy and existing products are not selling, it may be hard to convince financial backers that a new product or process stands a chance. When the resources are ample, the faith to use them may be absent; when, under full employment, the willingness to strike out in new ways is strong, the resources to do so may be absent.

The 1930's give an example of the third situation, the late 1940's of the first, the 1950's of the second. Since it seems likely that full employment will, by and large, continue, it is on the second situation that we shall concentrate, and we shall therefore seek our evidence in the recent past. Is it in fact true that in the 1950's British business has been short of finance? The following figures suggest at first sight that the overall position has been quite easy:

Surplus of U.K. Company Receipts over Payments, after Taxes and Dividends, and after Buying Fixed Assets and Stocks

£mn.	Surplus after all *payments* of taxes, dividends, and interest	Surplus after all *appropriations* for taxes, dividends, and interest
1948	169	30
1949	150	215
1950	348	245
1951	131	−286
1952	356	385
1953	436	429
1954	489	297
1955	129	15

Source: derived from *National Income and Expenditure*, H.M.S.O., 1956.

This table shows that companies have had money left over after paying their taxes and dividends, and after paying for all their new machinery, buildings, stocks of goods, and work in progress. These payments have covered both the making good of depreciation and additions to the stock of capital. Part of the surplus is due to the time-lag in collecting taxes or paying dividends—which tends, when taxes and dividends are rising in money value, to leave an extra sum each year in the hands of a company. But the last column shows that, except in one bad year, there has still been a surplus after a full appropriation for taxes and dividends; and this is in a period when there is no doubt that the stock of capital goods has been increased as well as maintained.

But these are fragile figures, and they break if much reliance is placed on them. The surplus has to pay for overseas investment, as well as for building up reserves at home. Overseas investment for persons and companies together is variable and frequently large; there are no separate figures for companies, but it is a fair guess that their overseas investment absorbs a considerable part of the surplus shown above. Furthermore, to do business of increasing extent on a rising price level may need more cash or near-cash holdings, which must also be provided from the 'surplus'. Finally, a figure which comes from a heterogeneous collection of companies, including merchants, insurance companies, and banks, is obviously difficult to interpret. It may be that, although companies as a whole have had a surplus, companies in manufacturing industry at home have been short of money from their own resources, and have had to borrow (on balance) to finance new investment. This view is supported by a recent survey of the experience of certain public companies engaged in manufacturing, building, and distribution, over the period 1948–54.[1] What no overall statistics can prove is that the situation has been easy for all companies; it may be that rapidly expanding companies have had serious difficulties in raising money.

We can, however, eliminate another hypothesis, which is that British industry has been held back by physical shortages or lack of money to such an extent that it has been barely able to replace its capital as it wears out. Evidence presented by Mr. P. Redfern and the Central Statistical Office [2] show that the country added to its stock of capital (i.e. 'capital formation' has exceeded 'true depreciation') in every year from 1948 to 1955; and there is reason to think that the estimate of the addition is on the cautious side. Within the total, additions to plant and machinery have been, in real terms, at well above the pre-war rate, and an apparent lagging in the total investment in manufacturing and distribution proves to be due to the fact that few commercial buildings have been erected. The total net investment in manufacturing plant and machinery increased by some 45 per cent. from the end of 1938 to the end of 1953, the whole of this increase being in the post-war period; and the average age of plant had fallen. In the course of so substantial an addition to, and rejuvenation of, capital, the opportunities for taking advantage of new scientific and technical knowledge must have been extensive. The rate of increase of the stock of industrial plant and machinery appears, for instance, to have been at least as great as that in the U.S.A. in the prosperous years before 1929: [3] and this is on the evidence of a period which precedes the great industrial construction boom of 1955–6.

Any shortage of funds, therefore, is relative to a great activity in adding to plant and machinery. It is frequently said that the U.K. is falling behind its industrial rivals because it is devoting so small a proportion

[1] A. Luboff, *Accounting Research*, April 1956, pp. 154–200.

[2] *Journal of the Royal Statistical Society*, Series A, vol. 118, part 2, 1955, pp. 141–92: see also *National Income and Expenditure*, H.M.S.O., 1956.

[3] R. Goldsmith in *Income and Wealth*, Series II, Bowes and Bowes, 1952, p. 307.

of its production to investment. Crude international comparisons of this kind are liable to be extremely misleading, because different kinds of capital, replaced at different rates, are used in the different countries. For what it is worth, however, the evidence is that recently there has not been much difference between the U.S.A. and U.K. rates of investment relative to national product. The U.K. has 'made room' for an exceptionally high rate of investment in plant, machinery, and housing by running down its capital equipment in the form of commercial buildings, roads, and railways, and the programme is, therefore, somewhat unbalanced; but to suggest that it is discreditably small is hardly fair. Of course, if people had saved more, industry could have got on faster still, and with less trouble from inflation; yet much has been achieved.

The evidence of the case-studies on shortage of finance is difficult to interpret, since some firms may give no signs of difficulty because they have become accustomed to tailoring their development plans to their financial resources. Out of 138 firms for which information exists, lack of finance was a definite hindrance to the full use of science and technology in nineteen, while in 119 no definite hindrance from this cause could be identified. This suggests that the problem is occasional but not general. However, of the nineteen firms suffering difficulty from lack of finance, ten were technically very progressive, and thirteen were in fact rapidly expanding, which suggests that the problem affects some of those who might be leaders in the application of science and technology. Yet even among the nineteen the difficulty was not always that money could not be obtained, but that the firm could not stomach the conditions for obtaining it. Some examples will make the position clearer.

One firm is a long-established private company, a family concern, which has gone through a period of re-awakening since the key position in it was taken by a young member of the family with a degree in engineering. Half the works has been re-equipped with up-to-date machinery, and the next step will be the re-equipment of the other half. The speed with which this can be done depends on the availability of money, since skill is already available and markets are waiting. The firm has already borrowed substantially from its bank; it could probably borrow more in the City, or 'float' itself as a public company, but no action is taken because of a fear of losing family control.

A second firm was founded by a brilliant scientist during the 1930's. It has expanded very fast, and there is a continual stream of new ideas coming from its research department. But expansion has meant heavy calls for both fixed and working capital, and there is now not enough money available inside the firm to bring into use the full flow of research ideas. There has been some recourse to outside finance. The firm has become a loose subsidiary of a large company, but as the Managing

Director wishes to retain full control over research and development policy, the parent company is regarded more as a technical associate than as a source of scarce finance.

A third firm is a subsidiary of a large public company. Under able management, it has achieved a higher efficiency than its parent, and this both results from and provides the excuse for a high degree of autonomy of operation. The firm's development programme is limited by shortage of money, but it does not ask for more from its parent company because it fears to disturb what it regards as a satisfactory position of autonomy.

A fourth firm is a public company which has shelved a project for a revolutionary process development because of its view that the cost of raising money on the Stock Exchange would be too high—said to be the equivalent of an interest rate of 12 per cent. on the sum actually becoming available for investment.

So far, therefore, we would conclude that shortage of money is an occasional hindrance to the full use of science and technology, when taken in conjunction with other features or attitudes of the firm. How far can this shortage be blamed on high taxation? This is a question to which it is difficult to give a meaningful answer. The fact that a particular company has been forced to raise outside money, when it would much prefer to finance development from its own retained profits, proves nothing, for there is no reason why the capital needs of individual companies should correspond to their ability to retain profits. The reaction of all companies taken together to high taxation has been a very heavy fall in the proportion of income distributed in dividends and interest, from 93 per cent. of gross trading profits and about 60 per cent. of total income in 1938 to around 30 per cent. of profits and 25 per cent. of total income in recent years. The people who receive large amounts of dividends are also, by and large, the big savers: and the reduction in the proportion of income distributed (and also in the real value of the amount distributed) means a lowering of the level of the reservoir of loanable funds which might come to the aid of rapidly progressive firms which find it difficult to raise capital.

But a great many companies have been able to finance both replacement of capital and expansion wholly or largely from retained profits; in other words, in a period of inflation and full employment, it has generally been possible to pass on the burden of taxation to the consumer or the shareholder. The burden would be a much more serious matter if, in difficult markets, it could no longer be shifted in this way. The heavy reliance on internal finance has another aspect; it means that development is taking place in existing and prosperous companies rather than in new firms or in firms which are unable to retain large profits. The weighting of the scales against new firms makes it more difficult to break into an industry which is complacent in its technical backwardness; while a declining industry, which might be revived by new techniques, may find itself with neither the profits to finance the change itself, nor the ability to attract money from outside.

Furthermore, an apparent adequacy of ploughed-back profits might be, once material shortages have disappeared, simply the obverse of an unwillingness to progress in size or technique. We have examined a sample of over fifty public companies, for which we have ratings of technical progressiveness, to see what relation exists between those ratings and the need to raise new money. The results, however, show no discernible relation over the period 1951–4; many of the most progressive firms have had no need to raise capital from outside. A study over a longer period might show different results.

We conclude that, although it is difficult to identify the harmful effects of high taxation in draining away money which is needed for the finance of technical advance, there is no ground for complacency on the matter. If the economic climate changes, the present weight of taxation might be a serious hindrance; and even now it is possible that taxation hinders advance precisely where that advance is most needed.

Difficulty in raising capital—our third question—has two aspects: a shortage of 'capital waiting to be raised' and an imperfection of the institutions which get the money to the borrower. The first is simply a way of looking at the shortage of saving, of abstention from the current use of resources. On this subject it is difficult to add to the commonplace observation that it would be nice to have more saving. But we would like to draw attention to the fact that a large part, probably much the greater part, of private capital investment is financed by savings made by the *same* people or bodies. The decision to save and the decision to buy buildings or equipment are made by the same people—as when a board of directors refrains from increasing a dividend in order that it may have funds to erect a new factory. Whenever this is so, there is at least a chance that savings plans may be able to be adjusted to fit investment plans. The real problem is, therefore, that of the firm which is growing too fast to live on its own fat, and we have noted that thirteen of the nineteen case-study firms reporting financial troubles were expanding rapidly. The other side of this problem is the shortage of free savings of private individuals. Thus in the year 1955 private individuals had available £814 mn. of new money for investment, of which £351 mn. was in fact invested in small businesses. Of the remainder, £40 mn. was added to National Savings, £74 mn. to bank deposits, and £488 mn. to accumulated life insurance funds; £283 mn. was spent on housing, with a net borrowing of £176 mn. from building societies, but in addition £191 mn. was spent on building society shares or deposits. The amount left over was *minus* £437 mn.[1] This is accounted for partly or wholly by an increase in consumer credit: but clearly there cannot have been much available for private 'Stock Exchange' type investment,

[1] *National Income and Expenditure*, H.M.S.O., 1956.

apart from the proportion of life insurance funds (about a third) employed in that way. It is this fact which gives rise to discussion of the 'shortage of risk capital', and it would seem likely that such a shortage, though of marginal importance relative to capital investment as a whole, would bear with special severity on the lively and vigorous firms who are most likely to be open to new scientific and technological ideas.

This is not, however, how some of the principal lenders view the matter; to them the problem appears, not as a shortage of money for lending, but as a shortage of credit-worthy borrowers. To see the matter clearly, we must now examine the main sources of outside capital for industry.

At the head of the list we would put bank lending, for we would like to emphasize the fact that, despite the supposed limitation of bank lending to short-term finance, we have found it to be extremely important in supporting the long-term capital investment programmes of firms. The connexion is usually nominally indirect, the bank taking over the finance of stock and work in progress, and thus releasing resources which the firm uses to buy capital equipment. Nevertheless to a number of the firms we have visited the condition of their adoption of a new method has been an ability to raise a bank loan. We find that, during the long period of 'cheap money' and easy credit, bank lending became considerably less conservative than is suggested in the banking textbooks; and consequently our conclusions may not apply to the period of dear money and restricted credit which began in 1955.

The other main sources of outside capital are as follows:

(i) *New issues to the public.* For a large, well-established company these are reasonably easy, and (if the issue can be made to existing shareholders) the costs of issue are not high. If the company is 'new' to the Stock Exchange, the costs of a small issue (normally made through a specialized issuing house) may be much greater, perhaps over 20 per cent. of the proceeds. Many issues are in fact made, not to provide new money, but to buy out existing interests; the costs are then lower, because a past record relating to the assets in which an interest is being purchased is available. The Stock Exchange will not handle very small issues, because the marketability of the shares would be too low. Broadly speaking, the results of these factors are:

(a) The new issue market is not suitable for issues smaller than £50,000, or for companies whose assets are less than £100,000.
(b) The raising of 'new money' by a company new to the Stock Exchange is expensive and difficult, especially if the amount required and the assets of the company are small.
(c) On the other hand, a really large company can to some extent suit its methods of capital-raising to the moods of the market, and to its own capital structure, and the terms on which it can raise

money are not necessarily related to the riskiness of the venture on which it proposes to spend the money. Thus, if I.C.I. wanted £20 mn. to finance production of a new and risky synthetic fibre, the terms on which it could raise money would be related to the 'blue chip' status of I.C.I. as a whole, and not to the riskiness of the particular venture.

(ii) *Company nurseries*. We use this term to cover the various institutions which lend money to firms, mainly with the intention of 'nursing' them over a period of years until they are able to make a public issue. This type of business is done by merchant bankers and as a companion to new issue business, by specialist development companies, and by the Industrial and Commercial Finance Corporation (which was set up by the Bank of England and the joint stock banks). Some of these bodies— e.g. the Charterhouse Group—are actively interested in nursing their charges to the point of public issue: the I.C.F.C. is prepared to be a sleeping partner, and to wait a considerably longer period. On a different level, the Finance Corporation for Industry assists in financing large projects which for some reason are not considered suitable for immediate support by public issue: a large part of its loans have been to the steel industry.

(iii) *Private individuals*. A number of observers have remarked that finance by private individuals is more prevalent than one would expect under present-day rates of personal taxation; and a good deal of business is clearly still arranged by accountants and solicitors who know of funds seeking investment.

(iv) *Hire-purchase finance*, *extended credits*, etc. Some small concerns augment their resources by buying machinery on hire purchase, or by obtaining easy payment terms from suppliers.

(v) *Insurance and other companies*. Some firms are able to obtain help from insurance companies, or loans from other industrial companies on terms which do not involve the loss of their independence.

Our inquiries in the City of London have brought to our notice two views about the adequacy of this machinery for providing capital. The first denies the existence of any significant difficulty at all. According to this view, the smallest borrowers can get help from banks and hire-purchase firms; the medium borrowers from a number of institutions in the 'company nursery' class; the large borrowers by public issue of shares. It is not denied that there are many disgruntled inventors who believe themselves to have been frustrated by the refusal of finance; but these prove (it is said) to be wholly uncreditworthy, and indeed the main problem is not the lack of channels of finance but the lack of creditworthy borrowers with good ideas awaiting exploitation.

The second view agrees with the first that in general the channels of finance are adequate, and that there is a lack of creditworthy borrowers;

but is prepared to concede that a few classes of borrower may find unreasonable difficulty, in particular:

(a) those wanting sums between (say) £10,000 and £30,000, who may have difficulty in getting so much from a bank or from private lenders, and yet be too small to be of much interest to the City institutions;

(b) those wanting money for three to seven years—i.e. for a period rather long for a bank loan, but too short to be counted as 'permanent' finance.

Representatives of both views emphasized that the City has been very ready to adapt itself to the needs of industry; and that it was false to look back to a 'golden age' in which capital was easily obtainable.

Looked at from the point of view of the borrower, the City views outlined above may seem complacent; for it is evident that the key question is how to define 'creditworthy'. The Charterhouse Group lays down the following conditions:

'An undertaking seeking finance . . . must therefore

(1) be established on a commercial basis and capable of further development;

(2) have a satisfactory record of trading covering at least three years; this does not necessarily mean that a profit must have been earned in each year;

(3) be under competent and continuing management.'

The Group 'does not normally undertake . . . the financing of new and untried processes or inventions'. These conditions are not particularly stringent, and do not appear to be stringently applied. But they do rule out the financing of companies *ab initio*, on which Professor Tew quotes [1] Lord Piercy (the chairman of I.C.F.C.) as follows:

'. . . The other case, which is frequently raised—and I must say that it is one that we (i.e. I.C.F.C.) frequently meet—is that of people who want to start a business but have no capital. The most common case is that of the man who wants a few thousand pounds; but we have had applications for borrowing as much as £100,000. The case is one which cannot altogether be dismissed. There is an argument of this kind: an established company may have a board of directors with very little shareholding among them all, who yet for practical purposes exercise absolute control of very large resources. Why cannot such a position be created *ab initio*? Chiefly, I suppose, because starting *ab initio*, creating and organizing a new business, if it is on any scale, is a very difficult task, and calls for exceptional qualities. This I take to be one of the lessons of experience, and bitter experience at that. To encourage such an enterprise is only reasonably safe where the financier knows so much about the business and

[1] *Economica*, August 1955.

the people that he can assess the risk of success and where, added to this, he is able to give some attention to the development of the enterprise. Financiers in such a situation are not non-existent, but they are scarce; and it will still be true that the promoters of such enterprises will mostly find themselves thrown back on getting the first few thousands from their personal friends and acquaintances before they can interest a general finance house.'

We did not find, in I.C.F.C. or elsewhere, any serious concern about the difficulty of obtaining a technical assessment of an invention or process; though we think that it is likely that experts, asked by a finance house to give an opinion of a radically new idea, would sometimes be quite wrong. But the knowledge 'about the business and the people' to which Lord Piercy refers is of a more comprehensive kind. It was suggested to us that the common reason for the failure of a small borrower to be creditworthy is that he does not command the *diversity* of qualities needed in successful business. He is perhaps a brilliant technician, but no manager of men; strong on production, but weak on marketing; or knowledgeable of his trade, but innocent of the mysteries of finance. A larger business unit will normally buy all the various kinds of expert advice required by its trade; a small one is often uncreditworthy because it is unbalanced. This lack of balance means that it is not merely a poor risk to a financier, but probably a poor risk to the nation also—there is no necessary divergence here between private and social interests.

Another aspect of the lack of creditworthy borrowers is the unwillingness of firms to seek finance, of which we have already given some examples. The finance houses and other lenders appear to use their power with moderation, but the belief that 'he who pays the piper calls the tune' is strong, and many small firms (especially family firms) put the maintenance of complete independence higher than an increase of prosperity. It is this which perhaps explains, what would otherwise be a puzzling discovery, that a number of firms complaining of a shortage of finance are completely ignorant of the institutions which could help, and appear to have made no effort to find out about them. They are really grumbling at the fact that taxation leaves them insufficient profits to finance development; they are not prepared even to contemplate the possible loss of independence involved in going to a finance house, for they are unwilling to surrender any part of their equity.

It is sometimes asserted that, although there has been no general shortage of capital, there has been a shortage of risk capital. This is not quite the same thing as an unwillingness to take risks; for a company's capital structure must be looked at as a whole, and there would be nothing incongruous in a large company raising money on debentures for a risky purpose—provided that the capital structure of the company remained reasonably balanced. There is, owing to the tax system, an incentive for companies to raise money by debenture issues rather than ordinary shares, and it could be argued that, having heavy debts, companies would then become more conservative in their attitude to technical improvements. But this is an uncertain argument, at least in a time of general prosperity in which inability to pay debenture interest is unlikely.

But the capital market is reasonably free; an unwillingness to lend in the form of risk capital might be expected to show itself in a difficulty in raising ordinary share capital except at high expected yields, and in an increase in the spread of yields between safe and risky investments. There is no evidence whatever of any such general change. The ratio of the yield of ordinary shares to the yield of fixed interest securities has indeed been much the same in the post-war as in the inter-war period.

So far we would conclude that *well-established* firms ought in general to be able to find capital to take advantage of all ordinary scientific and technical improvements—with the exception, of course, of those which require an initial outlay out of all proportion to the size of the firm. A firm might also be unduly handicapped if it was in an industry especially unattractive to investors, e.g. one which had suffered a long decline. It remains difficult, and perhaps more difficult than in the past, for *new, young, or small* firms to find capital. It does not follow, of course, that their frustration is the frustration of scientific progress, unless the larger firms in the trade are (perhaps because of general conservatism, or because of their heavy commitment to methods which would be displaced by the proposed development) unwilling to progress themselves. But the case-studies confirm that this unwillingness can on occasion exist, and they also yield examples of small firms which have been able to progress in technique or to develop a new product because of good luck in finding a private lender. There are others who have had no such luck; and we conclude that, while the facilities of the capital market are in general good, there is some hindrance to the adoption of new scientific and technical ideas due to the natural difficulty of providing finance, with independence, for new, young, or small firms.

Even if, despite taxation, technical advance at a reasonable rate is possible, it may not occur if it is *believed* to be impossible. It is, therefore, relevant to observe that, especially in the years before 1955, the hindering effect of taxation was a frequent theme of company chairmen. Thus, Sir Bernard Docker said on 10 December 1954, 'Everything possible must be done, and the matter is urgent, to reduce the fantastic burden of taxation. When three-fifths of the profits of a company like B.S.A., which is only one of the numerous companies which, by exports, help to sustain this country's economy, are taken in taxation, with inevitable results on capital replacement and other new projects, the warning is plain for all to see.' Mr. H. W. Secker (chairman of Thos. W. Ward, Ltd.) said on 19 November 1954, 'We were given some benefit in the last budget in the form of investment allowances, but I still

consider that much more help must be given to industry in this direction
if we are to introduce the improvements in machinery and methods necessary to bring our costs to a competitive level in international trade. (The
amount paid in taxation) is, to quote an Indian proverb, "Like taking
half a fowl for cooking—leaving the other half for laying eggs".' A
feature of many of these statements is that they are ill-defined: it is not
certain whether the company has in fact been prevented from improving
or extending its production by the weight of taxation, or whether it has
been prevented from distributing as much to shareholders as the
directors would like. Many of the companies whose chairmen make
these complaints are in fact rapidly progressive, and show impressive
increases in assets and earnings. One company was prepared to admit
to us that it had no developments held up by lack of finance, and that the
bitter complaints about high taxation in its annual report were meant to
justify to the shareholders a failure to increase the dividend. But in so
far as taxation is genuinely believed to prevent the introduction of improvements, it may have some effect; it is at least ready to hand as an
excuse for inaction.

The problem of the effect of high taxation on the incentive to advance
is a complicated one. It might at first sight appear obvious that, if a
new process is expected to yield 20 per cent. on an investment in it, and
is just sufficiently attractive to be adopted, then the fact that the tax-
gatherer reduces the net yield to (say) 10 per cent. will cause the process
to appear unattractive, and it will remain unadopted. But it could also be
argued that all other ways of producing income are also affected by
taxation; that it is *relative* yields, rather than absolute, which determine
the employment of funds; that if a new method has a relative advantage
before tax, it will nearly always have an advantage after tax also, and will
thus be adopted in any case. Or it can be said that the calculations of
expected yield are so rough and uncertain that they should not be regarded as major determinants of the adoption of a new method. In the
first view, taxation is harmful: on the second, harmless: on the third,
irrelevant.

If we can suppose that the motives which affect business men in 'real'
investment are similar to those in 'financial' investment, then the behaviour of the Stock Exchange lends support to the view that it is relative yields which matter. If the willingness to invest in stocks and shares
were related to the *net* yields obtained, then one would expect that the
general level of gross yields would be higher than in the past. There is
no evidence that this is the case. In particular, there is no evidence that
new money is, because of high taxation, being raised on terms markedly
less favourable to the borrower than in the past.

We referred this problem to our Accountants' Group, which reported that it was agreed that little importance should be attached to
high income and profits taxation as a discouragement to the adoption of

new methods. In the business decisions of which they had experience, regard was paid to gross and not to net returns. We then asked that this statement should be re-examined, to bring out its full implications, and in a further report the Accountants' Group added to the statement the following qualifications:

(a) It applies only to activities at home: in activities overseas, the varied tax rates of other countries are undoubtedly taken into account.

(b) Although tax rates may not formally enter the calculations which precede a decision to adopt a new product or process, they sometimes have an effect on the general level of prices which a company hopes to obtain for all its products: thus they indirectly affect the price set and the sales expected for a new product, and in consequence affect the gross return.

(c) High tax rates lead to a bias in favour of quick returns.

It might be thought that some additional guidance could be obtained by looking at an extreme case—the man who owns his own business, and pays surtax, and thus pays at a high rate on his income. But although the high taxation of individuals may conceivably affect their willingness to work, a highly taxed owner of a business has a strong incentive to spend money on improvements which can be charged against profits.

We conclude, on the evidence available, that the effect of high taxation on the incentive to undertake product or process development is not a direct one. No evidence of a direct disincentive effect appears from the case-studies. The basic reason for this is that the profits retained or capital borrowed by companies have got to be employed somehow; and if new processes are going unadopted because of high taxation, where are the alternative and superior ways of using profits which are so attractive? The tax-gatherer is round every corner, and this fact leaves the choice to be made on relative and not on absolute yields. But we think that the *indirect* disincentive effects of high taxation are important. One is cited in (b) above, that the *general level* of profits before tax may be raised, and with it the expected profit on a new product; and this may so raise its price and restrict its market that it is not worth developing. This is especially likely if the new product has to carry a specific tax, such as purchase tax, in addition to its share of general company taxation.

But there are other possible indirect effects, though we cannot claim that they are confirmed by the case-studies. Thus if a choice has to be made between applying a traditional method or venturing on a new one, the expected returns are not the only relevant factor; the uncertainty of the estimates is also important. In re-ordering a machine long in use, the manufacturer is dealing with something whose costs are well known, whereas a new machine may give unpredictable trouble. Taxation cuts down the margin against disaster when one ventures into the unknown. But of course a whole market situation may (because of the progress of one's competitors) be so fluid that the uncertainty has in any case to be faced. The argument of this paragraph would therefore apply mainly to slow-moving 'traditional' industries—taxation having the effect of discouraging those who would break away and apply new methods. But it may be in general presumed that, even if taxation leaves the order of profitability of a series of possibilities unchanged, it diminishes the sensitivity of choice between them. It is usually easier to go on with a well-tried method than to change to a new one: so the smaller advantage of the new (after tax) may be too weak to overcome conservatism.

Again, if taxation *distorts* relative yields, it may make old or inefficient methods more attractive than new or superior ones. This is liable to be a result of heavy indirect taxation: thus, the high tax on petrol relative to kerosene encourages the use of the kerosene-burning tractor, which as a machine is relatively inefficient, and also produces an inconvenient distortion of the demand on refineries.[1]

Finally, mechanical explanations of the behaviour of business men are dangerous. A reduction in taxation might alter the climate of opinion so that business *thinks* it has a greater incentive to invest, even though it is difficult to trace the exact reasons for the opinion. Thus the introduction of the investment allowance in the Budget of 1954, with a good deal of official propaganda in favour of more capital expenditure in industry, appears to have been part-cause of the 1955–6 investment boom, whose embarrassing dimensions caused the withdrawal of the investment allowance in February 1956. Our Accountants' Group stressed the important psychological effect of the allowance, which was viewed as a subsidy to investment, whereas the initial allowance (which preceded and followed the investment allowance) was regarded as a tax-free loan liable to repayment. To many firms the evidence of official approval for investment was important. The psychological effect was fully confirmed by the case-studies.

In thus mentioning the important indirect effects of taxation on the incentive to apply new methods, we are in a sense guilty of the obvious remark that it would be nice if taxes were lower. It does not follow that, if the present revenue has to be raised, some shift of tax burdens would on balance improve the health of the economy; though it would no doubt be possible, at some cost elsewhere, to increase the incentive to adopt new methods.

Let us therefore now turn to the special effects of the form of the tax system. After a careful review of this large subject, we think that there are two special problems worthy of consideration: depreciation allowances and death duties. The treatment of research expenditure by the

[1] *Petroleum Taxation*, Shell Petroleum Co., 1954, p. 11.

tax code is now reasonably generous, and we have already mentioned the possible distorting and restricting effect of high specific indirect taxes, and the possible bias in favour of raising money by loan rather than by an issue of shares.

Any disincentive effect of depreciation allowances arises either from a belief that the amount allowed to be written off for tax purposes, based on historical cost, is (in an inflationary period) inadequate to provide for replacement; or from a belief that the period of write-off is too long, perhaps especially when the plant is experimental. It appears likely that the amounts allowable for tax purposes in recent years have, for manufacturing plant and machinery, been related to values of about 50–60 per cent. of replacement cost. This means that companies must provide the difference from taxed profits, and may be in difficulties if they have omitted to do so. But if there were to be a change to replacement cost depreciation allowances, and tax rates were adjusted to yield as much as before, the result would be a shift in the burden of taxation between firms related to their use of capital equipment. It seems to us that this could only have a distant relation to the incentive to adopt new ideas, and that the complaints about the amount of depreciation allowances are in the main equivalent to complaints about the general weight of taxation. It should be noted that if a firm is growing the sums annually becoming available from (historical cost) depreciation allowances are not necessarily below the cost of replacements required in the year; and that the tax code gives an incentive to retain profits, by prescribing a lower rate of tax on undistributed profits.

The complaints about 'write-off' periods have gained strength from the fact that the U.S.A. has, from time to time, allowed accelerated writing-off of assets needed for a purpose of national importance. This, of course, only achieves a shift of the tax burden from year to year, and its main importance appears to be psychological—it seems easier to scrap a machine if it has been written off in your books. In addition, however, a larger tax allowance in the first year helps with the problem of paying for the new equipment—the initial allowance achieving the same purpose in the British tax system, though it must be remembered that the lower tax payment will usually be made a year or so *after* the equipment is installed.

Apart from special arrangements for rapid amortization, it is generally believed that the approved periods for writing off plant for tax purposes are shorter in the U.S.A. We have therefore examined British and American allowances, taking plant which can be written off in ten years in the U.K. and in six years in the U.S.A.: the British allowance being taken on the 'reducing balance' and the American on the 'two-thirds in the first half of life' principle. We conclude that, as long as the investment allowance continued, the British system gave (at current tax rates) a slight advantage, but that the abolition of the investment allowance means that the tax avoided in the first five years of life is somewhat greater in the U.S.A. We see in this position no solid ground for complaint about the British system, and no grounds for thinking it a special hindrance to development.

About death duties we take a different view. The Federation of British Industries and the Association of British Chambers of Commerce have both drawn attention to the difficulties caused to small family businesses by death duties, and we have sought the advice of our Accountants' Group on the matter. The essential point is that estate duty is a large tax (35 per cent. at £50,000 and 80 per cent. at £1,000,000 net capital value) which has to be met in cash. In consequence, if the control of a family over a business is to be maintained, money must continually be withdrawn and held idle in order to meet estate duty without the sale of a controlling interest in the business. Alternatively, time and ingenuity must be employed in arranging to reduce the estate by gifts *inter vivos*, or the business must be disposed of during the lifetime of the main proprietor. The former, commonly carrying with it an early transfer of control to the next generation, often leads to family difficulty and the loss of the ability and experience of elder directors; while the early disposal of the business implies that short-term developments, yielding a quick return and expected to improve the chances of a good sale or flotation of the concern, will be favoured rather than slow-yielding developments. Flotation as a public company is difficult for small concerns, and it often threatens family control unless the family is numerous and well-knit. Consequently often the only way of disposal is to merge the identity of the company with a larger concern.

Sections 46 and 55 of the Finance Act, 1940, although necessary safeguards against avoidance, have increased the fear of estate duties. Section 46 is aimed at those who make over property to a controlled company (i.e. one under the control of not more than five persons, close relatives counting as single persons) receiving in exchange benefits excessive in relation to the services rendered. The Commissioners of Inland Revenue then have power to bring a portion of the assets of the company into assessment, and to recover the duty from the company itself. Section 55 provides that, where a deceased person has a controlling interest in a controlled company, his shares are to be valued on an 'assets basis', i.e. on a fair current valuation of the net assets of the company, including goodwill. Owing to the poor marketability of the shares of a small private company, the valuation on an assets basis may greatly exceed the market value, and (although the Inland Revenue are normally reasonable in their application of the section) it is believed that an estate may be rendered insolvent by the inadequacy of the realized market value to pay the estate duty. In any case, the valuation is a matter of great uncertainty, and large changes in assessments are liable to occur. It should be noted that the Finance Act, 1954, improves the situation somewhat, and substitutes the sale value if the assets are sold within three years.

The net effect of all these difficulties is to cause undue attention to be given, by owners of sole or large interests in businesses who have attained the age of (say) 50, to devices for minimizing the effects of estate duty. These devices, and especially the withdrawal of funds to be held idle to meet estate duty, are inimical to the development of the business (including the improvement of its technical equipment) and may prevent far-sighted planning of that development by concentrating attention on short-term gains. The danger is particularly acute in some declining industries, in need of technical improvement, which are dominated by small family firms.

If it could be assumed as universally true that the family firm is un-progressive, and that the assumption of control by larger firms would speed up technical progress, these harmful effects of estate duties would not be a matter for concern. But the case-studies show that no such universal generalization is valid. We conclude that there is a likelihood that the weight of estate duties is a hindrance to the adoption in certain firms of improvements in product or process, in which those firms might have been pioneers.

L

Chapter 14

A FAVOURABLE MARKET

AMONG the reasons advanced for the technical superiority of the U.S.A., there often appears the advantage given by the great size of her market. The 'size' of a market is not, however, an idea whose meaning is self-evident. The turnover of a grocer's shop is determined by the number of people in the area it serves, and by the wealth of those people, or their willingness to spend money on groceries. But this 'area served' depends not simply on the accidents of geography, but on the sales policy of the grocer. By aggressive salesmanship he may be able to invade the territory of other grocers and steal their customers; in other words, to enlarge his market.

Similarly the size of the market of an industry depends on the wealth of the area which it serves, but that area is not wholly independent of the sales policy of the industry. It is true that some industries are by their nature limited to the area of their mother-country; building in traditional materials is an example, though even in that industry the function of organizing building is freely exported by the contracting trade. But in general there is no such natural restriction in manufacturing industry, and the idea that 'the market' means 'the home market' rests on the fact that many foreign markets are uncertain, expensive to reach, and surrounded by tariff walls or other restrictions. This limitation cannot be generally applied—no one would think of defining the market for British shipbuilders as the British shipowners, and the technical development of the motor industry would be difficult to explain without reference to its export markets. Yet for a new or radically changed product it will often be true that the establishment in the home market must come first, and that it is on the basis of a lively home trade that the producer can venture into the export market.

It is a long jump from this, however, to the proposition that British technical progress is held back by the small size of her home market. In terms of annual income the British home market is larger than any other except those of the U.S.A. and the U.S.S.R. The U.S.A. home market is about five times as big as that of Britain. On the other hand, the size of that market is in part illusory, for the great distances of overland transport give some local protection in each region to industries making heavy or bulky products; and, in contrast, the compactness of the U.K. means that her home market can be speedily exploited. Furthermore, the U.K. has easy access to the colonial markets and to much of the rest of the Commonwealth, and (as the second largest trading nation in the world) she has widespread and well-established trading connexions. This means that, except for products which must be floated on a purely local market, the potential British market is very large indeed.

The smallness of a market is relevant only if the minimum economic units of production are large. The advantages of a large market lie in the speed with which production can be built up to an economic level, but the advantage becomes slight if all the economies can be obtained on quite a small output. One would therefore look for the effect of market size in the development of processes requiring great size and heavy investment (e.g. nuclear power stations, continuous strip mills), or of products which will have a minor and specialized use in industry, and consequently require a large industrial base to make them worth producing at all.

We have nevertheless found that there are a number of cases in which the size of the British home market is apparently too small to *encourage* rapid progress. The disadvantages we have found must apparently apply with greater force to the whole of the rest of the world, outside the U.S.A. and the U.S.S.R., and we must therefore be cautious in assessing their importance: small countries like Switzerland do not find it impossible to be technically progressive. Yet there remains a significant harmful influence of the subdivision of the world into separate economic units—a subdivision which has gone far in the present century, and whose effect may be increasingly harmful as technology becomes more complex. The nature of the harm is suggested by the emphasis given to the word 'encourage' above; a small market may not be an absolute barrier to progress, but the prizes for success are less obvious, and consequently excuses for inaction are more readily made. In certain industries the British market has not been big enough to encourage the growth of specialist producers of equipment—who themselves might have created new possibilities of progress. We have found examples of this relating to paper, bread, rubber, plastics, fine chemicals, aircraft, and scientific instruments. There are some cases where one or a few specialist producers exist, but progress in design is slow: in a bigger market there would be more specialist producers, more competition in design, and a better chance that good designs would be produced. There are also some industries for which 'bread-and-butter business'—i.e. the normal, stable selling lines—will not support the development costs for the more chancy products which might include the occasional winner. We have seen possible examples of this relating to scientific instruments and pharmaceuticals. This problem is not simply one of the size of the market, but of the size of firms relative to the size of the market. It is only big and wealthy firms that can risk the very speculative developments, such as the production of new drugs which will take several years to prove. A large market may support several large firms in fruitful rivalry with one another.

The theoretical size of a national market is not always a relevant concept; for some goods that market is split up into fractions by an insistence on variety or a carelessness of the benefits of standardization. This is a matter to which we shall return in the next chapter. The textile and clothing industries provide some interesting examples. On the one hand, there are profitable export markets for goods of the highest quality, exploiting to the full the consumer's desire for luxury and fashion. To support such production, it is desirable that there should similarly be a varied and fashion-conscious market at home. Yet on the other hand, in a country of the size of the U.K. too much insistence on variety and fashion stands in the way of technical economy. We think that the variety produced in the U.K., in these and other industries, may on occasion inhibit the rapid application of new knowledge, especially where the knowledge requires for its best use long runs and mass production. We note that standardization provides no complete answer; there are virtues in variety, especially if one is trying to sell in rich and quality-conscious markets. But standardization and simplification of components need not mean a reduction of variety in the finished article, and British industry has far to go in this field.[1]

A matter which is allied to the size of the market is the size of the scientific effort of the country. We have shown in Chapter 5 that, as a proportion of national product, British expenditure on research and development is as high as or higher than that of the U.S.A. But in absolute terms it is of course much smaller; and although it might be further increased if there were a larger supply of scientists and technologists, it is difficult to see how a country of the limited size and wealth of the U.K. can avoid neglecting areas of basic and applied science. What applies to the U.K. applies, of course, with greater force to almost all other countries; for instance, the national product of the Republic of Ireland is only 3 per cent. of that of the U.K., and the amount of original work which it could support from its own resources is therefore very small. The smaller or poorer a country, the more essential it is that it should be non-parochial in its attitude and ready to pick up ideas from overseas. Indeed, all countries, whatever their size, stand to gain from a readiness to adopt ideas from overseas, and we have the impression that the U.S.A., despite the great size of her own scientific effort, is more alert than Britain in seizing on new knowledge from abroad.

The size of a market is not the only important matter; its rate of growth is also relevant. The British real national product doubled in the last three decades of the nineteenth century, doubled again in the first half of the present century, and may well double yet again by 1980. The U.S.A. national product quadrupled in each of the first two periods.

[1] For some examples of successful standardization, see *Times Review of Industry*, May 1956, p. 39.

The rate of growth in both countries owed much to the rise of population; but, whatever its source, the growth is clearly a stimulating influence, offering the promise that time is on the side of the venturesome, that tomorrow's markets will be bigger and richer than those of today, that over-optimistic forecasts will come right in the long run. But, of course, the growth of the economy does not occur in every industry, and we have been impressed by the remarkable difference in outlook and atmosphere between industries which are expanding at a great rate and those which are static or contracting. The latter find it difficult to attract competent technologists or managers; it may be that a technical change could arrest the process of decline, but (unless the change is overwhelmingly obvious) the long-standing habits of pessimism inhibit and delay decisive action; energy is spent on defending existing markets, and not on opening new ones. As we pointed out in Chapter 9, the distribution of talented manpower is to some extent a matter of fashion, and a contracting industry is not only unfashionable but dangerous—it may collapse before a new entrant's working life is over. On the other hand, a rapidly expanding industry, especially if it is also new and fashionable, adds to all its obvious advantages the intangible quality of optimism. People feel that natural forces are working in their favour, and there is a greater willingness to take risks and to reach forthright decisions quickly.

The difference may be seen by comparing the railways (a static industry), and cotton and linen (which are in decline), with the electronics industry. The decision to abandon steam traction on the railways was reached with painful slowness, and its execution may now be delayed by the difficulty of recruiting new technical staff to an unfashionable industry. From the users' point of view, rail transport has progressed little in speed or convenience during the last half-century, and indeed it has often retrogressed. There is no real doubt (in Great Britain) about the continuing need for railways, and the measures, commercial and technical, needed to maintain their attractiveness are not difficult to discover. Yet railway management appears to have found it extremely difficult to reach definite decisions, to put them into effect speedily and in sufficient measure, and to persuade the public and the Government of their necessity. We doubt if the cold hand of Government control is a sufficient explanation of this, though it has undoubtedly made a bad problem worse. Positions of responsibility in railway management are usually reached by seniority, and in a static industry there is little inducement for lively minds to come in from outside.

The cotton and linen industries are, in our observation, by no means devoid of firms which show an interest in new techniques, and the Shirley Institute and the Linen Industry Research Association have had a most valuable stimulating effect. It would appear so far that improvements in technique are unlikely to rescue these industries from their troubles, which spring from a fundamental change in demand. But the troubles could at least be greatly alleviated by a quicker adoption of new ideas, and especially of those which arise out of operational research and work study—usually known in the cotton industry as 're-deployment'. The slowness of the industries to adapt themselves seems to us to spring again from the unattractiveness of declining industries to vigorous management, and from the concentration of energy on the protection of existing positions. In contrast, the electronics industry is effervescent; its output has grown five-fold since before the war, and it has thrown up numerous small firms under vigorous technical and commercial management. We doubt if some of these firms will survive the hazards of expansion, but the industry plainly has plenty of points of growth. It shows to an exaggerated degree the optimism which Viscount Chandos expressed about the whole electrical industry in his statement to A.E.I. stockholders in 1956:

'It seems to your Directors that such industries as the chemical and electrical industries must be amongst the leaders in the last half of this century. Ever since 1900 it is broadly true to say that the use of electrical energy has doubled every ten years. We have had to judge whether this tendency will continue during the next ten or twenty, and it appears to us likely that it will' (Viscount Chandos then cited, as particular reasons supporting this general assumption, the developments in nuclear fission, in electric traction and in electronics) 'Ladies and Gentlemen, in this industry to stand still is to die. Your Directors believe that there is only one place for your Company, and that is in the van. In short, whether or not there are fluctuations in demand from year to year they believe in boldness . . .'

A similar optimism can be found in the industries which are associated with lively new developments: for instance, those involved in the development of atomic energy, and those supplying components or equipment to the electrical, oil, and vehicle industries.

Thus far it seems that the principle of natural selection among industries is that they are fortified by success, and not by adversity. But can success go too far? Do the easy conditions of a 'sellers' market' lead to complacency, and a willingness to continue with old methods which are still profitable? That this will happen is not as obvious as might at first sight appear, for although easy market conditions may reduce the *incentive* to progress, they also greatly reduce the *risks* of doing so, and abundant profits help to furnish the means for technical change. In a severe depression, the risks are high and internal finance often lacking, and it would be reasonable to expect that technical change would be slowed down; it would be odd if we concluded that it would also be slowed down by the opposite circumstances.

In fact—as one might expect where there is a balance of opposing forces—the answer is that there is no general answer. The evidence of the case-studies leans by a small majority (thirty-one to twenty-five) in favour of the hypothesis that the post-war sellers' market has helped the rapid application of science and technology. The firms confirming this hypothesis include not only those which could do more because they were richer, or were willing to do more because risks were less, but also firms which benefited from a less conservative attitude in their customers. The firms refuting the hypothesis include some which, as a policy or through pressure of circumstances, look for new developments when the order-book shortens. There were also some which seem merely to have relaxed and taken no trouble: and some (though only three) in which the insistent pressure to produce more pushed resources away from research and development. But we think that the right interpretation of the evidence is that the sellers' market exerts a pressure towards the application of science and technology, mainly because it is associated with a labour shortage, but that this pressure is not universally sufficient to overcome the inertia of firms or the contrary forces affecting them.

Some firms would indignantly deny that their slowness in applying a new idea is due to complacency or laziness, and would claim that it is wise policy to let others bear the costs and risks of development, and come in when the new idea is proved. If the product or process is likely to go through a series of steps of improvement, it may indeed be dangerous to lock up capital in the tools for 'Mark I', only to find a competitor has jumped straight to Mark II, and that it is now too expensive to follow his example. The history of the aircraft industry would seem to bear out the contention that a producer who gets in the lead must expect to lose it before he has had time to write off his research and development costs over a reasonable output. A producer who tried to be in the lead all the time would always be developing, and never producing. But despite these difficulties, even in the aircraft industry it pays to be first sometimes; and the evidence of the case-studies strongly suggests that the safer general principle is that it pays to be first in the field. The majority in favour of this is fifty-three firms to twenty-one, and of the twenty-one cases which apparently dispute the principle seven relate to developments taken up twenty or thirty years ago, and another seven are in the more traditional and conservative branches of engineering. The principle is subject to the qualification that one should be first in the field with developments which, after a proper evaluation of the possibilities of the market, are found to be needed. Those who rush ahead on a 'hit-or-miss' principle are likely to miss uncomfortably often.

This is an encouraging result. If the risks of being a pioneer exceed the advantages, there is a real danger that progress will be held up while firms are metaphorically bowing to each other and saying 'After you,

Claude'. But if the richest prizes go in general to the pioneers, there is prospect of a competition in pioneering which could greatly speed up the pace of progress.

Why is it considered to pay to be first in the field? The answer is in part that the first arrival can protect himself against competition by taking out patents or maintaining the secrecy of processes, or can at least levy tribute in the form of royalties from those that follow. As we shall see in the next chapter, however, the degree and period of protection thus obtained is often not very great. We would suggest that a major advantage in first arrival may be a marketing advantage: the prestige which attaches to the first creator of a product or process, the free publicity which may accompany a discovery (for instance, in the pharmaceutical industry), and the advantage of time in building up contacts with customers. Despite a chequered history, the firm of Marconi long had an advantage by carrying the name of the great inventor; the Italian creators of the light-weight motor-scooter have won markets from which it will not be easy to dislodge them; it will be a long time before other plastics manage to become as familiar to the man in the street as Bakelite, or other man-made fibres as familiar as rayon and nylon.

We would not wish to elevate 'Be first in the field' to be a universal principle. There must obviously be developments whose value is so uncertain that it is best to let others take the risk. But the marketing advantages of pioneering are a reminder of a principle which has more claim to universality, that it is no use producing goods if you cannot sell them. The whole value of a development may be lost, and progress be considerably set back, if there is no sales organization to back the efforts of research and production. The firm which is speedy and successful in scientific and technical progress is one in which research, production, and sales are co-ordinated: this is a conclusion strongly confirmed by the case-studies. We have not found many developments which appear to have been frustrated largely by the inadequacy of sales organization, but this is because technical progressiveness and good salesmanship are, in the larger firms at least, concurrent symptoms of good management, so that it is not easy to find firms which are good in one and not in the other. There were nevertheless thirteen firms of which it could be said that development was being frustrated by poor salesmanship. This means, of course, poor salesmanship in relation to the needs of the users; thus a seller of electrical equipment complained of the lack of technically trained sales staff, leading to waste of the time of development staff—this is an industry where salesmen must be technologists. Other industries need an aggressive but non-technical sales staff; some companies admitted that developments were delayed or took a long time to establish themselves because they had not obtained enough people with the gifts of salesmanship.

In small firms it is much more difficult to secure sales ability and technical ability at the same time, and for this reason many small firms flourish best if they have no sales problem—for instance, if they are normally engaged on sub-contract or component work for a big firm, or if they live on Government contracts. It is in this way that many 'back-yard boffins' in the electronics and scientific instrument industries manage to keep an independent trading existence.

But it can be argued that, even if there are not many developments which are being frustrated by bad salesmanship, there may be many which are slowed down. The sales staff reduce the risks of production by offering a reasonable assurance of being able to sell in quantity without undue delay; the market research staff help to ensure that what is being made is in accordance with the needs and wishes of the market. It is not, of course, true that anything can be sold in any quantity by sufficient sales effort, but there is no doubt that the rate of build-up of sales can be greatly affected by the competence of salesmanship. Market research (which is done far too little in the U.K.) makes pioneering easier by reducing the risk of deciding to produce the wrong thing. It has been suggested to us that the success in Britain of a number of firms with an American origin is due to their competence on the sales side, and that this has enabled them to be speedy in technical development.

We think that there is substance in these arguments. There has, for instance, been much public complaint about the sales efforts for synthetic detergents. The competitive element in those efforts is perhaps a waste, but there is no doubt that these new products (whose minimum economic scale of production is understood to be large) would never have established themselves without high-pressure salesmanship to build up a market (at the expense of soap) as quickly as possible. Without the sales effort it would not have been worthwhile for a manufacturer to wait for the slow infiltration of the new product. There are still some British manufacturers who confuse any substantial sales effort with the fraudulent claims of dishonest advertisers. But if we define it as a scientific inquiry to find out what the consumer or user wants, and a well-planned and honest effort to tell him what is available, then we think sales effort may be an important condition for the rapid application of science. As we have seen in Chapters 6 and 7, it is important that companies should choose research and development projects with a knowledge of the market possibilities, and this in itself implies a desire to obtain a systematic knowledge of the market.

The conclusions of this chapter illustrate a point which is important in this whole report. The application of science and technology in industry is not something which can be fitted at will to the productive machine, like some optional gadget on a car. It is a component part of a complex process which begins with the basic research and ends with the sale of the finished product. It can be made useless by weakness at the production or the sales stage, just as much as by weakness in research or development. It can be speeded up by the favourable sales conditions of a large and expanding market, just as much as by the skill and ingenuity of the researchers themselves.

Chapter 15

A FAVOURABLE ENVIRONMENT

THE preceding chapters have been concerned with some factors which are internal to the firm—for instance, its managerial system—and some which are external, such as the market for the product and the sources of finance. There now remain for discussion a number of other features of the environment of industry, or of the atmosphere or climate in which it lives, which influence the attitude to new developments in products or processes.

The first of these is the extent of competition. We are not here concerned with the arguments for and against free competition in general. It is sufficient for our purpose to observe that there is no reason why competition should always favour or induce technical progress. On the one hand it can be argued that free and lively competition keeps a firm 'on its toes', always looking out for new ideas and better processes in case its rivals should obtain an advantage. On the other hand, much research and development work requires a long view, an ability to plan for many years ahead. A firm, especially a small firm, snatching an uneasy living, in constant danger of losing markets to its rivals, is in no position to take a view much beyond the end of its order book.

It is certain that competition is not a *sufficient* condition of technical progress. If society has not set up a system of technical and scientific education, if it has not made provision for the conduct of basic research, competition cannot induce technical progress other than that due to simple inventiveness. Basic research, on which most industrial research and development is founded, is mainly carried on outside the range of business competition; and so also is the important part of industrial research which is financed through the Department of Scientific and Industrial Research. Education also is a function of the non-competitive part of society. If competition is to favour technical progress it must be backed by an educational provision which is both general (e.g. training in physics and chemistry) and particular (training in the technologies of particular industries). But even the latter is not a natural product of competition. In most of the industries which we describe as 'craft industries' competition has existed, but it has not called into being adequate facilities for technical education. The growing provision for education and research in these industries has, apart from some effect from the competition of more scientific firms abroad, taken place in spite of competition rather than because of it. Competition may indeed make it more difficult to obtain recognition of the industry's interest in education and research.

This suggests that we should look at the conditions in which competition takes place, rather than at the simple facts about its intensity. But there are other reasons why we need, to get to the root of the matter, more subtle distinctions than those based on counting the number of competing firms. The essential point is not the possibility of competition, but the actual attitudes existing between potential competitors—attitudes which may or may not be expressed by any formal relations, such as cartel agreements, existing in the trade. In other words, we have to inquire what business men think about their relations with other business men—an inquiry much more difficult than the discovery of facts about restrictive practices.

The importance of a study of attitudes is suggested by the difference in the climate of opinion about relations between firms, as it exists in the U.K. and the U.S.A. In the U.K. there remains, from the experience of the 1930's, a certain respectability attaching to the ideas of 'orderly marketing', of 'rationalization of industrial structure', of 'prevention of cut-throat competition'. Indeed, the word 'competition' has had an evil smell for much longer; in 1907 Marshall found it necessary to write:

'We ought therefore not to brand the forces, which have made modern civilisation, by a name which suggests evil. . . . It is perhaps not reasonable that such a suggestion should attach to the term "competition"; but in fact it does. In fact, when competition is arraigned, its anti-social forms are made prominent; and care is seldom taken to inquire whether there are not other forms of it, which are so essential to the maintenance of energy and spontaneity, that their cessation might probably be injurious on the balance to social wellbeing.' [1]

In the U.S.A., on the other hand, free competition enjoys in general a social prestige, as part of the 'American way of life'. Its victims may squeal, and attempt to protect themselves behind barriers of restriction; but they cannot usually expect their actions to be respectable or to attain public approval, unless (like tariffs) they hurt the foreigner. Public opinion, indeed, shows from time to time a doctrinaire disapproval of monopolies, or indeed of any 'big business', regardless of their virtues.

Such a summary, of course, fails to bring out the diversity of opinion which exists in both countries. But there must be at least a tendency to favour in each country those firms which are best fitted to survive in the prevailing climate of opinion. Both the virtues and the vices of competition will flourish more freely in America, where they have greater public approval.

Our evidence does not enable us to go into this matter very deeply, but we suggest that it is desirable to distinguish the following varieties of

[1] *Principles of Economics*, Macmillan, I, i, 4 (from 5th edition).

attitude among the industries of the U.K. Our classification, however, is neither exact nor comprehensive.

1. *Expanding industries with competition based on product and process developments.* These are the industries, in general new and based on science, in which there are possibilities of rapid technical change. Competition in development is often a matter of technical pride as well as of a struggle for markets, but no firm which is to survive can fall far behind its rivals in paying attention to new knowledge. Research and development can go forward in the assurance that there is likely to be a good flow of results and room in the market for their profitable application. In such industries there tends to be a recognition of the community of interest in technical education and in the results of research. There is thus considerable freedom in the exchange of technical information—in short, a non-parochial approach to industrial problems.

This balance of competition, based on development, and safety, based on growth, is likely to favour technical change. The competition does not depend on having a large number of firms (as in electronics): it may be intense between a very few firms (as in synthetic detergents).

2. *Expanding industries in which competition is negligible.* There are some cases where a firm is, in effect, the industry; others where there are several firms in the industry, but they do not compete. We must also distinguish two kinds of expansion, typified by Terylene and by electricity or steel. In the first case the expansion is created *by* the producer, following his own research and development: in the second case the expansion is created *for* the producer by an investment boom or by the growth of the economy.

The theoretical danger in industries in which competition is negligible is that, though the conditions for technical progress may be ideal, the incentive to action may be lacking. But where the product or process comes from a firm's own research department, that firm has every incentive to create an expanding market, and it has the impetus to further development provided by the research workers who have successfully brought forth the innovation and are confident that they can do more. In our observation, the monopoly in a successful innovation is often temporary; once a development is proven other firms come in either on licence or with an alternative product. Rayon and polythene are examples. Large firms, if their research and development are successful, are always likely to have one or two monopoly products for the time being. Indeed, a firm which is never in this position never pioneers.

Where an industry is expanding not so much because of its own technical innovations as because of external pressures, the possibility that monopoly agreements will hinder technical progress is greater. But we have not found good examples of this, and we think that the

danger is not great.[1] (There is a possibility, of which the steel industry
provides an example, that expansion will be so 'orderly' that it fails to
match an increase in demand, and consequently delays technical change
in other industries—see p. 112.) Where the industry has considerable
opportunities for technical change, it will probably support research
departments of good size and status which will be pushing forward innovations and searching out new knowledge. Technical pride will take
the place of competition as an impulse to progress. Even where the
potentialities of technical development are slighter, it must be remembered that monopolies or closely associated groups of firms are vul-
nerable to public criticism, and the impulse to be reasonable in pricing
policy and to appear progressive in outlook is therefore strong. Finally,
any sluggishness in an expanding monopolistic firm may be due, not
directly to its monopoly protection, but to the complications caused by
its size—a subject to which we have referred on p. 125.

3. *Defensively restrictive industries.* Some of the expanding industries
discussed in the last section are monopolistic almost by historical
accident. We must now distinguish industries in which the defensive
purpose of monopolies or restrictive agreements is more obvious.
Monopoly or restriction is the response of the industry to actual
or threatened market difficulty. There is no doubt that there is in
British industry a great number and variety of defensive and regulatory
agreements and 'understandings'. For instance, in the cement industry
an agreement was made in 1934 to fix prices and to regulate output on
a quota basis. This was the consequence of a price decline, due to
excess capacity, which had continued steadily since 1924; neither
occasional agreements to abstain from price-cutting, nor a partial
process of consolidation, had been effective in checking this decline.
The increase in building activity after 1934, and the revival after the
war, in fact removed the original incentive to restrain trade. The fforde
Committee [2] found, moreover, that the Cement Federation arrangements
had not in fact led to a restriction of output through excessive prices.

These restrictive agreements are sometimes spoken of as 'protecting
the inefficient', the idea being that prices are kept high enough to cover
the costs of a high-cost producer. But we do not think that detailed study
of particular agreements will support this view. The people who receive
the greatest degree of protection are those with the biggest bargaining
power in the negotiation of the agreement, and it will often happen that
the high-cost producer is in a weak position and cannot prevent the
agreement being framed in such a way as to squeeze him out.[3] We note
that the British Non-Ferrous Metals Federation, giving evidence to the

[1] Some possibility of sluggishness in the oxygen industry is suggested by paragraph 245 of the Monopolies Commission *Report on the Supply of Certain Industrial and Medical Gases*, H.M.S.O., 1956.
[2] *Report of the Cement Costs Committee*, H.M.S.O., 1947.
[3] B. Fog, *Journal of Industrial Economics*, November 1956.

Monopolies Commission on the supply of semi-manufactures of copper, argued that in fixing their prices the trade associations showed 'a constant bias towards the lower-cost producer' and that the prices tended, therefore, to reflect the more efficient techniques. They were able to give examples of occasions when members had ceased to make products for which their costs were high and the prices fixed unremunerative.[1]

The effect of defensive agreements on technical progress depends once again on the relation between progress and safety. The agreement may provide the shelter within which technical development can with reasonable safety be pressed forward, or it may provide the chance of avoiding technical change and continuing with antiquated methods. Most of the recent evidence about restrictive practices is contained in the reports of the Monopolies Commission, and indeed it has been an unhappy effect of the activities of that Commission that business is now more than ever secretive about restrictive practices. We have therefore examined all the Commission's reports with care, to see if an effect, one way or the other, on technical progress can be established.

We obtain from this study an impression that the strength and importance of restrictive agreements—at least of those so far investigated by the Monopolies Commission—can be greatly exaggerated. Elaborate machinery may exist (as, for instance, in the London Builders' Conference) and yet have hardly any apparent effect. A second conclusion is that there is no striking evidence of a deliberate suppression of new knowledge. Dissatisfied inventors often imagine that they are frustrated by the wicked machinations of monopolists, but there usually seems to be some sound commercial reason for a refusal to develop their inventions. There is an inference that, where new entry to a trade is made difficult, progress will be obstructed; thus, in the report on Dental Goods, the Commission concludes (p. 73):

'The discouragement offered to new manufacturers is liable to impede the introduction and promotion of new materials and equipment, an effect which is particularly undesirable in an industry serving the needs of public health.'

This, however, is not a proof that new developments have been impeded, still less a proof that any such obstruction is more important than the beneficial effects of protected stability. In the case of acrylic teeth, discussed in the Dental Goods report, the effect of the agreements seems to have been an attempted diversion of business to member firms, but there was no effective obstruction of the development. The agreements in the match industry appear to have obstructed independent producers (such as the Co-operative Wholesale Society) in their efforts to obtain the best machinery. There was at one time a system of

---

[1] *Report on the Supply and Export of certain Semi-Manufactures of Copper and Copper-Based Alloys*, H.M.S.O., 1955, p. 92.

fines (under the 'Phoebus agreement') for producing electric lamps which lasted too long, but it was never operative in the British industry, and in any case there is alleged to be a necessary conflict between long life and operating efficiency in electric lamps. The Hard Fibre Cordage Federation appear to have prohibited the manufacture and sale of first quality manila trawl twine, but this is of trivial importance.

On the evidence, therefore, we conclude that the dangers to technical progress set by restrictive agreements are limited and to some extent theoretical; they are dangers which might reasonably be expected to occur, rather than dangers which can be proved to have occurred. This conclusion is supported by the case-studies. We have heard rumours of restrictive agreements which are framed in such a way as to impede technical change, but in the field covered by our detailed studies we have found only two minor cases in which development of products or processes have been held up because of restrictive practices on the side of management. It is possible that the 'restrictive habit of mind', which runs to the protection of an agreement not to compete, may be associated with sluggishness in accepting new ideas. But we think that this is a factor small in importance compared with the provision in the industries for research and education. Those 'restrictive' industries which were most sluggish in accepting new ideas were those which gave least attention to technical and management education and to research—that is, those industries in which the firms were most parochial. In any case, agreements not to compete usually give a poor and uncertain protection against the competition of substitutes, the dangers of vigorous firms breaking the agreement, the competition to be met in foreign markets and from foreign firms in the home market, and the pressure exerted by large buyers. The danger that they will give so much safety that firms can go to sleep is therefore not great. Nothing in this section, of course, touches the general question of public policy involved in agreements to fix prices or divide markets; we are solely concerned with the effects of such agreements on technical developments.

4. *Competitive depressed industries.* There are some industries which are subject to periods of contraction or depression, but in which there is no possibility of achieving the protection of a restrictive agreement—commonly because the numbers of firms to be covered would be too great, or because there are strongly opposed interests among them. Such industries are, so to speak, unwillingly competitive (though some of the business men in them may be belligerently competitive), and it is here that we may expect to find that in the constant struggle for a place the stability necessary to encourage long-term developments is absent. Sections of the textile and clothing industries, of the furniture trade, and of retail distribution provide examples. There is a striking contrast between the attitude of firms in expanding industries, laying their plans for development ten or fifteen years ahead, and the attitude of firms in

competitive depressed industries, which go on using old methods because it is never certain if the market will stand the cost of an improvement.

The pottery industry is an extremely interesting case for study. Some sections of the industry—which is made up of table-ware, tiles, sanitary ware, and electrical porcelain makers—have restrictive practices, while others have not. The industry was depressed between the wars, but has been prosperous since. Between the wars technical progress tended to be least in the most competitive section of the industry—namely, the table-ware section. This has led to the argument that it was the stronger Trade Associations in the other sections which made technical progress possible. This argument, however, overlooks the technical and market differences between the sections. The two sections which were technically most progressive between the wars were tiles and electrical porcelain. The tile section produces a small range of standard products which, unlike table-ware, lend themselves to mass production techniques, while the housing boom of the 1930's created a demand for tiles, and gave a profitable opportunity for investment in new methods. Furthermore, the Tile Association was one of the pioneers of research in the industry and has encouraged the free exchange of technical information. The electrical porcelain section produces to specification, often one provided by the buyer. This, together with the increased demand which came with higher electricity output, gave manufacturers an incentive and an opportunity to evolve new methods of production. It is significant that since the war, when output for table-ware has been high, this section of the industry has been just as 'progressive' as the other sections. (See Appendix III.)

'Progressive' here is used in a relative sense. One of the most significant things about the craft industries is that the scientific basis of the process of production is very imperfectly understood, and that the provision for technical and managerial education is small compared with that in the modern industries. In the craft industries technical change is particularly sensitive to market conditions, more often than not because there are few really big technical developments which it would be worthwhile for one or a few firms to introduce when the market outlook is poor. The 'time horizon' must be short, because so little is done to dominate market conditions.

Once again, therefore, we have to make the troublesome insistence that there is no simple answer. Technical progress is encouraged by a favourable balance between safety and competition, the nature of the balance required depending on the circumstances of the industry. Expansion is a favourable influence, but neither free competition nor monopoly can be singled out as necessarily encouraging technical progress.

There is one special aspect of monopoly which we have examined,

M

namely the effect of patents. A valid patent confers a monopoly for a period, normally of up to sixteen years, but it discloses the facts of the invention and therefore invites those who wish to use it to apply for a licence to do so. As between two independent inventors, the right to a patent depends (in the U.K.) on the time of application. In consequence an inventor who neglects to make application may find that he is unable to work his own invention without paying royalties to another inventor who has obtained the patent. If he is not concerned to obtain a monopoly, he can prevent the granting of a valid patent covering the same subject-matter by publishing his invention at large, and thus dedicating it to the public use. Otherwise he will clearly be wise to make an immediate application covering all patentable material. It has been suggested that this leads to defensive patenting of things which may never be important to the patentee.

This complaint may be valid, though we doubt if it has much importance; but the relevant question is whether the British patent system as a whole achieves a reasonable compromise between the protection of inventors and the encouragement of technical progress. We think that it does. The degree of protection given by a patent is more limited than may appear at first sight. In any complex field of technology, what is invented may be found to follow by slight improvement on some invention already made and in use. The questions of novelty, of the extent of the use of the inventive faculty, of the precise necessity of the various claims made to the successful use of the invention, may all be in doubt, at least to such an extent that it would not be worth the cost and the risk of maintaining the validity of the patent in the Courts. A high proportion of patents are allowed to lapse after four years, when renewal fees become payable, and many others are in fact readily available on licence. Indeed, the patentee must be ready to develop his invention himself or to grant a licence to do so on reasonable terms, for the Comptroller-General of Patents may grant compulsory licences 'if it is shown that the patentee is exercising his monopoly in such a way that the fullest practicable use of his invention or the fullest development of industry is not being achieved'.[1]

The bias of the patent system is therefore towards the disclosure and use of inventions, rather than their concealment or suppression. We are informed, however, that owing to the inadequate staffing of the Patent Office the grant of a patent takes from two to four years. During this period there may be uncertainty about the necessity of seeking a licence for the use of the invention, or about the conditions appropriate to such a licence; indeed, since the delay is mainly prior to the publication of the complete specification, the invention may remain unknown. To some small degree these factors may slow down the rate of application of inventions.

[1] D. Hennessey, *Research*, vol. 7, 1954, p. 439; cf. also note 1, p. 27 above.

It has also been suggested to us that British inventors are prejudiced because of the difficulty of obtaining protection overseas, and particularly in the U.S.A. It is undoubtedly both tedious and expensive to obtain adequate protection in the principal foreign countries, and there are grounds for thinking that a U.S.A. patent is more difficult to obtain than a British patent. But the difficulty applies to American inventors as well as British—there is no evidence known to us of discrimination against the foreigner; and, because it follows a searching examination, a United States patent is well respected and gives good protection. A patent easy to obtain is likely to be difficult to enforce. While the degree of international protection available is unsatisfactory, we doubt if it could be shown that this imposes special difficulties on the British, but not on foreign, inventors.

The laying down of national standards specifying such characteristics as dimensions, qualities of materials for particular purposes, methods of test, and methods of installation, use, and maintenance, is often referred to as an aid to productive efficiency. President Hoover said:

'They (standards and simplification) have played an enormous part in our whole economic development. They are at the back of all mass production. They make possible more continuous employment by manufacture for stock instead of dependence upon immediate and specialised orders. They have made it possible to conduct this fabulous productive machine with the least amount of spare parts and inventories in the hands of the consumer industries. They have sharpened competition. They have cheapened the cost of production in millions of directions . . .' [1]

British industry is often said to be relatively slow in perceiving the advantages of the standardization of components and of concentration on simplified ranges of types and sizes; consequently the advantages of large-scale production are not fully exploited.

This criticism may have some validity, but its relevance to the speed of application of new scientific knowledge is not clear. 'Mass production' or 'long runs' are a way of extracting the last fraction in efficiency from a settled productive process. But in doing so they sometimes impede changes in the productive process, or at least delay them to some, perhaps distant, time for re-tooling. Where there is an immense investment in single-purpose tools and dies, it is difficult to vary the planned method of production. Standardization does not, however, always lead to inflexibility; with its partner, the simplification of design, it may make technical change easier. This is because it leads to economy in the use of scarce labour (including designers and draughtsmen), and facilitates a fuller use of machines, thus encouraging earlier machine replacement. An industry whose product is wholly unstandardized, but

[1] Quoted in *How British Standards Serve Industry*, British Standards Institution.

is constantly varying to suit the needs of customers, may have to leave unused scientific or technical developments whose adoption would limit the ability to meet special needs.

It is also suggested to us that the movement towards standardization, excellent as it is in its immediate results, may tend to preserve certain specifications or methods when they ought to be changed. If this is so, it is not the fault of the British Standards Institution, whose committees keep British Standards under frequent review. The trouble—whose occasional existence seem to us likely, from the evidence of our case-studies—is inherent in the process of standardization. A British Standard is in effect the definition of the best technical practice *which is generally acceptable* to the making and using trades, for no standard is published unless it has 'the substantial support both of manufacturers and users and others concerned'.[1] Once published, it has undoubted prestige, and is liable to be regarded, in its successively revised versions, as being the best up-to-date practice. This makes it all the more difficult for a minority with better ideas to overcome the convervatism, perhaps based on lack of knowledge, of buyers or manufactures who insist on British Standard specifications. Such obstruction is all the more likely to be caused by 'standards', such as Government specifications and local authority bye-law regulations, which are only revised at long intervals. Yet this contingent danger to progress may be a small price to pay for the value of standardization.

We have taken a special interest in the possibility of hindrances to the speedy application of new knowledge caused by lack of co-operation from labour. Such hindrances are frequently reported; they commonly take the form of an insistence on the continued employment of men who are made redundant by a technical change. New machines or methods are also liable to produce jobs which do not fit into the accepted descriptions, and technical change is thus a fertile ground for inter-union demarcation disputes. There have been disputes of the first kind, for instance, over mechanical handling in the docks (though there has also been a dispute caused by the absence of mechanical handling); the second type was involved in a long struggle in the shipyards over the drilling of holes.

We are not satisfied, however, that the resistance of labour to technical change is as simple a matter as may appear from newspaper reports of strikes against the introduction of this or that new machine. Under full employment, changes involving the dismissal of men or a serious lessening of their earnings (or worsening of their working conditions) are not very frequent; it is often possible for management to absorb men who are displaced in some other part of the business. We have been impressed by the number of cases in which wholesale reorganization

---

[1] *Annual Report*, British Standards Institution, 1954–5, p. 17. 'Substantial support' does not, of course, require unanimity.

and the introduction of new and labour-saving methods have taken place with the ready co-operation of workers and their unions. Except perhaps in depressed industries, acceptance of technical change is the rule, resistance the exception; and where there has been resistance, there has usually been a history of labour trouble on issues quite different from the introduction of new machines. Where there is a long record of suspicion between management and labour, any change is seen as a possible intrigue by management to worsen the position of the workers, and the reply of labour is to insist on excessive guarantees that this cannot occur. An atmosphere of suspicion and distrust makes it difficult for management to convince labour of the facts, for the facts will be believed to conceal some hidden purpose; the problem, common to all large organizations, of keeping subordinate workers informed about intended change is thus made more difficult. Where in one firm a new machine can be proudly displayed as something marvellous which 'we' have got, in another it is grudgingly received as a change made by 'them', whose purpose is concealed. This lack of communication and failure to carry the consent of the workers lead sometimes, we think, to demarcation disputes which apparently have nothing to do with the actions of management.

If, therefore, a 'labour restrictive practice' is regarded as something which issues from the conservatism of the unions, whatever the attitude of management, we must record that we have found no evidence which would justify the conclusion that such practices are a serious hindrance to technical advance. What we have found is that bad labour relations can be such a hindrance, expressing themselves in a suspicious attitude to change. The leadership of most of the unions and of the Trades Union Congress take a moderate and enlightened view of the labour problems involved in technical change. The extent of labour troubles is easily exaggerated—on an average day, more than 99·9 per cent. of workers are *not* on strike—and on the whole the last decade has been a period of industrial peace. Our general conclusion is that the hindrances caused by labour, though significant and in part removable by good management, cannot be regarded as a major determinant of the speed of scientific and technological advance, at least in the period 1945–56.

We find, however, that some firms avoid trouble with labour by going slow with innovations; so that the absence of difficulty over labour restrictive practices is evidence, not of the absence of restriction, but of its avoidance. There must obviously be some limit to the rate at which a group of workers will accept change (though the factors influencing that rate are complex), and a good management will judge the speed with which it can make changes accordingly. But we have no direct evidence that avoidance of trouble with labour is an important factor slowing down technical advance.

If this chapter had been written ten years ago, it would have given much attention to the special problems created by Government controls, which were then an important part of the environment of industry. But practically all detailed controls over materials and prices have now been swept away, and the Government's regulation is exerted through such instruments as the Budget and the Bank Rate, whose effects are to be found in the matters discussed in Chapter 13. The nationalized industries, however, are still subject to control over their capital investment programmes, and in some cases over their prices. B.O.A.C. cannot buy foreign aircraft without permission; capital expenditure on coal, railways, or electricity is liable to be cut back (and might in other circumstances be speeded up) not for any direct commercial reasons, but to balance the investment programme of the nation as a whole. We have been unable to make a direct study of the nationalized industries, but from various scraps of evidence we have formed the impression that this subjection to a Government control which varies with the winds of economic circumstance is destructive of that stability necessary for speedy and resolute technical decisions. We do not, however, deny the need for some means of controlling capital investment by the basic industries.

One remaining form of control which might have an effect is that over industrial location. In order to undertake any substantial new factory building (exceeding 5,000 square feet), it is necessary to obtain an industrial development certificate from the Board of Trade or other appropriate department. Planning permission must then be obtained from the local authority; there is a statutory period of two months for reaching a planning decision, but this is often extended by agreement. There is a possibility of considerable delay in dealing with the conditions to be imposed on the development, the supply of water, the disposal of effluent, and so on. Nevertheless, since the relaxation of building controls, the time taken to pass a project through the stages of permission has been reduced, and (provided the applications are made skilfully and in due time) we think that the delay to development cannot be serious. We have no recent evidence of projects being held up unnecessarily at this stage.

It is easy to fall into the habit of regarding the actions of Government as red tape, controls, burdens on the vigour of private enterprise. But it is only fair to observe that the net effect of Government action on the rate of adoption of new scientific and technical knowledge must be strongly favourable. The education of scientists and technologists is predominantly State financed, and much of it is so expensive that it would be beyond the resources of individuals. A significant part of the country's research effort, including such vitally important fields as nuclear engineering, is to be found in Government laboratories. The research associations and research stations draw on Government funds. The Department of Scientific and Industrial Research has a great record in the encouragement of science. The quotation from Professor Pope in Chapter 1 (p. 6) is happily long since out of date.

Owing for the most part to the needs of defence, much special Government help is given to industry in the form of research and development contracts. The case-studies reveal numerous instances of companies which have been assisted in their establishment or growth by these contracts, which enable the State to carry risks too large for private firms. We have heard complaints about the form and administration of the contracts, and we note that a few firms try, as a matter of policy, to avoid them, but we have no doubt of their general effectiveness in speeding up the selected developments.

The Advisory Council on Scientific Policy in its Sixth Report (Cmd. 8874, 1953) noted that:

'Without Government help of this kind, it is almost certain that our aircraft industry would never have achieved its present pre-eminent position. . . . The practice has undoubtedly achieved very useful results in the fields of civil aircraft and Post Office equipment, and, although it has not long been in operation in the fuel and power field, the results are already encouraging.'

The Advisory Council in consequence suggested:

(a) that civil departments might place (further) development contracts for 'long-term' needs, e.g. of energy and raw materials;
(b) that the research associations might bring into being, with public assistance, Development Companies;
(c) that the National Research Development Corporation might be given power to help with development arrangements in industries where the research association could not carry the burden unaided.

We have referred in Chapters 5 and 7 to the work of N.R.D.C. and of the research associations, and to the creation of Shirley Developments, Ltd., to sponsor machinery development in the cotton industry. We are not aware of any substantial change in the use of development contracts.

Our review of the influence of the industrial environment can appropriately close by referring again to the importance of the climate of opinion—the attitude of business men and of the public. We have already discussed this matter in relation to competition and restrictive practices, but it has a wider importance. We have referred repeatedly, and especially in Chapter 10, to the importance of the relations between firms to the speed of application of new knowledge; to the 'gate effect', when a development in one firm sets off new developments in others; to the 'chain effect', when advance requires the simultaneous action of a linked series of firms. Anything which helps to break down the isolation of firms will speed up the spread of new ideas and make easier a concerted advance. Consequently it is important that the general business attitude should not be one of dour secrecy, but should show a willingness to give and receive knowledge to the utmost that commercial considerations allow. We think that there is some movement towards a freer interchange of knowledge, but (especially in some of the older industries) there is a long way still to go.

There is another sociological field which we have not fully explored, but whose importance is beyond question. What is the kind of business man who is admired by his fellows, and how can the ideal be changed? There are traditional industries in which men are proud of doing what their fathers did, and the ideal is the man who is master of an inherited craft. Before the days of science such an attitude was vitally important, to secure the transmission of knowledge without loss to succeeding generations; it is still important in the crafts which remain untouched by science. But the attitude can be a great hindrance where old methods should be tumbled to one side by the stream of new knowledge. There are 'new' industries where men are proud of *not* doing what their fathers did, where the ideal is the innovator, and a new idea has an appeal from its very novelty. Farming can show both extremes—the traditional farmer, who will learn very little, and the 'modern' farmer, who is quick to try out a new tool or seed or insecticide. People may laugh at the supposed American worship of novelty, but we would suggest that the creation of a public opinion which is proud of technical change is no small part of the conditions for achieving that change.

Chapter 16

THE TECHNICALLY PROGRESSIVE FIRM

IN the earlier chapters we have mentioned many characteristics of the firms (and farms) which we judge to be technically progressive, that is to say to be keeping close to the best which could reasonably be achieved in the application of science and technology. In this chapter we try to bring together the various elements of our picture of the technically progressive firm, and to list the signs and characteristics which distinguish the progressive [1] from the unprogressive firm. We have added to this a special study of the characteristics which change when a firm wakes up, and moves from an unprogressive to a progressive state, and of the factors affecting such a change. We think that this may help to suggest some of the points of pressure which are most likely to yield results in speeding up the application of science. As can be seen from the list of characteristics, we have been interested in the non-technical qualities of the firm—its managerial efficiency, its interest in cost accountancy or market research, and so forth. This enables us to come to some conclusions about the relationship between technical progressiveness and what might be called *general quality*. Because we live in an economy in which, to a considerable extent, profit is both the motive of production and the provider of the means of expansion, we have also examined the relationship of technical progressiveness to *financial success*. Does it pay to apply new scientific and technological knowledge? If it does not, then the forces of natural selection determining the survival and growth of businesses are to some extent working against the application of new scientific knowledge.

We have first to face the difficulty that the definition of a technically progressive firm lacks precision. It is not enough to say that in practice different observers can be found to agree on a rough classification of progressive firms, for it might be that their impressions were the joint result of the observation of a series of characteristics which people naturally associate with progressiveness. We should then find an association between the ratings of progressiveness and the characteristics on which those ratings were (perhaps subconsciously) founded, but this association would convey information about the minds of the observers, and not about the real world. The danger is a serious one, for in the course of an investigation one naturally forms preliminary hypotheses— for instance, that progressive firms are ready to share ideas with others; and once such a hypothesis is formed, it may begin to enter into the

---

[1] Throughout this chapter, the word 'progressive' means 'technically progressive' on the above definition.

reasons for the classification of the progressiveness of firms later interviewed.

While admitting this difficulty, we do not think that it affects the extreme examples of progressiveness and unprogressiveness. Whatever its other qualities, we think that there is no difficulty in recognizing a firm which is in the forefront of discovery in applied science and technology, and which is quick to master new ideas and to perceive the relevance of work in neighbouring fields. Similarly, there is no difficulty in recognizing a firm which is quite uninterested in science and technology, and is perfectly content to continue with its traditional methods without even examining the alternatives. What we have done is to examine the group of highly progressive firms, and to draw up a long list of the characteristics which seemed to be common to all or most of them. We have then tested the less progressive firms by these characteristics. Firms of a moderate level of progressiveness give widely spread results. The significant outcome is that there are twenty-four characteristics which are not only (by definition) *present* in progressive firms, but also prove to be generally *absent* in unprogressive firms. These we may fairly call 'characteristics related to progressiveness'. There are a further five characteristics which show no such close relation to progressiveness.

The twenty-four characteristics are not, of course, relevant in all firms, nor observable in all firms; and, where observable, they are not of equal significance. We therefore devised a system by which marks, on a scale from 0 to 8, were assigned to each firm for each characteristic, and these were weighted, as between firms, to allow for differences in relevance and amount of knowledge. Since the characteristics were chosen as those of progressive firms, they naturally score high marks— 97 per cent. of the possible maximum for the six most progressive. But the six least progressive firms scored only 14 per cent.

We hope to present our statistical findings in a separate paper. We should mention at this point, however, that we offer no judgement on the statistical significance of the associations observed, for such a judgement would be meaningless without more knowledge of the distribution of the measures employed. All we claim is that certain associations, which on general grounds are reasonable, do in fact seem to exist in a sample of some fifty firms for which our information is sufficiently extensive.

The twenty-four characteristics are as follows:

1. *High quality of incoming communication.* The more progressive the firm, the higher the quality of the technical literature which it takes, and the better its contacts with scientists and technologists of good standing and wide experience in universities and in other institutions and firms. The reading of backward firms is usually confined to the lower qualities of trade journal, and such firms rarely have contact with 'outsiders' of a wide range of vision. In consequence, the backward firm

may not hear of an idea for several years after it is first made known. It should be noted that it is quality which matters, rather than quantity; one of the most progressive firms in our sample deliberately restricts the number of journals coming into its research department.

2. *A deliberate survey of potential ideas.* In the firm which is neither parochial nor adoptive the ideas stimulated by incoming communication, as well as those arising within the firm, are deliberately and regularly surveyed in order that those offering the best promise of reward may be developed. We have quoted an outstanding example of this on p. 62. At the other extreme we find the self-satisfied parochial firm, discussed in Chapter 10, which is protected from new ideas by its own complacency. To quote one Managing Director: 'I consider our ancestors were clever—I think they had worked out what was the nearest to the ideal. . . . So it seems foolish not to take advantage of what they did.' The adoptive firm (p. 109) is open to new ideas if they are presented ready developed by the 'host' on which the firm is a parasite. It thus occupies an intermediate position.

3. *A willingness to share knowledge.* The greater a firm's technical achievements, the readier it is to share its knowledge with other firms and to contribute to journals, conferences, and so forth. The progressive firms in our sample were astonishingly ready to throw open their factories to visits by competitors, though we gather that their more backward competitors rarely take advantage of this. On the whole the moderately progressive firms are also willing to share their more limited knowledge; and we must record our pleasure at the help freely given to us by a wide variety of firms in the course of our studies—a help which hardly fits in with a general accusation that British industry is secretive. But the most backward and parochial firms are secretive on technical matters.

4. *A willingness to take new knowledge on licence and to enter joint ventures.* Progressive firms are willing to be adoptive when it is convenient—that is to say, to supplement their own research and development by buying knowledge from other firms. They are also more ready to share in joint ventures in research, development, or production. Such ventures are unthinkable to the parochial firms.

5. *A readiness to look outside the firm.* This characteristic is included to test one aspect of 'parochialism' (see Chapter 10). We have tested it by setting up a classification of the extent to which the firm looks outside itself and sets its standards of performance by what it sees in its competitors or other firms. The classification differs according to the size of the firm: thus a large firm obtains the highest marks only if it provides for extensive overseas travel, is conscious of the best standards of performance set anywhere in the world, and is ready to interchange technical information with firms in other countries: while a small firm cannot usually be expected to provide for more than occasional overseas

visits but should (to reach the highest class) have extensive British contacts, both inside and outside its own industry. The analysis confirms that the technically progressive firms look outside themselves for their standards of performance.

6. *Effective internal communication and co-ordination.* We find that the following qualities are on the whole present in progressive, and absent in backward firms:

(*a*) There is effective team-work by departments when new developments are being planned. Thus evaluation of the potential market, of the costs of production, and of the capital position of the firm, involves and interests various departments of the firm well before a decision to undertake a new development is made.

(*b*) Responsibility, authority, and the objectives of the company are so specified and understood that individuals and departments work together effectively.

(*c*) The differences in outlook in research, development, production, and sales do not hold up projects, or lead to their being pigeonholed; and Board decisions (where required) are given without undue delay.

7. *High status of science and technology in the firm.* This characteristic should perhaps not appear, since it is obvious that a firm which makes full and speedy use of new knowledge must give a larger place to science and technology than a backward firm. But it also tends to give them a higher status; there are not only *more* research, design, and development staff, but they are more important in the firm, and are represented by a powerful and sympathetic voice on the Board.

8. *A consciousness of costs and profits in the research and development departments (if any).* Many firms have no research, design, or development department; this characteristic is of use only in comparing degrees of progressiveness in those which have. The more progressive firms give more attention to economic justification in choosing projects for research and development and in deciding which are worth continuing after the preliminary investigation. Cost-consciousness, in the sense of economizing in the use of scarce scientific and technical staff was (as we have noted on p. 104), not well developed, even in the progressive firms.

9. *Rapid replacement of machines.* Progressive firms replace machines earlier; this is a natural consequence of their desire to be technically up to date, but it may be significant that many regard it as the right *policy* to scrap early. This is consistent with our observation in Chapter 15, that depreciation allowances are not the major factor in determining replacement policy.

10. *A sound policy of recruitment for management.* The progressive firms tend, more than the unprogressive, to recruit people with con-

siderable training; for example, their recruits include a significant proportion of graduates. In firms in which 'family' succession is able to provide for the filling of management posts, the more progressive firms give the younger generation of the family a wider education and training. A large proportion of the unprogressive firms restrict their recruiting to those who leave school at 15 or 16, except for the occasional professional recruit such as an accountant. Such people, when later promoted to managerial posts, tend to solidify the traditional outlook of the firm. (See p. 131.)

11. *An ability to attract talented people.* The progressive firms have on the whole a greater ability, as well as a greater desire, to attract trained and able staff. The factors influencing this ability have been discussed on pp. 115–117.

12. *A willingness to arrange for the effective training of staff.* The more progressive firms have a greater interest in arranging for the training of their staff, whether through internal training schemes (in large firms) or through effective use of local technical college and university facilities. The less progressive firms must, of course, do the necessary apprentice instruction, but beyond that they are satisfied with vague admonitions to 'go to night school'. But we have the impression that still more attention might be given to training, even in many progressive firms.

13. *Use of management techniques.* The progressive firms tend to use such techniques as method study, work measurement, production planning and control, standard costing and budgetary control; the backward firms do not.

14. *Identifying the outcome of investment decisions.* This difficult subject is discussed in Chapter 8, where we draw attention to the general tendency to take investment decisions without detailed calculations of the probable outcome. This analysis shows, however, that the technically progressive firms make some sort of calculation, though it is often only partial or only 'on the back of an envelope', but that there is an almost total absence of any such calculation in backward firms.

15. *High quality in the chief executive(s).* The importance of the 'key personality' (or occasionally of a dominant group of people) has been mentioned on p. 115, and it was stressed in the report of the Manchester Joint Research Council.[1] The quality of the key personality, commonly the chief executive of the firm, is not easy to judge, and we have had to do the best we can on the basis of our own impressions of the man and his work, and the evidence of his subordinates. The evidence strongly confirms the hypothesis that technically progressive firms are led by men of high general quality.

16. *Adequate provision for intermediate managers.* A limit to the number of intermediate managers (between the top executives and the

[1] *Industry and Science*, Manchester University Press, 1954, p. 109.

shop-floor supervision) is set by the size of the firm and the nature of its processes. Comparing firms of similar size and environment, we find that the unprogressive firms have relatively fewer intermediate managers. Senior management is thus burdened with trivial matters, and has neither time nor the mental agility to think of long-term policy. By providing for more intermediate management posts, the progressive firm frees senior executives from the worry of day-to-day problems, and incidentally provides a better ladder of promotion and a way of training for higher management. There can, of course, be too many levels of management,[1] but we have not found firms which have obviously erred in this direction.

17. *Good quality in intermediate management.* There appears to be a relation between the quality of intermediate management and the progressiveness of a firm. The most progressive firms are found to have, for example, production departmental managers who comprehend the technology of the process for which they are responsible, and who can and do initiate technical change. The unprogressive firms, by contrast, tend to have in the similar positions people who work to rule-of-thumb methods, and who are convinced of the eternal validity of the processes with which they are familiar.

For what it is worth, our evidence suggests that the intermediate or moderately progressive firms are above average in the quality of senior management but below average in the quality of intermediate management. If this finding were confirmed by further study, it would suggest that such firms should give special attention to the number and quality of subordinate managers.

18. *An ability to bring the best out of managers.* This characteristic can best be studied in firms which, having been unprogressive, have been revived under new management. Junior managers in such firms have told us that their former chiefs gave the impression that they 'knew all the answers', that there was no need to listen to or to act on the advice of subordinates. The junior managers were frustrated, and felt that their problems were not understood. With the change of management, they found their advice and suggestions listened to, and they were stimulated and encouraged to do their best by the needs of the new situation. Our main study suggests to us that an ability to stimulate subordinate managers is often found in technically progressive firms, but that unprogressive firms are apt to frustrate them.

19. *Use of scientists and technologists on the Board of Directors.* We have seen in Chapter 12 that this is not a necessary condition of progressiveness, but it is a characteristic frequently found in progressive firms, and absent in unprogressive firms.

20. *A readiness to look ahead.* There is evidence that the 'time horizon' is further away, and the 'planning period' longer, in progressive

[1] P. F. Drucker, *The Practice of Management*, Heinemann, 1955, p. 177.

firms. In backward firms the chief executives are frequently immersed in daily detail (see No. 16), and (even if they had time) this makes it difficult for them to make the change of mental gear needed for looking far ahead. This characteristic might be related indirectly to progressiveness through financial success, for it is difficult for a firm with poor profits to look far ahead.

21. *A high rate of expansion.* 'Expansion' here means the rate of increase of assets. A high rate of expansion may be the consequence of technical progressiveness, through the intermediate stage of financial success; or it may be the stimulus of progressiveness in an industry which is growing.

22. *Ingenuity in getting round material and equipment shortages.* The progressive firms are, on the whole, much more ready to find ways of overcoming shortages—for instance, by making the goods themselves, by scouring unusual sources for imports, or by preparing powerful cases in order to overcome restrictive controls. The unprogressive firms tend to regard a shortage as though it were an Act of God or of the Queen's enemies.

23. *An effective selling policy.* We have referred in Chapter 14 to the fact that technically progressive firms are often found to be vigorous and effective on the sales side as well. A good test is the reaction of the firm to the post-war sellers' market: progressive firms tended on the whole to regard it as inspiring them to fresh efforts, or as giving them an opportunity to prepare for bad times, or at least as giving them no reason to relax their normal pace of development: unprogressive firms tended to sit back and enjoy a period of easy selling.

24. *Good technical service to customers.* Progressive firms tend to help their customers to understand the properties and right use of their products, and to overcome any difficulties which the customer might find. This often involves using scarce technological skills—either in a technical sales force, or by a readiness to send design or production staff to give help to customers. As one firm put it, 'The designer will sit on a new machine until all the bugs are ironed out'. By contrast, unprogressive firms often had to be pressed very hard before they would give any help, and would then send junior staff 'to give the job the once-over'. Such firms not only failed to help their customers; they failed to derive information which would have helped them to improve their product.

The following five characteristics were included on our original list for testing because of their possible relevance, but they proved to have no regular or definite connexion with our assessments of technical progressiveness:

1. *Membership of an industry with a strong scientific or technological background.* This may appear an odd result; the point is that, although 'modern' industries (see p. 110) do appear to contain a high proportion

of progressive firms, it is not possible to assert the converse: the 'traditional' industries show a wide spread of technical progressiveness.

2. *Adequate buildings or site.* The case-studies revealed many firms which were badly housed or on constricted sites, but there was no definite indication of a relation to progressiveness.

3. *Scientific or technological training of the key personality in the firm.* This is a companion of No. 19 above: whereas the evidence suggests that scientists are often found among the directors of progressive firms, the grounds for concluding that the leading personality in the firm (e.g. the Managing Director) is likely to be a scientist are inadequate.

4. *Resistance to innovation on the shop-floor.* This refers to personal problems like the conservatism of foremen and operatives, and not to Union resistance, but the discussion in Chapter 15 is relevant. Only 12 per cent. of the firms reported any significant difficulty, and they were about equally divided between the progressive and the unprogressive.

5. *Adequate finance.* As Chapter 13 shows, certain types of firm are especially liable to find difficulty in obtaining or retaining money for their development. This analysis showed that shortage of finance had not significantly affected backward firms; its effect on the progressive firms was too various to confirm this characteristic as one which is related to progressiveness. This conclusion relates, of course, to a period of inflation.

These five characteristics are not, of course, *unrelated* to the rate of adoption of new scientific knowledge—better buildings, less resistance on the shop-floor, or better finance would (for instance) all help forward technical progress. The point is that the relation is a complex one, so that one cannot say that the characteristics are *necessarily* or *generally* associated with progressiveness, or their absence with unprogressiveness.

The conclusion to be drawn from our analysis of the characteristics of technically progressive firms is clearly that the firm which is good in applying science and technology is also of good 'general quality'. We have referred on p. 134 to three firms for which this is not true—firms whose dominant attitude is that of achieving the maximum development and application of new scientific ideas, despite some backwardness in other respects; and we have mentioned that in these cases it has been found necessary to improve the general quality of the firm's operations, if its technical progress was not to be frustrated.

The concept of 'financial success' is not easily defined, especially when we are using the results of a short and unsettled period. From Moody's company records[1] we have selected a sample of 500 firms principally engaged in manufacturing or extractive industry in the U.K.,

[1] We acknowledge the kindness of Moody's Services Ltd., in making these available to us.

and whose shares are quoted on the London Stock Exchange. This is therefore a sample of *larger* companies, and our results are subject to that limitation. After hearing the advice of our Accountants' Group, we have used three different criteria of financial success:

(a) Trading profits as a percentage of fixed assets and stock, for the average of two recent years (normally those ending in 1954 and 1955).

(b) The trading profits for the four years ending in 1952 to 1955 as a percentage of those for 1948–51.

(c) The increase of net tangible assets from 1948 to 1954 as a percentage of the 1951 net tangible assets.

Each of these criteria enables us to arrange the 500 firms in order, from the 'best' to the 'worst', the three arrangements being related, but far from identical. The 500 firms already include some of those covered by the case-studies, and other firms can be assigned to their appropriate place on the 'ladder' provided by the sample of 500. Thus firm A in the case-studies is found to have, on criterion (b), a percentage approximately equal to that of the 152nd firm of the sample of 500. It is therefore allotted a 'mark' of 152 on the scale of criterion (b), which ranges from 1 for the most successful to 500 for the least successful firm. These marks can then be set against the ratings of technical progressiveness.

There is no evidence of a relationship between profits as a percentage of assets and technical progressiveness; this figure seems to be mainly determined by the nature of the industry. There is apparently a weak relationship between the increase of net tangible assets and technical progressiveness. Both criteria, (a) and (c), are perhaps rendered uncertain by the variety of practice about the valuation of assets; and unprogressive firms sometimes show profits as a high percentage of assets, because their assets are old and well written-down. There is a much stronger relationship between criterion (b), the increase of profits, and technical progressiveness. Thus relatively unprogressive firms (rated 4 or 5 on a scale of progressiveness from 0 to 10) average around 250–300 in their position on the scale of criterion (b): progressive firms, rating 9, average about 130. But there is a considerable spread of results, and the number of very backward firms which are public companies quoted on the Stock Exchange is too small to give evidence below progressiveness rating 4. Furthermore, it is not proven that technical progressiveness is the cause of fast-rising profits; it may be that the profits are the stimulus or the necessary means for the progressiveness.

However, the most likely explanation is that the relationship works both ways, and that technical progressiveness is often the condition of financial success; this is supported by the evidence in Chapter 14 suggesting that it 'pays to be first in the field'.

In a review of 152 case-studies, we find sixteen firms whose general

N

quality (in production, sales, costing and so forth) appears 'better' than their record in applying new technical developments. Six of the sixteen are certainly financially successful. But these exceptions to a general principle that technical progressiveness, general quality, and financial success are related prove to be mostly in a state of transition; eleven of the sixteen are taking steps to increase the scale of research and development, in some cases backing this by taking new products or processes on licence from overseas countries.

Among the sample of 500 firms, those with poor profits records include a higher-than-average proportion of smaller firms. 'Smaller' is here a relative term; being public companies with a Stock Exchange quotation, the firms would be better described as of medium size. The case-studies, while showing outstandingly progressive firms which are of small size, also show many more small backward firms; we have no examples of really large firms which are comparably backward, but several of large firms which are very progressive. These results can partly be explained by the obvious fact that a backward firm is more likely to stay small; but we think that they support the conclusions of Chapters 11 and 13, that while progressiveness is possible (and does occur) at all sizes of organization, there are special disabilities attaching to certain types of small firm which make financial success (and presumably in consequence, outstanding technical progress) more difficult to achieve.

We have made a special study of firms which are moving, or have recently moved, from a backward state to one in which they are making considerable use of new developments. These firms were mostly of medium size, and in long-established engineering or craft industries.

Four patterns of change were identified:

(1) Some firms were forced, by industrial change of which they were not the originators, to employ staff of higher quality or training. This may happen, for instance, through the appearance of highly complex equipment requiring competent engineers to run it. The changes, in our observation, start from a general 'policy' decision to adopt the new methods; this decision is often taken without a realization of the changes in people and in practice which will be induced. The change so induced is slow, for it takes time to appreciate the need for and to attract the new staff, and they may have to rise in status before they can begin to induce further changes in out-of-date methods. There is a danger that the new staff will be frustrated by conservative management, and that good people will therefore leave the firm. We have cases in which the change from backwardness to progressiveness has taken place gradually over a period as long as thirty years; this has covered the realization of the need for new people, their recruitment, their acclimatization in the firm, their rise to power in their own departments (usually production), and their levering out of backward management in other departments.

(2) Some firms had been reduced to decay and near-bankruptcy by incompetent management, and had then been revived following purchase by a more efficient group of firms or by financiers. Change can then be rapid; new brooms have no hesitation in sweeping clean, and the purchasing group may bring the knowledge and the resources in men and in capital needed to raise the firm's standard of performance to that achieved by the purchasers elsewhere. The whole process can be complete in two to five years.

(3) On the evidence of our sample, the most common cause of technical change is a change of senior management: in family firms this is commonly a coming to power of a new generation of the directors. In cases under this heading, the degree and the rapidity of revival vary widely; in the most outstanding cases, the new directors have a background of education or training far removed from that of their predecessors—in one company, a complete change to young (late 30's) directors with experience in several other firms; in another, the death of the owner of a medium-sized firm led to the succession of a son without any previous industrial experience whatsoever. In most of the less outstanding cases, also, there is some difference in the background of the new generation of directors. In several firms in the Potteries, for example, a considerable part of the change in performance can be traced back to the influence of Dr. Mellor, first Principal of the Pottery School at the North Staffordshire Technical College, both through the formal technological courses he inaugurated and through the impact of his personality and ideas.

(4) Finally, there are a few cases of change which has followed, or been made possible by, Government protective action. Thus the imposition of the McKenna duties appears to have been a condition, though not a sufficient condition, for scientific change in the papermaking industry. In the jute industry (see Appendix III), the greater security given by import controls and by Government purchasing has freed managers from the immediate struggle for existence, and they have been able to give attention to the introduction of new equipment which had been developed in other industries. We would not put forward protection as a general method of improving the efficiency of backward industries; we think that its success in the jute industry is related to the higher quality of existing management in that industry, and to a strong additional stimulus from the shortage of labour.

The extent of change depends largely on the extent of the experience of management; people of high education and wide industrial experience can carry change further than those who have limited education and experience in a single firm. The main barrier to *rapid* change appears to be the traditional methods and attitudes of existing managers. The conservatism of intermediate management can seriously restrain a new direction, and in extreme cases members of the lower ranks of management have had to be dismissed or prematurely retired. There is naturally great reluctance to do this.

Apart from this, there are natural limits to the speed of change; it is no use trying to alter everything at once, and changes in management have usually been followed by a period dedicated to 'getting efficient on the present basis of operations' before the firm has turned to major changes of process or product. In other words, attention is usually directed to other aspects of the 'general quality' of the firm, before 'technical progressiveness'.

This survey of firms which have changed their outlook underlines the great importance of trained, lively, and receptive management. Better finance, attractive propaganda, the influence of example can all have their place in speeding up the change, but the change has to start from a man. This suggests that those of our original twenty-four characteristics which relate to the quality of management—Nos. 10, 11, 12, 15, 17, 18, and 19—may be the most fundamental. But it must also be remembered that, as we pointed out in Chapter 10: 'The industries most firmly stuck in the mud of unprogressiveness are less likely to secure the talented direction which might pull them out.'

Chapter 17

A PROGRESSIVE ECONOMY

W E started this book by affirming our belief that the full and speedy application of science is necessary to economic progress, and should be one of the most important objectives of national policy. The factors influencing the speed of that application seem to us to be much more complex than is usually recognized, and they vary in their incidence from industry to industry, from firm to firm, and from year to year. It is so easy to write dangerous half-truths and generalizations on this subject that we consider our work half-done if we have persuaded readers to look at it in its full complexity. It is not our purpose to say in detail what we think should be done to speed up the application of science; this is a matter to which our committee is now turning its attention, and we hope that this report will stimulate public discussion of it. But that discussion may be helped if we indicate what we consider to be some of the broad conclusions of our study.

First, British industry is not universally backward in scientific matters, but is uneven in its development, with a great range from the best to the worst firms. We have found many firms which need fear no comparison with similar firms anywhere in the world; but we have also found firms which have shocked us by their ignorant complacency. Although all countries must expect to have some unprogressive firms, we do not think that this justifies the parochialism of large tracts of British industry.

But the situation we have observed is in process of change. Industrial research and development are growing rapidly, but their growth is mainly recent, and they will yield greater rewards in the future. Indeed, the growth has a feed-back effect, creating for itself some of the conditions of further growth. The increase in industrial applied research makes us doubtful if there is any present validity in complaints of lack of balance between basic and applied research; in fact we have traced some of the deficiencies of application to the inadequacy of British basic research in certain fields (Chapter 3).

Next, there are some supposed reasons for scientific and technical backwardness which we think without substance, or of uncertain effect. Thus we have not found that Government control or 'red tape' is a serious influence, and indeed we suggest (p. 174) that the net effect of Government action must be favourable to the speedy application of science. Though we have mentioned many problems of changing the form and quality of management, we think that, given a basic ability in senior management, forms of organization or methods of management do not have any certain effect, which would enable us to pick out one as specially favouring scientific advance (p. 65). We have not found, however, sufficient attention paid to the appropriateness of management structure to the problems in hand. Small firms suffer from more difficulties than large, and we find more backwardness among the smaller firms; but this does not justify a general condemnation of small units of organization, for we find (p. 126) that it is possible for technical progressiveness to occur, and it does actually occur, at all sizes. The effects of high taxation on the resources available for development, or on incentives, appear to us to be uncertain (p. 142), at least as regards the recent past. If scientists hold senior positions in management, or are directors, there seems a moderate probability that the firm will be found to be technically progressive; but the cause-and-effect relationship is not certain, and firms can achieve considerable technical progress with no scientists or technologists in leading positions.

We have tried to throw light on the problem of the communication of scientific ideas by drawing attention to the receptiveness of firms as often being more important than the method of communication (p. 34). We have also noted the growing importance of the 'scientific middleman' who writes simplified articles for trade journals or visits firms on behalf of an advisory service. The 'small size of the British market' turns out to be an idea which needs analysis (p. 154), and we have suggested in what sense the size of the market can be said to be a limiting factor in scientific advance. We have also referred (p. 156) to the fact that it is natural for even so large a country as the U.K. to have to rely on foreign sources for many results of both basic and applied research. The 'shortage of capital' appears on analysis (p. 147) to be a problem most likely to be felt by new, young, and small firms, but we draw attention to the fact that the trouble is often not that it is impossible to find capital, but that firms are not willing to face the implications (e.g. in loss of family control) of accepting it. The effect of restrictive practices is found, on the management side, to involve a difficult balance between the advantages of competition and security, and we are not disposed to regard the effect on the application of science as large (p. 169).

The factors we have so far mentioned are various and complex, and many of them are inherent in an advanced industrial society. We do not think that any of them have a leading importance in determining the pace of the adoption of new ideas. We would summarize what we conceive to be most important under the following six heads:

1. Technical progressiveness is related to the general quality of the firm; and attention to other aspects of its general quality—for instance, to management efficiency or to salesmanship and market research—helps to create the conditions for technical progress. In other words, the use of science is not an optional extra to be attached to the firm, but an expression of the whole attitude of the firm.

2. Effective industrial research and development must be closely related to production and sales policy and needs. This means that careful thought must be given to the scale of research and to the choice of research projects, so that both may be fitted to the general policy of the firm. It means that those who manage research must be able to judge the possibilities of projects on economic as well as scientific grounds.

3. The interconnections of firms are important—suppliers stimulating their customers and providing technical service, manufacturers encouraging the development of new raw materials. Hence there is a danger to the progress, not just of one firm, but of a whole chain of firms, when one company is 'parochial' in its attitude—self-satisfied, surrounded by the barriers of ignorance, complacency, and secrecy.

4. Even the parochial firm is open to some general influences from outside which may change its attitude; and it is important that these influences should give a high status to the firm which is scientific and progressive, and not to the one which is content to repeat the errors and virtues of its predecessors. The general climate of opinion is important.

5. The rate of technical advance is limited by the number of good minds which can be brought to bear on the problems of research, of development, and of management. This number is not capable of indefinite increase, and it therefore becomes all the more important that the educational system should work with the least possible wastage of ability. We are not satisfied that the British system accords with the needs of modern industry.

6. In particular, we note that there is a constantly increasing demand for scientists and technologists. In the early stages of the application of science to industry, a few scientists are engaged, mostly in basic research; later a larger number is required, to provide for industrial applied research—this is the stage now reached by Britain; and finally a much larger number still is needed, in the control of production processes—a stage reached by the U.S.A. We have no doubt that many more scientists and technologists must be trained, if Britain is to consolidate her industrial research and apply it in complex processes; but we think that it will be very difficult to increase the supply without considerable changes in the educational system.

We conclude this report by referring to two findings, one of which is encouraging, while the other shows the magnitude of the difficulties which remain. We find that technical progressiveness is to some extent related to financial success, and in particular that it may pay to be first in the field, rather than to allow the pioneering to be done by others. If these findings are correct, the forces of natural selection, stimulating the growth of profitable firms, are allied to those of technical progress. But, on the other hand, we suggest that backwardness is self-perpetuating, both in firms and industries; the backward firm, even if it can be made to desire technical progress, is ill placed to command the resources (and in particular the human ability) necessary to begin that progress. It will take much ingenuity by industry and government to break up the crust of habit and to divert lively and able minds from the places where change is most likely to those where it is most needed.

Appendix I

THE SCIENCE AND INDUSTRY COMMITTEE

THE origin of this book is to be found in a decision of the Council of the British Association for the Advancement of Science, meeting at Belfast in 1952, to appoint a committee 'to study the problems of speeding up in industry the application of the results of scientific research'. The committee's first instructions were to prepare a programme of work, and the first half of 1953 was spent in a preliminary survey of the problems. This convinced the committee that substantial new investigation would be needed, and it decided to look both for additional sponsors of the work and for extra funds.

Some months of negotiation followed, as a result of which the Royal Society of Arts and the Nuffield Foundation agreed to join the British Association in sponsoring the investigation. The interest of the Royal Society of Arts is shown by its full title, 'The Royal Society for the Encouragement of Arts, Manufactures and Commerce', while the Nuffield Foundation has within the ample scope of its trust deed 'the advancement of social well-being'. The reconstituted committee, with representatives of all three sponsors, met for the first time in April 1954. This report, however, is the result of the work of the whole period from 1952 to mid-1956. It is not the only result of that work; it is expected that other reports and articles will follow.

The British Association committee was able to bequeath to its successor an agreement with the Board of Trade to supply funds for research under the 'Conditional Aid' scheme; and these funds were later augmented by the Department of Scientific and Industrial Research, under the same scheme, to make the total sum available about £20,000. As stated in the Foreword, therefore, the committee gratefully acknowledges that the preparation and publication of this book have been made possible by a grant under the Conditional Aid scheme for the use of counterpart funds derived from U.S. economic aid: that is to say, that the book is a by-product of United States generosity.

The committee's field of work is defined by the following terms of reference:

'To identify those factors which determine, in different industries and in different types of firm, the speed of application of new scientific and technical knowledge; to examine their relative importance, their inter-relations, and their correlation with characteristics of the firm or industry; to obtain evidence of the effectiveness of measures already taken to speed up the application of science in industry, or to remove hindrances to such application; and to examine the possible results of other proposed measures.'

At the beginning of 1955 these were extended, as a consequence of an invitation from the Treasury and an offer of additional funds, to include 'factors influencing innovation' and 'the collection, in the course of the case-studies, of material which would contribute to knowledge of the background of investment decisions'. ('Investment' is here used in the economist's sense, relating to building, the installation of plant and machinery, and the accumulation of stocks of goods.) This book, however, is concerned with the factual part of the main terms of reference; the committee is regarding the examination of 'other proposed measures' as a separate task, and it intends to report separately on the extended terms of reference.

The British Association's definition of 'science' is a broad one, covering both social and natural sciences, and the committee was able from the beginning to have the help of physicists, chemists, engineers, economists, and business men, drawn from industry, agriculture, professional practice, and the universities. During 1955 and 1956 the committee was fortunate enough to be advised on certain aspects of its work by a group of accountants, convened on the committee's behalf by Professor F. Sewell Bray. The members of the committee and of the Accountants' Group were as follows:

List of Members of the Science and Industry Committee

Professor C. F. Carter (*Chairman*)
Sir Ernest Goodale, C.B.E. ⎱(*Vice-Chairmen, from* 1954)
Mr. L. Farrer-Brown ⎰
Professor B. R. Williams (*Secretary*)
Mr. M. G. Bennett (*Treasurer*)

Sir George V. Allen, C.B.E. (1954–)
Dr. T. E. Allibone, F.R.S. (1953–4)
Mr. J. C. Beavan (1956–)
Professor A. J. Brown
Professor A. K. Cairncross, C.M.G. (1954–5)
Mr. R. V. C. Cleveland-Stevens (1954–)
Mr. R. H. Fry (1956–)
Mr. A. C. Hartley, C.B.E.
Dame Caroline Haslett, D.B.E. (1954–5, deceased 1957)
Professor K. S. Isles (1954–)
Professor H. D. Kay, C.B.E., F.R.S. (1954–)
Mr. J. H. Leycester (deceased 1953)
Mr. D. N. Lowe, O.B.E. (1952–3)
Mr. K. W. Luckhurst (1954–)

Professor J. A. L. Matheson, M.B.E.
Dr. A. C. Menzies (1954–)
Mr. J. E. Morpurgo (1954–)
Dr. R. W. Powell (1952–3)
Mr. A. R. N. Roberts (1955–)
Mr. J. M. Robertson
Sir John Simonsen, F.R.S. (1954–, deceased 1957)
Dr. R. E. Slade
Sir Richard Southwell, F.R.S. (1952–3)
Professor M. Stacey, F.R.S.
Dr. George Taylor (1952–3)
Dr. Barnes Wallis, O.B.E., F.R.S. (1954–5)
Dr. S. Whitehead (1955, deceased 1956)
Mr. A. H. Wilson, F.R.S. (1954–)
Dr. T. Wilson, O.B.E.

List of Members of the Committee's Advisory Group of Accountants.

Mr. E. H. Davison, A.C.A.
Mr. J. A. Jackson, F.C.A., F.S.A.A.
Mr. H. L. Layton, F.C.A., F.S.A.A.
Mr. S. L. Pleasance, F.S.A.A.
Mr. A. P. Ravenhill, F.C.A.
Mr. W. G. A. Russell, F.S.A.A.

together with Professor F. Sewell Bray and Mr. T. W. South of the Stamp-Martin Foundation in the Incorporated Accountants' Hall.

The members of the committee gave active and frequent help, in the day-to-day conduct of research as well as in committee meetings, but the main burden had, of course, to be carried by full-time staff, who were organized in two research units. One, the Keele unit, was under the direction of Professor B. R. Williams; it was housed, with the ready co-operation of the University authorities, at the University College of North Staffordshire, Keele, Staffordshire. The function of this unit was to study the actions of firms who were facing, or had faced, particular opportunities of scientific or technical development, and the ways in which it did this are set out in Appendix II. The other unit, housed by the Queen's University of Belfast, and under the direction of Professor C. F. Carter, was instructed to bring together and examine existing evidence, and to conduct such special inquiries as might be necessary (other than those involving visits to firms).

The committee was throughout fortunate in the quality and keenness of its staff, who were:

	Keele	Belfast
Research:	Mr. W. P. Scott (1953–6)	Mr. M. J. M. Erritt (1953–5)
	Miss M. G. Hanna (1953–6)	Mrs. J. M. Alexander (1955–6)
	Dr. D. L. Cardwell (1954–6)	Mr. D. P. Barritt (1955–6)
	Miss M. I. Burnikell (1955–6)	
Clerical:	Miss J. S. Martin (1955–6)	Miss P. Clarke (1953–6)
		Miss M. R. Sharkey (1956)
		Miss E. Ellison (1956)

To all of these the committee offers its grateful thanks. They have greatly assisted in the preparation of this report, but they are not responsible for any bias or errors. Nor is the committee to be held responsible, for it is too large a body to agree on every word of a lengthy document, and it therefore deputed the writing of this book to its Directors of Research.

Appendix II

THE CASE-STUDIES

OUR case-studies were of three types—general case-studies, industry case-studies, and cases of specific innovations.

In the *general case-studies* we selected a sample of firms of differing sizes, efficiencies, and types of ownership, from a variety of industries. The sample was not a random one—it was chosen to throw as much light as possible on the problem. To understand the complex of factors that impede or encourage the rapid industrial application of science and technology, we needed case-studies of firms of many types—large and small, public and private, successful and not successful in applying science to industry, enthusiastic and lukewarm about applied science, experienced and inexperienced in research and development, engaged in traditional industries and in new ones based on science, in industries that have developed a scientific understanding of materials and processes, and in industries that have not. With two research workers we expected to do 100 case-studies, and with this number there was a high chance that a random sample would fail to bring out the necessary distinctions between different types of firm. Later our research staff was increased, but the need for a sample obtained by deliberate selection remained. We made 152 usable general case-studies.

We first visited firms known to welcome our investigation. They enabled us to experiment with techniques of inquiry and to test the relevance and completeness of the hypotheses formed during the first year of the Committee's work. At each firm we visited we formed ideas of other firms to visit—firms in the same trade that were said to be different in size or achievement, and firms in other trades that were said to help or hinder in the chain of relations affecting innovation. We checked these suggestions with members of the Committee, or with research associations, trade associations, or university scientists. In this way we also obtained advice on relevant technical problems. Periodically we examined the sample built up in this way, and by adding extra firms, corrected it for any unbalance in size, efficiency grades, or type of industrial process used.

There was a continuing tendency for stupid and unprogressive management to be under-represented in our sample—if only because we often could not get a usable case-study from them. To offset this we took care to include in the sample firms that had taken over 'dead' firms and given them fresh life. We then made a special study of the measures taken in that revivification.

Firms in the sample were visited by the research team, who gathered background information about such matters as size, products and processes, capital employed, rate of growth, numbers of scientists and technologists employed and their position, and the experience and 'paper' qualifications of members of the Board. They then studied the problems of communication and decision within the firm—the management structure, the basis of decisions to adopt or reject new products or processes, the means of gathering information about possibilities of product and process change, the expenditure (if any) on research and development, the choice of research and development projects, and the process of adaptation to an innovation. Where innovations had been made, brief case histories were compiled giving their origin, the incentives to undertake them, their progress through the stages of research and/or development, the decisions to adopt or reject them, and if adopted the subsequent difficulties of actual application, whether within the firm or in the market. These case histories provided a most valuable method of getting the facts of the situation in each innovating firm. The problems of applying science in each firm were then related to the general prospects of applied science in the industry—the supply of scientists, technologists, and technicians, the extent of knowledge of properties of materials and processes, growth in output, the degree of dependence on firms in other industries when innovations are attempted, and the degree of progressiveness of these other firms.

In thirty-one cases a conference was arranged between representatives of the firm and members of the Committee, or other experts, who had special knowledge of the scientific or technical problems involved, to discuss the information gathered by the research team. These conferences, in which discussions proceeded from the case material embodied in a 'briefing' document, were of great value. We were able not only to add expert knowledge and understanding of scientific and technical problems to the resources of the research group, but also to conduct an open investigation with the firm into the impressions gained and the judgements formed in the collection of the case material.

The composition of the general case-study sample by type of ownership was as follows:

	Employment by firm—					
	Up to 100	100 to 500	500 to 2000	2000 to 5000	Over 5000	Total
Public company	—	3	27	20	19	69
Subsidiary of public company	2	9	7	3	2	23
Private company	17	19	15	8	1	60
	19	31	49	31	22	152

The industry and size-group composition of the general case-study sample was as follows:

Orders	Minimum List Headings	Standard Industrial Classification	Employment by firm—			
			Up to 500	500 to 2000	Over 2000	Total
II	10–19	Mining and quarrying	—	—	1	1
III	20–29	Treatment of non-metalliferous mining products other than coal	4	8	1	13
IV	30–39	Chemicals and allied trades	4	4	6	14
V	40–49	Metal manufacture	—	3	2	5
VI	52	Agricultural machinery (except tractors)	3	2	—	5
	54	Machine tools	—	4	2	6
	55	Stationary engines	—	—	1	1
	56	Textile machinery and accessories	—	—	1	1
	58	Constructional engineering	—	1	1	2
	69	Other non-electrical engineering	12	6	5	23
	70	Electrical machinery	1	1	1	3
	71	Electric wires and cables	1	2	3	6
	73	Wireless apparatus (except valves) and gramophones	—	—	2	2
	75	Batteries and accumulators	—	—	1	1
	79	Other electrical goods	3	2	4	9
	50–79	*Total—Engineering, shipbuilding and electrical goods*	*20*	*18*	*21*	*59*
VII	80–89	Vehicles	—	4	3	7
VIII	90–99	Metal goods not elsewhere specified	4	—	—	4
IX	100–103	Precision instruments, jewellery etc.	2	3	3	8
X	110–129	Textiles	1	4	3	8
XII	140–149	Clothing	—	1	1	2
XIII	150–169	Food, drink and tobacco	4	—	3	7
XIV	170–179	Manufactures of wood and cork	2	—	1	3
XV	180–189	Paper and printing	5	4	2	11
XVI	190–199	Other manufacturing industries	1	—	4	5
XVII	200–202	Building and contracting	1	—	1	2
XIX	220–239	Transport and communication	—	—	1	1
XX	240–246	Distributive trades	2	—	—	2
			50	49	53	152

The distribution by ratings of technical progressiveness (see Chapter 16) was as follows:

Technical progressiveness	General sample only	General sample plus certain firms from industry studies (see below)
High	60	62
Medium	64	86
Low	25	45
Not known . .	3	3
	152	196

In the *industry* case-studies a 10 per cent. random sample of firms was chosen for the pottery industry. Thirty-three firms were included, and in addition eight firms which supply equipment to the industry. In jute and cutlery a small sample of firms was chosen, after discussions in the industry, to include firms of differing sizes and degrees of 'progressiveness'. Nine were chosen in jute and twelve in cutlery. Equipment suppliers were also visited. We also added to the number of paper firms in the general sample to bring it into line with the other industry studies; nine paper firms were included. The object of these case-studies was to examine in greater detail than was possible in the general case-studies the process of technical change. We chose for this purpose long-established industries in which research was of recent growth. Appendix III shows the impressions gained from these studies.

The case-studies of *specific innovations* were undertaken to give a detailed understanding of the passage from invention to innovation, and of the different reactions to the same invention of firms in the same or in different industries. We used the thirty-three firms of the pottery industry study to examine the introduction of the tunnel oven (see Appendix III); we investigated the use of the tower crane in five firms in the building industry, and the use of shell moulding in twenty-seven firms making or using metal castings. We also studied the progress from invention to innovation for the Raper Autoleveller, both with the inventor and with the firms involved, and we followed up the introduction of ion-exchange resins and of silicon iron, respectively with three and four firms principally concerned.

The constitution of the industry samples and the shell moulding 'innovation' sample was as follows:

| | Employment by firm— | | | | | |
	Up to 100	100 to 500	500 to 2000	2000 to 5000	Over 5000	Total
Pottery (Total) . .	5	22	*14*	—	—	*41*
Public company .	—	2	6	—	—	8
Subsidiary . .	1	2	1	—	—	4
Private company .	4	18	7	—	—	29
Jute (Total) . .	—	4	4	—	*1*	9
Public company .	—	1	1	—	1	3
Subsidiary . .	—	—	—	—	—	—
Private company .	—	3	3	—	—	6
Cutlery (Total) . .	3	8	*1*	—	—	*12*
Public company .	—	2	1	—	—	3
Subsidiary . .	—	—	—	—	—	—
Private company .	3	6	—	—	—	9
Paper (Total) . .	—	*1*	6	—	*2*	9
Public company .	—	—	3	—	2	5
Subsidiary . .	—	—	1	—	—	1
Private company .	—	1	2	—	—	3

	Employment by firm—					
	Up to 100	100 to 500	500 to 2000	2000 to 5000	Over 5000	Total
Shell moulding (Total).	9	*10*	*4*	*3*	*1*	27
Public company .	—	3	1	2	1	7
Subsidiary . .	1	2	1	1	—	5
Private company .	8	5	2	—	—	15
Total of all the above .	17	46	28	3	4	98

Altogether, the number of firms visited by the research staff was 269. The number which did not yield usable information was twenty-three; of this twenty-three only six refused to help with the investigation. In addition, during the conduct of these case-studies the research staff made 109 visits to universities, Government departments, research associations and trade associations, to gather information, expert judgements, or advice relevant to the conduct of the case-studies.

Appendix III

EXAMPLES FROM THE CASE-STUDIES

THE nature of the industry and 'specific innovation' case-studies was indicated in Appendix II. From these we have chosen four to give a further indication of the helps and hindrances to change. These are the introduction of the tunnel oven in the pottery industry, and studies of the cutlery industry, the jute industry, and the paper industry. The field workers in the first were Mr. Scott and Miss Hanna; in the second, Miss Burnikell and Mr. Scott; in the third, Miss Hanna; and in the fourth, Mr. Scott. These reports are their summaries of the much fuller analyses which they made.

All these studies were in long-established industries. The first three—the pottery, cutlery, and jute industries—are not growing rapidly; the paper industry, on the other hand, is growing fast. In the tunnel-oven case we have examined not only the strategic factors in the adoption of this innovation, but also the process of development. In the cutlery industry there have been no big innovations of this kind, and there we have examined the impediments to the rapid industrial application of science which come in a small industry with a strong craft tradition. In the jute industry, where there have been significant changes in machinery, in training, and in management methods, we have tried to isolate the critical factors in the change. The paper industry (or some firms in it) has grown a long way from its craft origins. There we have examined some of the steps in the change, in which scientists and engineers, after a considerable process of adaptation in technical methods and management structure, have played a considerable part.

The examination of these industries, other than pottery, has been based on very small samples. We have, therefore, presented the material in a somewhat general form. The value of this sort of inquiry is not in statistical conclusions but in the significant cases and in the understanding obtained of the effect of the special problems of the industries on the nature and rapidity of change.

(a) The introduction of the tunnel oven in the pottery industry

The pottery industry is a long-established industry and proud of its craft traditions. The great majority of firms are private limited companies—there are twenty-five public companies (half of them still family concerns), twenty-nine subsidiaries of other public companies, and about 290 private family firms. The industry is, like cutlery,

o

highly localized—over three-quarters of the 73,000 pottery workers are employed in the Stoke-on-Trent area. The industry as a whole is not rapidly expanding—the numbers employed now are much the same as they were in 1912, while output has increased only 20 per cent. since the depression. The average size of establishment is larger in pottery than in cutlery (see below). Although 92 per cent. of the total of 342 establishments employ less than 500 people, about a third of the employees are in establishments with more than 500 workers.

The pottery industry has not (at any rate until recently) had available any background scientific knowledge on the properties of its raw materials, or of the change which they undergo during manufacturing operations. The industry's reputation has accordingly been founded on manual skills, on the craft ability to form complex patterns and to feel and overcome mysterious variations in the materials, and on the maintenance of traditional firing practices. There is no normal apprentice training and operatives have acquired the craft mystiques from workshop practice; supervision has been in the hands of the most senior and most able craftsmen; in the main higher management has been by family directors who also have grown up within the local craft tradition.

This traditional 'craft' pattern has recently shown some signs of changing. The change has been due to a variety of factors; the stronger pressure of the competition of substitutes and of labour shortage, and the greater opportunities of change created by the growth of technical education and research.[1] There are very few graduates in natural science in the pottery firms, but there is an increasing number of ceramic technicians and technologists trained in the Technical College at Stoke. The impetus for the foundation in 1914 of the pottery school at the North Staffordshire Technical College came from Dr. J. W. Mellor, F.R.S. The impact of his courses and of his personality moulded the attitudes of many of his pupils who, twenty or thirty years later, have succeeded to senior positions in the industry. These pupils, in their turn, are giving to their firms a new outlook on the possibilities of technical change in pottery practice.

The main centre for scientific work is the British Ceramics Research Association, which had an income of £170,055 for the year 1954–5,[2] and in 1956 a staff of 180 (65 graduates or equivalent). This Research Association was formed in 1947 by the amalgamation of the British Pottery Research Association and the British Refractories Research Association. The Pottery Research Association was formed in 1937, as a

[1] See p. 169 above, and B. R. Williams in *Manchester Guardian Survey of Industry, Trade and Finance*, 1957.
[2] Department of Scientific and Industrial Research, *Report for the year 1954–55*, Cmd. 9680, H.M.S.O., 1956, p. 125.

condition of receiving protection against imports. The Refractories Research Association was formed in 1920. The Research Association runs library, information, and 'trouble-shooting' services for its members, and conducts technological research, though the lack of basic knowledge about clays and their reactions to changes in moisture and temperature has led it to concentrate much of its effort on basic research to remedy this deficiency.

The industry falls into five or six sections, distinguished by nature of product. The sections are: glazed tiles, electric porcelain, sanitary earthenware, table earthenware, fine china, and ornamental fancy goods. The 'craft' tradition is least apparent in the tiles section, which now mass-produces a small range of shapes and sizes, and in the electric porcelain section, which has benefited from its necessarily close contact with a 'modern' industry.

The first process is the preparation of the clay (the body) which is then thrown on the potters' wheel or moulded or cast into the appropriate shape. This is followed by the first—the *biscuit*—firing operation, to a temperature varying between 1150 and 1300° C. for earthenware and china.

The ware emerges from the biscuit-firing, hardened in the appropriate shape, and glaze is then applied. This glaze is baked on to the ware in the *glost* firing operation, the temperature being of the order of 1050–1150° C.

Decorative patterns (which in some cases are put on before the glaze) may then be applied to the glazed ware, and baked on in the *decorating* oven (to a temperature of 700–850° C.). Complex decorations, and gold-enamelling, may require repetition of this last stage.

Traditionally, these firing operations have been carried out in the picturesque bottle ovens: the ware is placed in saggars (containers), which are stacked to a height of 12–20 feet in the oven, which ranges from 12–20 feet in diameter; the oven and its contents are raised to the appropriate temperature, usually by a series of coal-fires around the periphery; then the oven is allowed to cool, the saggars removed, and the ware taken out of them. The filling and emptying of the oven takes about three days; the firing and cooling requires another five or six days for the biscuit process, three days for the glost, and one and a half for the decorating. These time limits are set by the physical problems of raising the temperature of the whole structure.

Bottle ovens require a considerable quantity of labour, and involve strenuous work in carrying and placing of saggars; there is heavy fuel consumption, and no heat-recuperation, for during the cooling process the accumulated heat is allowed to dissipate into the atmosphere; repeated 'baitings' (i.e. stokings of coal) are required, and this often has to be left to the discretion of unsupervised night-workers; there is considerable temperature variation between different parts of the oven; the firing cycle is determined mainly by the physical difficulty of raising the oven and its contents to the required temperature, and *not* by the most efficient time/temperature firing curve appropriate to the ware; and the coal-fired bottle oven creates a vast smoke nuisance.

The most common alternative type of oven is the tunnel oven. This is a continuous firing process, consisting of a tunnel through which pass trucks loaded with the ware. The middle of the tunnel (the firing zone) is maintained continuously at the desired maximum temperature; some heat drifts towards the 'pre-heating' zone at the entry end of the tunnel, and helps to heat the ware before it reaches the firing zone. Between the firing zone and the exit, the ware gradually cools, some of the heat from this being recirculated into the pre-heating zone.

Modern tunnel ovens are heated by gas, oil, or electricity—fuels which can be more closely controlled than coal. In electrically heated ovens, and in other ovens where there is a muffle between the inside of the tunnel and the combustion of the fuel, it is possible to dispense with the saggars, and to place the ware 'open' on furniture arranged on the trucks.

A typical modern tunnel oven is some 170 feet long; the cross-sectional area available for placing ware is about $3\frac{1}{2}$ by $2\frac{1}{2}$ feet. It has a capacity equal to that of three, four, or five intermittent bottle ovens. The usual time-cycle for firing in tunnel ovens, from the entry of a truck into the kiln to its exit, is: biscuit firing, three days; glost, one and a half; decorating, half a day.

As compared with bottle ovens, tunnel ovens save labour, and the arduous task of dealing with saggars is eliminated; fuel consumption is reduced since the tunnel oven is heat-recuperative; the feeding of appropriate fuels can be automatically controlled; temperature variations are substantially reduced; the firing cycle is controlled by the nature of the ware and the process, rather than by problems of raising the temperature of the whole structure; and there is no smoke nuisance.

The tunnel oven of today, following improvements in the inter-war period, shows substantial savings in operating costs; reduces firing costs; usually produces better average quality of ware; and leads to improvement in work flow. These advantages must be weighed against higher initial outlay, and the loss of flexibility in dealing with fluctuation of output which is common to most continuous processes.

As neither the bottle oven nor the tunnel oven is a standard piece of equipment, the precise effect of a change from one to the other cannot be given. Nor can a single figure be given for financial saving, since on the one hand the best use of the tunnel oven requires change in ancillary drying equipment and in work-flow which has not taken place in every firm, and, on the other hand, the efficiency of the replaced bottle ovens varied. Savings in operating costs in case-firms thus show considerable variations.

Where one antique glost oven was replaced by a tunnel oven, the saving in operating cost was sufficient to pay for the new oven in a year; antique intermittent biscuit ovens were replaced and the saving in operating cost was sufficient to pay for the new tunnel kiln in three years. It is more usual, however, for firms to recover the cost of the initial outlay in a range between six years for a biscuit tunnel oven and two for a glost oven.[1]

The quality of ware fired in tunnel ovens is more uniform than that from bottle ovens—and in over 95 per cent. of the firms visited it was reputed to be better. These quality-savings are important: it is common in some sections of the trade to find 20 per cent. of ware is rejected between the original making and the dispatch of the finished product; and we have cases where the improved method of firing has reduced this loss factor to 15 per cent. or substantially less. This is equivalent to a 5 per cent. increase in output at no extra cost.

The continuous nature of the operation greatly facilitates smooth work-flow; indeed, in some case-firms, the installation of a tunnel oven, which demands smooth work-flow if it is to be run most efficiently, has led to a general improvement in managerial procedures.

There are, then, considerable advantages in the tunnel oven, but these must be balanced against a higher initial outlay (say £20,000 for a glost earthenware tunnel, as against say £8,000 for a series of bottle ovens with similar capacity); and against the loss of flexibility inherent in the continuous method, particularly in the case of the biscuit tunnel oven. The Potteries have suffered severely from fluctuations in trade; in times of recession bottle ovens can be fired less frequently, but the tunnel oven demands continuous operation. Many manufacturers argue that a tunnel oven is only efficient when it is full, but this is an exaggeration. We have examined cases where the tunnel is the more economical as long as throughput exceeds two-thirds of normal capacity; moreover, some firms have two tunnels per firing process, and can conveniently close down one during a recession. Even so, there is not, for most firms, the same possibility of economically firing very small outputs.

The tunnel oven is most used in the later stages of production. Approximately 90 per cent. of decorated ware is fired in tunnel ovens, 80 per cent. of glost, and 50 per cent. of biscuit. The first successful tunnel was installed in 1912,[2] but it is only in the last decade that application has

---

[1] For published information on savings see A. Dinsdale, *The Development of Firing in the Pottery Industry*, in *Ceramics: A Symposium*, British Ceramic Society, 1953.

[2] See E. Rosenthal, *Pottery and Ceramics*, Penguin Books, 1949.

become fairly widespread. The following table gives a rough indication of the number of tunnel ovens in use at various periods:

Date	Cumulative total: Tunnel ovens installed
1912	1
1926	32
1934	74
1939	124
1944	128
1953	390
1955	490

Why should there have been a forty-year time-lag between the first success of this revolutionary method of firing, and the time when its use became fairly general in the industry? Revolutionary conceptions generally require significant development work before they can be used in production, and in this the tunnel oven was no exception. What technical resources were available to carry out this development work?

This is a small-firm industry, in the sense that 92 per cent. of establishments have less than 500 employees. In traditional industries small firms can rarely afford the luxury of a separate research and development department. Even now, in the pottery industry, not more than a dozen firms have such departments, and these are small. Their efforts are concentrated on control and short-term work.

The tunnel is essentially a one-off product, designed afresh for each installation to meet the heat and output requirements of the individual pottery firm. New ideas were incorporated in new ovens, judged on their performance, amended and tried again in later installations, or dropped as unsatisfactory. Progress followed full-scale trial and full-scale error. Thus the development work, as in the case of silicon steel mentioned on p. 25, was costly and complex. A tunnel oven cannot be scaled down to get laboratory information on heat flow, while due to the late development of research into the behaviour of clay bodies practice was ahead of theory in firing. In 1942 L. Bullin wrote[1] of the absence of published work on tunnel kiln efficiencies, and of the need for a close collaboration between manufacturers to correlate the dimensions and results of kiln operation, so that the most efficient could be studied in detail by the Research Association. As Bullin pointed out, until the advent of the Research Association there were few in the industry capable of the analysis. The Association established suitable methods of test (British Standard 1388, 1947) and so obtained more detailed and better co-ordinated information than was previously available. This played an important part in the post-war development of tunnel kilns.

The industry did not itself have enough technical resources to develop the tunnel oven, although there were capable and interested individuals

[1] *Transactions*, British Ceramic Society, September 1942.

in potteries who carried out experiments in firing. What other resources have been available?

The main raw material [1] is clay. There is little direct relationship between the marketing of clay and the installation of tunnel ovens. The clay-pits themselves used to be deficient in technological staff, and they have contributed little to the development of tunnel ovens. The tunnels are usually made from refractory bricks, and one firm of refractory suppliers has been prominent as a contractor designing, creating, and developing tunnel ovens. Other people with an interest include the suppliers of oil, gas, and electricity, the manufacturers of electrical equipment and of gas or oil burners, the makers of the trucks, of the kiln 'furniture', and of the propelling equipment.

There has, in fact, been a need for development by a chain of firms in different industries. To none of these industries has the potters' tunnel oven been of compelling interest, and the market has looked very small to the larger firms—it seems unlikely that the total value in any one year of tunnel ovens installed, complete with all equipment, has approached £1 million. There have been hardly any examples of a co-ordinated approach to development work by the various organizations and industries concerned; the development work has been performed largely by oven builders.

Before the war there were two main sources. The firm of refractory suppliers went in for tunnel ovens to provide a further outlet for its refractories. During the 1920's it purchased the tunnel oven business of the discouraged pioneer, Dressler, and acquired the rights to build a decorating kiln developed by two English potters. The other source was an associate of an American company which specializes in tunnel ovens. Since the war other manufacturers have entered the field, among them a Continental firm and an American subsidiary. An English firm which produces furnaces for the metal industry, partly as a result of licence agreements with a French firm, extended its range of ovens to provide for the pottery industry.

In the development work needed before the tunnel oven became generally applicable, there were two basic difficulties: the lack of knowledge about appropriate time/temperature firing curves, and the lack of control over heat distribution in the tunnel. These two basic problems were only gradually identified over a period of twenty years.

With the bottle oven the appropriate firing cycle was developed from experience. The oven was fired over a period of several days until it achieved what was judged to be the required temperature. It was not until the introduction of cones and rings, bending or contracting at particular temperatures according to known patterns, that the industry had any absolute means of assessing temperature. These devices were

---

[1] The consumption of coal was, in fact, some 20 per cent. heavier than that of clay when bottle-firing was universal.

available in this country about 1900, but were not then used for a systematic collection of data relating to firing.

Even if the industry had known the details of the firing cycle in bottle ovens, however, it would not necessarily have known the optimal firing cycle: on the one hand, the firing time in the bottle oven was conditioned by the difficulty of raising the temperature of the whole structure: on the other hand there was a lack of scientific knowledge of the change which the body undergoes during firing. An an example: biscuit china used to be placed in a bottle oven, gradually heated to around 1200° C. and 'soaked' between that temperature and the peak of 1240° C., for some six hours. The heating process could be rapidly accelerated in a tunnel oven; and after failures due to operating the tunnel oven with an accelerated heat treatment, the Research Association found (about 1950) that the temperature rise had to be checked for a while at around 1150° C. to allow fluxes to permeate the body. This check had been automatically achieved in bottle ovens, where the stoker had to shovel furiously in order to achieve even a slow temperature rise at such a heat.

Such observations have followed the development of effective heat-control in, and instrumentation of, tunnel ovens; but this, too, has been a slow and evolutionary development process. There have been three main steps in the securing of effective heat control. The first was to maintain a constant maximum temperature. The traditional fuel—coal —gave rise to temperature variations between successive stokings. By the time of the first war, after developments in pyrometry, a constant maximum temperature was achieved by using gas or oil instead of coal.

The second step was to secure even heat-treatment at maximum temperature, over the cross-section of the load. The same cones and rings guided efforts to achieve this; and a variety of full-scale factory experiments were tried before this stage was successfully achieved in the 1920's.

The third step was to secure control over temperature throughout the length of the kiln, including control over the cross-section throughout the length. It was realized a priori that heat tended to move convectively along the roof of the tunnel towards the ends—'a howling gale of it', to quote one manufacturer—but it was not until 1927 that the first use (for this purpose) of travelling pyrometers 'squarely presented the problem to the kiln manufacturers'.[1] A series of full-scale trials and full-scale errors led at first to effects which heightened the 'howling gale'. The working solution, achieved in the mid-thirties, lay in the positive method of using fans to direct the flow of heat and air, in reducing the cross-sectional area from about 6 × 5 feet to about 3½ × 2½ feet, and in leaving the absolute minimum of space between the ware and the tunnel walls.

[1] Dressler, Bulletin of the American Ceramic Society, Vol. 18, No. 11, 1939.

Thus although the first successful tunnel oven was built in 1912, it was not until the mid-1930's that the glost and decorating tunnel oven had emerged as a well-controlled firing process. Two biscuit tunnel ovens were operated with success before the war in the production of table-ware, but the biscuit oven could not be said to have a 'well controlled firing process' until the Research Association established the appropriate firing curve.

The length of the development stage (in which a considerable part of the progress was due to work in the U.S.A. and Germany) was due to a variety of factors. The pottery industry is composed of a large number of small to medium-sized firms without the technical or scientific resources to carry through development work of this kind. In any case few master potters were confident that the concept of the tunnel oven was sound, so there was no disposition to put down money to finance research and development. Some potters were experimentally minded— indeed, two potters, Moore and Campbell, invented and developed an electric decorating kiln for table-ware during the twenties. Development was, however, left mainly in the hands of tunnel-oven builders who, conscious of the size of the development effort and of the conservatism of potters, did not plan a systematic research programme into the problems involved, which is one reason why the key problems emerged only gradually. As the firing of clays whose chemical and physical properties were not fully understood could not be reduced to a science, developments in kilns depended on the kiln-builder finding a potter who was prepared to buy the kiln and share the risks of improvement. There was no great rush from potters to do this. By the end of the twenties, however, kiln design had advanced far enough for an increasing number of potters to be prepared to share the risk. Tunnel-oven development depended also on a chain of other developments—in electrical and gas equipment, in kiln furniture, in insulating bricks—and these developments were 'called forth' slowly.

There seems little doubt that if the pottery industry had been less of a craft industry the development stage in tunnel ovens would have been taken faster. Few master potters took the technical attitude, that if the tunnel oven was based on sound principles it could be made to work. Few took this attitude because few were trained in science or engineering. Equally if the pottery industry had been an expanding industry there would have been more opportunity to try out and develop the new methods without disruption of existing production, and more incentive to suppliers to make a systematic research and development effort.

The Working Party on Pottery reported that between the wars, out of some 200 factories, only seven consistently made a profit in the region of 10 per cent. on turnover. Turnover and capital were approximately equal. For the domestic pottery industry between 1923 and 1938 the average profit on turnover varied between 9 per cent. in 1923 and

1 per cent. in 1931, the mean for the whole period from 1923–38 being 4 per cent.[1] This profit record was a serious impediment to the installation of tunnel ovens. Banks were not prepared to lend except to the few firms with a good profit record, and the majority of firms were not prepared to borrow on terms that endangered family control. There was, moreover, a strong reluctance to put a 'load of debt' on the firm.

In such circumstances, the rate of installation has been conditioned by the quantity of funds accumulated out of ploughed-back profits, and profits were at a very low level between the two World Wars. We have no doubt that higher profits would have hastened the widespread application of tunnel ovens.

But why did not the potential savings over-ride these considerations? Why did not depression give a greater incentive to cut costs? The answer lies partly in an inability to determine what the potential savings were. The form of development was such that kiln-builders could not sell on the basis of specified performance. Further, every potter proudly claims that his own 'body' is different from anybody else's, that he has to adopt different methods to produce his ware. He has accordingly wanted a tunnel oven designed specially to meet real or imputed differences in the product, and has placed little reliance on estimates of performance for his particular model.

Costing systems in three-quarters of the firms visited were poor or non-existent. Consequently, there has been a tendency to talk loosely and inaccurately of the level of savings; and in such circumstances it has been natural to let the fear of committing substantial resources influence notional ideas of savings. For example, in one firm, the chairman weighed up the risks involved against the 'small' savings which a biscuit tunnel oven would show; he firmly decided that he would not be so foolish as to risk his money in so big a gamble for so small a reward. His estimate of savings was simple: 'It hardly saves any fuel'. Yet when a new director instituted costing he found that labour was the major element in firing costs, and that a tunnel oven would reduce operating costs for the process by more than 30 per cent.

Another factor impeding the innovation was the lay-out of factories. Many were on small restricted sites, had grown up piecemeal around bottle ovens, and could not accommodate a tunnel oven without substantial rebuilding and interruption of output. Fear of subsidence damage to long tunnel ovens was another impediment.

The rapid rate of introduction since the war has been partly due to the success of the pre-war installations and to a growing knowledge of the factors making for successful construction and operation. Knowledge of the advantages and operating costs of tunnel kilns was built up in the period before the war. In 1937 the British Pottery Manufacturers Federation issued a book on *Pottery Ovens, Fuels, and Firing*, and a series of

[1] *Working Party Report on Pottery*, H.M.S.O., 1946, pp. 3, 6.

papers were read before the British Ceramic Society describing the experience of pioneer firms with their tunnel ovens. Such publication of the successful outcome of experiments with tunnel ovens was important, for the strength of the craft tradition in the industry meant that suspicion of a new method would disappear only when the firms that took the risk were known to have prospered. Firms that had installed ovens before the war were known to be planning additional installations. This is the sort of information that is persuasive to firms that do not rely on costing, particularly when complemented by Research Association bulletins on the performance of tunnel kilns.

There were three new factors, namely labour shortage, fuel shortage, and high profits. Full employment in Britain and greater diversity of employment in the Potteries has created new attitudes to labour-saving. Scarcity of labour has forced attention on to the tunnel oven as a means of saving labour. Another factor has been the fear that in the new labour situation the supply of stokers and firemen would disappear. The growing shortage of coal, the great rise in its price, and the expectation that there would be new regulations about smoke pollution forced attention to questions of thermal efficiency. During the war and after it profits were high. Money was available from ploughed-back profits to finance the tunnel ovens and the rebuilding that was often involved.

We have not identified any cases of labour (or Trade Union) hostility preventing the adoption of this innovation; but we have found cases in which top management has not had the foresight or the drive to overcome the antipathy of well-entrenched subordinates with a distrust of new methods. This is related to the lack in such firms of an effective intermediate level of management.

The level of taxation seems to have played very little part in determining the rate of installation of tunnel ovens. We have some small amount of evidence indicating that the differential taxation on *distributed* profits has led to an increase in the proportion ploughed back, so tending to hasten application; and that 'initial allowances' and 'investment allowances' have played a marginal role in influencing directors to go ahead with investments.

The rate of installation of tunnel ovens has varied both from section to section of the industry, between firms within the sections, and between processes within firms. Inter-firm variations can be explained by the varying progressiveness of the firms; within sections, the tunnel oven was used by the tile and the electric porcelain sections before the table-ware section. This has led some people in the industry to argue that the strong Trade Associations of the former two sections contributed to technical progress by preventing the 'cut-throat' competition in the table-ware section; but we do not place much emphasis on this argument. The sanitary earthenware section also has a strong Trade Association, but does not seem to have taken a pioneering attitude towards the tunnel oven. The leadership of the glazed tiles section appears to be related more to the nature of its production—a small range of products which lend themselves to techniques of continuous production —than to restrictions on competition; and one tunnel-oven contractor has suggested that the explanation for the leadership of the electric porcelain section is its 'engineering mentality', stimulated by the influence of customers in the electrical engineering industry. Furthermore, the tile and the electric porcelain sections were stimulated respectively by the housing boom and by the increasing consumption of electricity: during the 1930's they were the most prosperous sections of the industry.

The rate of installation of tunnel ovens has varied between processes, so that a high proportion of glost and enamel firing but slightly less than one-half of biscuit firing is now in tunnel ovens. Glost and enamel ovens show a high rate of return on cost, but even a biscuit oven 'pays for itself' in five or six years—when output is high. The slow progress in biscuit firing has to be explained in terms of higher capital cost, fears of inflexibility, and lack of space. As biscuit firing is a much longer process than glost or enamel, the kiln must be substantially longer and more expensive. For the same reason, economies of size are greater up to the maximum efficient size of cross-section. But except in very large firms which have more than one biscuit oven, size makes for inflexibility. A reduction in size of the oven, however, reduces the possibility of fuel economy as compared with intermittent kilns. In a fluctuating industry such as pottery, inflexibility is a considerable handicap; and even where the firm is large enough to overcome the inflexibility, there may be insufficient space for the long biscuit oven, or at any rate insufficient space to make possible a factory layout which would yield the greatest benefits from the tunnel oven. This factor has been important, particularly in the china section of the industry.

The problems of space and inflexibility have led to development work on intermittent electric kilns. Interest in tunnel ovens arose at first from the desire to improve thermal efficiency, but it is now clear that there are also substantial (perhaps greater) economies in the saving of labour and the even heat treatment which the tunnel oven makes possible. These latter economies can now be achieved from electric intermittents. They cost less, and need less space, than the tunnel oven; these are substantial gains to offset against higher running costs. A battery of 10 such ovens costs about £15,000, in comparison with the £35,000 for tunnel ovens with comparable capacity, and they do not have the same supposed inflexibility. Their development has been based on knowledge of heat-treatment painstakingly acquired at full scale during the evolution of the tunnel oven, and on recent improvements in refractories and electric elements.

To sum up: the rate of application of the tunnel oven has been conditioned by the difficulties of developing it to a state at which it would be acceptable to the master potters. Because of the lack of a scientific understanding of pottery processes, these difficulties have been but slowly overcome: because of the limited technical resources available to deal with them, it took a considerable time to identify the critical technical problems. Owing to the primitive costing methods of the industry, the identification of the economic advantages of the ovens was even slower.

At a critical period of the development—the 1930's—the rate of in-installation was retarded by shortage of finance, and by the lack of faith in new methods which one tends to find in old-established industries. These impediments were greatly reduced in the post-war period by the known success of pre-war installations, by the growth of technical knowledge, the labour shortage, and the high demand for pottery.

(b) The cutlery industry

The cutlery industry, as defined in Sheffield, produces table knives, pocket and sheath knives, pruning knives, razors, and scissors—each to a large number of patterns. As defined for Census purposes, cutlery also includes razor blades, table forks, and spoons of steel. The value of output in the 1951 Census was £19,500,000; £12,000,000 if we exclude razor blades. The number employed on Census definitions was just under 15,000. There were 243 firms that employed less than ten, and 165 establishments employing more than ten. Almost 70 per cent. of the workers were in establishments employing less than 500; more than one-half in establishments of less than 200. On the other hand, four establishments larger than 500 employ roughly 30 per cent. of the labour force. If we exclude establishments making safety-razor blades the percentage employed in these large establishments drops by more than one-half.

Many of the firms specialize on a section of the trade such as razors or scissors or pocket-knives, quite often producing them to a fascinating array of patterns; or in different processes such as forging, grinding, hafting, or polishing. Some separation of processes exists in all firms except the few large ones.

There is considerable reliance on handwork. The industry is, of course, 'long established', and it has a strong tradition of quality and craftsmanship. The 'secret in the workman's fingers' has been passed on by the father-to-son method of training. The father-to-son system exists still to some extent, but it has been weakened with the growth of semi-skilled jobs, as increasing use is made of machines and mechanical aids in production. Furthermore, the instability of the industry has led many cutlery workers to direct their sons into other industries. The difficulty in obtaining the right sort of labour has led recently to the introduction of an apprenticeship scheme, which will be discussed below.

In this very competitive and small-scale industry the past still seems to dominate the present. One can stand in a factory and easily envisage conditions 150 years ago, when a factory was little more than a gathering together of a number of craftsmen's workshops. Change, however, has been considerable. New steels and new materials for handles have been used, electricity has largely replaced steam as the motive power, abrasive composition wheels have replaced the old grindstones. Such changes in materials could easily be absorbed in the old methods of production so long as the suppliers provided sufficient technical information. After 1919, however, there were changes that entailed changes in organization and in forms of labour. The forging of table-knife blades on the anvil has been almost entirely replaced by machine forging, and the blades are formed either by the hammer or by rolling; bolsters are shaped hot in dies under the drop-stamp; tangs are drawn and shaped in reciprocating machines; machine-grinding has been brought to a satisfactory standard, though it is not universally used. Much of the heaviest work has been mechanized, and with a simplification of operations the use of machines and mechanical aids has been encouraged.

This change has been limited in scope and intensity. The Working Party on Cutlery spoke of an uneven but distinct advancement in methods of production. The main reason for limited change is that many of the machines involve mechanical imitations of hand operations, and unless products are re-designed to make these 'hand operations' very simple, the machinery does not always reduce costs. Hand polishing and grinding gives a better finish than machinery. Given the traditional forms of design, the number of patterns, and the variability of trade, small workshops or outworkers with very few mechanical aids are able to compete with the more mechanized workshops. Many of the problems in mechanization, however, arise from traditional patterns— for example, in the grinding and glazing of table and dessert knives difficulties arise from the 'habitual practice of forming curved surfaces'. Are these awkward surfaces, and a wide range of patterns, part of fine quality? If so, how much of this fine quality would the market buy when also offered ware, re-designed to suit mechanical processes, at a considerably lower price? The Working Party estimated that the world's markets can absorb 'maybe from 5 to 10 per cent. of fine, 15 to 25 per cent. of middle class, and upwards of 65 per cent. of cheap' cutlery. The British market will absorb a higher proportion of fine and middle quality than will poorer countries. Hitherto a large part of international trade has been in cutlery made from qualities of material lower than that used in Britain. However, low-priced ware need not be made of poor material. If we think of cutlery in terms of quality of material used and of finish, there is almost certainly a large field for mechanized production in the British cutlery industry in both medium quality and in the upper ranges of the lower quality. Mass production for export markets has been developed on the basis of patterns suited for mechanized production; and the products have sold well both at home and abroad.

It is, however, misleading to think just in terms of whether machinery reduces quality or whether it pays only with mass-produced goods. For there are many small factories in which the lay-out is very wasteful of labour, the forging and heat treatment of steel are conducted largely by rule-of-thumb methods, and loss of heat from furnaces is excessive. Improvements here could not reduce quality.

There is a pressure to improve operating efficiency, to increase mechanization, and to find new ways of treating materials. This comes from competition in export markets, from a shortage of labour to perform hand processes, and from large competitors who have given a close attention to cutting costs through standardization, better lay-out, and the development of more efficient machinery. Between 1948 and 1951 the persons employed in the over-500 group went up from 23 to 30 per cent., and the proportion of output produced by the over-500 group rose from 40 to 50 per cent. As these Census figures include safety-razor blades, they overstate the importance of larger firms in the other sections, but even if razor blades are excluded, the trend is quite definite.

But why has change not proceeded faster in this very competitive industry? We will run through the possible explanations.

The first is that we have over-estimated the potentialities of change. Seven firms in our sample of twelve have argued that their market is a quality market, and that further mechanization or standardization would be bad business because it would lead to a fall in quality and sales. This argument about quality does not hold for inefficient lay-out or furnaces; nor does it hold for other than fine-quality producers. Problems of standardization will be considered below.

The second possible explanation is that the conservative craftsmen in the industry impede change. A craftsman proud of his skill may resist the introduction of methods that threaten it. We have not, however, found cases of this. The main case of serious resistance to change was a new process that created an unpleasant smell. The unimportance of worker resistance to change is not surprising, for in the large firms there is less reliance on manual skills, while in small firms it is easy for the management to overcome or avoid resistance, at any rate at a time of labour shortage. Furthermore, more than one-half the labour force are women, many of them only loosely attached to the industry. Of course managers may possess a 'conventional outlook', and so impede change. We have in fact found conservative managers to be more important than conservative craftsmen. Top management posts in family firms are usually filled by family succession. Members of the family are customarily prepared for their jobs by 'experience within the firm'. Family succession without outside experience has bred a parochial approach.

There has recently been a change in the attitude towards higher education, though owners' sons with this education have shown a reluctance to follow their fathers into the firm.

In most small firms there is no management between executive family directors and shop-floor supervision. The latter, in the craft tradition, is usually in the hands of the most able and the most senior craftsman. Such craft foremen are able to advise and supervise the execution of craft practices; but their narrow background makes it difficult for them to comprehend the potentialities of modern management methods and technical practices. Nor is there provision for training courses to overcome these limitations. Under these conditions management has little conception of 'the possible' except in terms of 'the usual'. Absence of costing and of the possibility of comparing costs for like processes in similar firms helps to keep such management prisoners of convention. We have found several cases of 'foreman resistance' to changes in techniques.

We have seen a striking difference between these 'closed' firms and firms which have in management positions men with technical training or management experience outside the industry. We found these 'outsiders' both in new firms and in a few of the family firms. The new firms have shown an attitude to machinery, lay-out, the employment of engineers, and costing, very different from that in the parochial firms. They have, in other words, given close attention to the conditions of operating efficiency. We have also examined four examples of able outsiders introduced into conservative family firms—in one case by a younger member of the family with outside experience. In two cases the outsiders were frustrated by the lack of receptivity on the part of both directors and supervisors and left after a very short period in the firm. In the other two cases technologists were introduced, and made a substantial difference to the technical methods used by the firm.

Many firms are in antiquated buildings which have grown piecemeal over the years. These antiquated buildings cannot easily be adapted to achieve an efficient lay-out of work. Given the low profit margins in the trade and the high cost of new building, these antiquated buildings are an important impediment to operating efficiency. Firms that have managed to improve lay-out and reduce the number of patterns have been able to increase profit margins and plough back money for modernization. The biggest difficulty in the firms with bad buildings is to get started on such a process of improvement.

The next possible explanation is that there are far too few directors or managers with a training in science or engineering. This explanation in part overlaps the second—namely, the deadening effect of the parochial. For if more directors and managers did have such a training there would be fewer parochial firms. There are directors with scientific qualifications who have brought improvements in operating efficiency, but no more so than non-scientific directors in certain other firms. There are not a large number of usable scientific ideas lying round un-exploited simply because there is no one in the industry with any knowledge of science. There are, however, a number of problems that need research or development work for their solution—e.g. methods of forging more accurate blanks, the uses of induction heating, automatic handling or transfer devices, machines that do give fine-quality results. This sort of development does not come simply because a scientist is appointed to the Board. It requires systematic research and development work. Only two or three firms in the industry are large enough to finance any sort of development work.

For machine development the cutlery industry must in large measure rely on machinery manufacturers. The trade relies mainly on two small local engineering firms for supplies of its machinery, and even these are not strictly cutlery specialists. Certain items are available from makers of general machinery in Birmingham.

The Working Party reported that 'the efforts of individual firms are insufficient in themselves to encourage machinery manufacturers to design and produce machines for which the demand may be too small to justify the cost of development, but if the whole industry would join in the effort to discover and try out new methods and principles, machinery manufacturers would doubtless co-operate'. Even where standard machines are produced for certain operations in the cutlery trade, the variation in the type of work done by each firm means that standard machines need adaptation. Where there is a maintenance staff in the firm, minor adaptations can be carried out. But frequently something more than this is needed—particularly if an enterprising cutlery manufacturer has bought a machine used in another industry which seems likely to be useful in the cutlery trade. We have seen three ex-amples of machines lying idle because the purchaser was not able, and the maker not prepared, to adapt them. We have, however, in two firms been shown instances where the manufacturer has had co-operation from machine-makers for adaptation or genuine development. In both these cases the outside firms were not such as would normally be approached by a cutlery firm. They are firms which have a technical sales staff and development departments. Nevertheless, though cutlers would get on better if they had more contacts outside the industry, and if they knew more of the firms that might be interested in their problems, the machine manufacturers are not keen to undertake costly develop-ment on a machine that may only sell one or two.

The structure of the industry, the strong handicraft tradition, the fierce competition when orders are short, have not encouraged a co-operative spirit in the trade. Individual cutlery manufacturers have tended to watch competitors with suspicion and to guard jealously any novel ideas which they thought might assist them to get the better of

P

their competitors. In a small industry this secrecy and lack of co-operation is a great handicap in technical development.

The absence of any considerable degree of mechanization has enabled the industry to continue producing small quantities of a very wide range of shapes and sizes in conformity with the whims of a market which it has accepted as whimsical and which it has not sought substantially to influence. There has recently been some effort by case-firms to reduce the number of patterns in their catalogues; but they find that orders for redundant patterns are then channelled to outworkers who, with virtually no overhead costs to worry about, can readily meet a demand for an odd dozen or two of (hand-made) knives or scissors. Firms that do not calculate the cost of making odd lots find this diversion of orders to outworkers difficult to bear. There is, further, an awkward problem of adjustment for the small firms. For until the activity of the firm is re-organized and equipment is improved there will not be a significant reduction in price (or increase in profit margins), and the loss of orders in the meantime puts a greater strain on the financial resources of the firm. Further, to ensure a good outlet for a smaller range of products, the small firms will need a selling organization, instead of waiting for wholesalers or retailers to place orders for a wide variety of shapes and sizes. These difficulties can be overcome by a change in management methods and outlook; their existence, however, is an impediment to technical change.

We can judge from this brief review the main problems of making full use of science and technology in the cutlery industry. The industry is not based on science, and there is not therefore from the normal processes of higher education a supply of scientists and technologists ready-made for employment in the industry. On the contrary, the industry is craft based, and this, together with the predominance of small units and the parochial nature of the majority of firms, sets barriers to the use of scientists and engineers. The structure of the industry, with its large number of small firms producing a wide variety of products by methods which are often needlessly wasteful of labour and materials, has survived without radical change because there have been no mechanical inventions to transform processes of manufacture—machines have tended to copy hand movements. For the development of more efficient machines and new materials, the industry has relied on suppliers. In machine development the smallness and instability of the industry have not given suppliers an incentive to risk an expensive process of development. There is some evidence that the problems are very similar to those in France, Germany, and Switzerland.

The industry has not, as we have mentioned, remained static. There are now new pressures to change, such as the growing shortage of skilled labour and the competition from a few firms which have used well-known management and technical methods to achieve a large production of a few patterns at a low cost. As these firms are now large enough to employ technologists who can develop or adapt machinery for the special needs of the cutlery trade, the pressure on the smaller firms is likely to increase. A new opportunity of change is now provided by the Cutlery Research Council.

In 1918 there was considerable interest from the cutlery industry in a course of lectures given at the University of Sheffield on the application of science to the industry. Then in 1919 a Research Association was formed under D.S.I.R. This, however, collapsed for lack of support by cutlers.

In 1952 the Cutlery Research Council was formed. This Council is financed jointly by the member firms of the Sheffield Cutlery Manufacturers Association and D.S.I.R. It has two most interesting features. The first is that in an industry noted for its individualism a sufficient membership has been secured by organizing the Research Council through the Trade Association. The second is that this small Research Council, with an income in 1954–5 of £7,180, was relieved of the need to build laboratories by the British Iron and Steel Research Association, which has provided accommodation and access to its laboratories. It has also provided advice in the early stages, and has seconded one of its scientists to become Research Superintendent. Because of this help and technical collaboration with the British Iron and Steel Research Association, the Cutlery Research Council was able very quickly to provide a technical inquiry service and to start its research programme. Without this help a co-operative research association would have been out of the question.

The Council staff have been increasingly consulted by member firms in all fields. They have conducted short-term investigations or development work in measuring devices, forging furnaces, welding, glues, corrosion, and current production difficulties. They have started longer-term work on the properties and heat treatment of stainless steel, die-sinking by the electro-spark method, cutlery edges, and the surface finish produced by mechanical handling process. It is encouraging that the Committees of the Cutlery Council are now changing the emphasis from short-term work to longer-term work.[1]

The Cutlery Research Council is likely to have a two-fold effect in the industry. The industry now has at its disposal a ready source of technical knowledge. This should help to improve methods in a number of ways and to diminish the self-sufficiency of firms. Second, it will be possible for the Research Council to overcome the difficulty of developing new processes or machinery. The Research Council has better outside contacts than the individual manufacturers, and the outside manufacturer may think the prospects of sale are better if a development is sponsored

[1] Department of Scientific and Industrial Research, *Report for the year 1954–55*, Cmd. 9680, H.M.S.O., 1956, pp. 134–5.

by the Research Council; or, as in the case of furnaces and die-sinking, the development may be conducted within the Research Council.

The Research Council does not regard its research and development work as successful unless it is at the point where the man in the works is applying it successfully. This is without doubt the appropriate policy. It necessitates a considerable amount of liaison work with managers and workers—liaison work which is useful in getting a trial (and, if successful, an acceptance) of new methods, and in giving the research staff a keen insight into production problems and possibilities. For this liaison work the concentration of the industry is a great advantage.

It is too soon to judge the impact of the Cutlery Research Council, just as it is too soon to judge the effect of the Cutlery Apprenticeship Scheme, which was started in 1955. The old indentured apprentice system has largely disappeared, and both in the interests of recruitment and of labour efficiency a new scheme was needed to give training in engineering and production planning. The new scheme has the assistance and approval of the Trade Unions and the Ministries of Labour and Education. There is provision for indenture in the case of craftsmen, and for technical and general training, on day-release schemes, through the local College of Technology, and there is provision also for works visits during the period of training.

From the standpoint of applying science, the need to raise the educational level of the workers in the cutlery trade is great. This apprenticeship scheme, so long as it attracts a sufficient number of apprentices, should be of great benefit to the industry. With the industry developing on new lines, new skills that require technical training, and not simply a father-to-son craft training, are needed.

(c) The jute industry

The manufacture of jute was introduced into Dundee in 1822, when the fibre was processed on the existing flax machinery. The industry rapidly expanded up to the end of the nineteenth century, when competition from India began to make itself felt. The industry processes the fibre into yarn or cloth or finished goods such as bags. Because of its dependence since earliest days on the use of machines, the possibilities of technical change are rather different from those which occur in industries such as pottery or cutlery, where many of the processes are performed by hand. However, with minor exceptions, the methods of production, and indeed the whole outlook of the jute industry, underwent very little change in the period from the beginning of the century until the mid-1930's and, in particular, until the decade after the 1939–45 war. In the past ten years there has been considerable change in machinery and in management methods.

At the outbreak of the 1939–45 war the industry had an abundant labour supply in Dundee, where the bulk of the mills were situated.

It was composed in the main of a large number of small firms (which is also true today, in spite of certain amalgamations which have taken place since the war), and there was a wide variety in the number of spindles and looms in the different establishments. It had suffered heavily between the wars from the effects of the general depression and the intense competition from Indian manufactured jute goods, with resultant reduction in output and heavy unemployment.

Although a mechanized industry, in many respects it resembled a craft industry, with its reliance on traditional ways of doing things. The pattern was still one of a large number of operatives looking after machines within the traditional manager–foreman–operative framework. Ownership and management of firms were predominantly by families, and experience was acquired only within the trade. Managers and supervisory staff were also recruited from within and qualified by their mill or factory experience. Apart from certain arrangements within individual firms for the training of spinners and weavers, there were few educational facilities available to the trade. In one or two of the larger firms research facilities (mainly for routine testing) were established, but in the main attention was concentrated on survival within the existing framework of the industry.

There had been some change in machinery before 1939. The first significant developments available to the industry were High-speed Rove Spinning in 1929 and Sliver Spinning in about 1935. At that time the industry was using a great deal of very old machinery, and with certain exceptions there had been little attempt to do anything more than essential replacement. In spite of the low profits [1] and the general attitude to change, the pressure to reduce costs led to a certain amount of re-equipment on the spinning side just before the war. By 1939, 39 per cent. of the spindles in the industry were of the high-speed type, and a certain amount of new preparing and other ancillary machinery had been installed.

Nevertheless, it remained a largely traditional industry. The Working Party reviewing the industry just after the war advocated its re-grouping followed by substantial re-equipment. It argued that this could be done only if the industry was given an assurance that when necessary it would be afforded protection against low-priced Indian goods. The Working Party estimated that when the immediate post-war plans for re-equipment were completed it would be possible for the industry to

---

[1] Annual average profits as a percentage of capital employed, valuing plant and buildings at book values: based on figures for the years 1934–8 supplied to the Working Party by 38 producers:

Spinners	6·32 per cent.
Weavers	4·14 ,,
Spinners/Weavers . . .	2·70 ,,
All Producers	3·48 ,,

(*Working Party Report on Jute*, H.M.S.O., 1948)

have an output of yarn and cloth equivalent to approximately 94 and 81 per cent. of 1936 levels with about half the labour force. The nature of pre-war production had also acted against standardization of products—through the desire to stimulate demand in the home market for cloths in different weights and widths from the normal run of Calcutta cloths. The introduction of quality standards had received little thought, for the intense competition between manufacturers in pre-war days made price, and not quality, the main consideration of both buyers and sellers. Though the industry was faced with the problem of survival, the existing pattern of management and management training was not changed. The firms in the industry tended to operate in small watertight compartments, and there was little knowledge of modern standards of production efficiency.

During the war there were two major concentrations of the industry, resulting in greatly reduced capacity, and a good deal of the labour force left the area. As a wartime measure the Jute Control was established to exercise control over the distribution and use in the U.K. of raw jute and the products made from it. In July 1942 it also became the sole importer of raw jute and jute goods.

Since 1945 the industry has changed considerably. There have been certain pressures to progress. First, there has been a striking alteration in the labour-supply position. Many jute workers left Dundee during the war and did not return. Dundee was designated a Development Area, and the 'folk-memory' of conditions in the inter-war years has inhibited labour recruitment to the jute trade. There were in Dundee 13,911 insured workers in spinning and weaving in 1951, as compared with 26,172 in 1939.

Second, the continued operation of the Jute Control has, in conjunction with other pressures at work, helped forward a revival. Acting as the sole importer of jute goods, the Government undertook to import only that volume of goods necessary to bridge the gap between home demand and home production, provided the industry was efficient. These imported goods are sold at a price related to the cost of raw jute and to the U.K. conversion costs based on the trading results of a cross-section of the industry. This measure of protection provided a welcome relief from the difficulties experienced in the inter-war years and gave some degree of confidence and security to the trade. As prices were related to average conversion costs in a sample of the more efficient firms, there was an incentive to most firms to seek out more efficient methods of manufacture and management. Additionally, in ensuring a market for products, the Jute Control assisted the industry in getting together the necessary funds for re-equipment. The position of the Jute Control, until 1954, as the sole importer of raw jute was important in the early post-war days. Individual companies might have operated just as profitably in buying raw jute, but this would often have tied up large sums of money in stocks of the raw material—as at present. The capital thus freed was, therefore, available for the purchase of new plant. There has not been, however, any certainty as to how long such a measure of protection might last. This has encouraged the majority of firms to undertake technical change, so that they will be in a better position to face whatever the future may bring forth.

Third, there has been a change of outlook in this hitherto conservative and somewhat parochial industry. Those inside the trade have attributed the new spirit to a variety of causes—in particular to a 'change in generation'. A large number of owners of works are in the 30–40 age group, or even younger. But generations have changed before. A change of generation as such cannot explain the new spirit. Another explanation is that members of the industry have ceased to be so secretive and insular. This is attributed to the effects of the wartime policy of concentration, the working of the Jute Control, and the institution after the war of a co-operative Research Association. It seems likely that the alteration in outlook has been due to a combination of these circumstances at a time of labour shortage.

Finally, there has been a pressure to progress from the requirements of customers. The demands by some of the industry's large customers that products such as bags should conform to certain specifications has contributed towards the greater interest in quality control. Certain new uses for jute cloth have necessitated the purchase of new plant—for example, jute cloth used as a base for tufted carpets requires especially wide looms.

The change which has occurred since the war can be put into two broad categories—*technical change* and *change in management techniques*.

The most important single item of change has been the large-scale re-equipment and re-organization of the mills and factories. Between 1945 and 1955 £7½ million was spent, and there were in addition outstanding commitments in 1955 of over £2 million. A high proportion of this was devoted to new machinery for the spinning mills, electrification and improvement of lay-outs. About 95 per cent. of the spindles in use in the industry are now of the high-speed type, and there has been widespread installation of ancillary machinery. In some cases re-equipment has been completed, in others there are plans for a few years to come, involving a certain amount of change in each year. At present about 30 per cent. of the looms have been fitted with cop-loaders (which can be fitted to ordinary flat looms, enabling the shuttles to be replenished without stopping the loom), and at least five concerns have special weaving sections equipped with circular looms.

This re-equipment has been closely related to the availability of modern machinery. The two significant developments in the actual spinning process were available before the war, and before 1939 and since that date there have been additional developments in preparing and other ancillary spinning machinery. The developments on the weaving side have come later: the Saint Frères circular loom was introduced into this country in 1950, and the first of the automatic cop-loading devices appeared in the U.K. in 1949. In bag-sewing, developments have been of a more evolutionary character. The concentration on the spinning side of the industry has been largely due to the fact that new machinery was available for this section before it was available in the weaving section, and not to questions of relative profits or ease of application. For better machinery the jute industry relies wholly on machinery manufacturers. Sliver Spinning was first developed in the U.S.A. and the idea of the Good's Spreader also came in the first place from there. Both the significant developments in weaving had their origins on the Continent. The Saint Frères loom is being produced under licence in this country, and the cop-loaders have been further developed by machinery-makers. British machinery-makers have also developed certain new machines—for example, the Roll Former. However, though the jute industry simply adopts new machines, individual jute firms have themselves introduced improvements, such as ways of making possible the processing of longer lengths, while job evaluation and re-deployment of labour have led to increased output from machines.

The production of jute-spinning machinery is largely confined to four firms—supplying both the home and overseas markets. The bulk of the new spinning frames have been supplied by two firms, both of whom had experimental mills, though one of these is no longer in operation. Loom production is mainly in the hands of three firms, and these firms with another have also been responsible for producing most of the devices for making flat looms automatic and for supplying items such as bag-printing machines. Significant new items of equipment have been made under licence or have originated in other countries. In the post-war period, however, there has been a new competitive situation and an urge to be in the forefront. Machinery-makers, partly due to other work undertaken during the war, have devoted greater attention to development work. There has also been an improvement of their production facilities. In one case managers who have had a good deal of engineering experience outside the trade have been appointed. In certain of the larger jute firms there is greater willingness to co-operate with the machinery makers in the provision of facilities for trying out new devices and new machines under mill conditions, and in at least two instances manufacturers have shared the cost of a licence in order to expedite development work, and to ensure first deliveries to themselves of the new machines. Now, recognizing that most of the means of saving labour have been exploited, one machinery-maker has invented a method by which a long-established process can be altered to make possible the use of a lower quality jute, and yet not to give an inferior product.

The British Jute Trade Research Association was established in 1946. Prior to this the only opportunities for research were in two of the larger firms which had set up research departments in the inter-war period. They were originally for testing, but later their scope was widened. To-day, with the exception of these firms, the Research Association is still almost the sole source of scientific information which is used by the industry. Membership of the Association covers 97 per cent. of the producing industry, and its income for the year 1954–5 was £44,869.[1] While certain of the activities of the Research Association are directed to basic research which may not have any immediate practical outlet, other work, such as that on the finishing side of the process and on quality control, has an immediate bearing. Increasing use is being made of the Private Enquiry Service, by which members submit particular problems to the Association—only nineteen members out of 160 have not at some time participated in this service. At the request of various sections of the trade, the Research Association carries out on their behalf surveys of quality levels. This has stimulated interest in the use of better methods of quality control in manufacturing processes. The Research Association trains people from the smaller firms in the techniques of statistical quality control and advises on the setting up of control sections. In *all* the companies visited such control sections have been established—in most cases at the suggestion of and under the guidance of the Research Association, and manned by 'likely people in the works' who have been trained by the Association. Without exception, the case-studies have indicated widespread appreciation of these services of the Research Association. There is criticism that the Research Association does not do more technological development work, but it cannot cover all problems in ten years.

Parallel with the installation of new machinery, work study has been undertaken and there has been re-deployment of labour on a considerable scale. In an industry undertaking a programme of modernization designed, at any rate in part, to overcome an acute labour shortage, re-deployment of labour is to be expected. It is, nevertheless, surprising that the employment of industrial consultants has become almost a commonplace throughout an industry where the tradition has long been one of conservatism on the part of both employers and employees. Consultants have been used mainly to measure work and to recommend how machinery should be manned, though they have on occasions advised on the turn-round of machinery and on aspects of management reorganization. The jute industry was the first in Britain to introduce in 1952 a new wage structure based on job evaluation. Work to be applied under this must be studied by a competent Work Study officer or industrial consultant. The introduction of the scheme has been encouraged jointly by the Association of Jute Spinners and Manufacturers

[1] Cmd. 9680, H.M.S.O., 1956, p. 167.

and the textile trade unions. A Works Study Advisory Officer was appointed to operate the wage structure advisory service, and between 60 and 80 per cent. of the firms now use the system in varying degrees.

A firm of chartered accountants which worked for the industry as a whole during the wartime operation of the Jute Control had the idea of attempting to introduce uniform costing methods throughout the trade, in order to make it possible to compare figures for individual firms in the industry. No such universal scheme is yet possible, but most of the firms visited have adopted or are in the process of introducing some system of standard costing. In almost all cases this firm of accountants has been employed privately by the individual companies and has installed the system and trained staff members to operate it.

There has been a limited amount of change in the qualifications for senior and other managerial positions. Family firms predominate, and the most usual qualification of the owners of firms is 'experience of the trade'. The majority have entered the family business straight from school and subsequently acquired experience in the different aspects of the trade. The proportion of directors who have been technically or scientifically trained outside the industry is very small, but the proportion of the 'coming generation' is higher. Where additions have been made from outside the family there has been some attempt to introduce specialists in engineering or accountancy, though it has been suggested that this might not have occurred if members of the family of appropriate age had been available.

On the production management side there has not been in the past any tradition of technical training. The most usual qualification for a mill or factory manager is an 'engineering background'—he has been either apprentice-trained or experienced as a mechanic in the industry; though in certain cases his only qualification is simply general experience in some aspect of the trade. In some firms there was before the war a tendency for directors to carry out the detailed supervision of work— a tendency which left insufficient time and energy for the creation of more efficient methods of production. Now, directors are coming to appreciate the need to plan, to take an overall view, and to leave detailed supervision of work to lower management.

The introduction of new techniques and management methods requires a new type of manager. Some firms have not yet realized this, though there is now a definite tendency to select a different type of man —not a man with a different educational level or industrial experience, but one likely to be keen on the application of new ideas. Many firms in the trade are making use of management courses; in this connexion the Association of Jute Spinners and Manufacturers has been important in arranging such courses and in bringing others—external to the trade—to the notice of firms.

The manager–foreman–operative type of management framework

referred to earlier has undergone considerable change. There is no longer a surplus of labour and top management is attempting to make change normal. Because of this the traditional function of the foreman has become inappropriate: he is no longer required to supervise work of a standard type for which discipline can be easily enforced, but instead to appreciate and welcome new methods and to lead the operatives towards a smooth introduction of them. Since the war there has been a marked alteration in attitude to the importance of foremen. A great deal of interest is being shown in the training of such people. They are encouraged to attend training courses—both inside and outside the trade —and many firms have instituted a system of weekly or monthly discussion meetings for all foremen. Worker training, too, is receiving greater attention—in particular, that for weavers, who are in short supply.

One other aspect of the industry has received consideration in this period—the improvement of working conditions. About two-thirds of the spinning and weaving establishments have by now appointed someone in the capacity of personnel officer, though only four of these individuals are fully qualified.

Pressures to progress have been operating in the industry and considerable change has occurred. What have been the impediments to change?

Although Sliver Spinning machinery offers advantages which have acted as a stimulus to its installation in many mills, it has other aspects which have brought problems. In many cases it is considered necessary to have double-shift working: first, because the new equipment has a higher output, but takes up more space; production per square foot per hour has in fact decreased, and since the majority of mills have no room for immediate expansion, hours worked must be increased in order to maintain the same volume of output. Second, the need to recoup the relatively high depreciation costs of the new equipment is an added incentive to double-shift working. Where new type spinning machinery has been installed it has not always been possible to get sufficient workers to operate the two shifts, and so only one by day and a part of the night shift can be worked. We are told that in these circumstances it has not been possible to cover depreciation costs. Nevertheless, a system of double day-shifts is operating in many mills, and today approximately half the yarn spun and a quarter of the cloth woven is produced on shift systems. The position has been helped by the willingness of married women to work an evening shift. Recruitment of workers is improving. There is, too, a recognition of the advantages which re-equipment offers to both sides of the industry and of the fact that shift working, particularly in the spinning section, is a necessary concomitant of such re-equipment. In January 1956 just over one-third of the spindles of all types were operating on more than one shift.

The amount of modernization and re-equipment undertaken in any one period has in many cases been related to the amount of money available. More retained profit is available for investment than before the war, but there is a reluctance—in an industry of family firms—to seek financial assistance which would result in a loss of independence. Many of the buildings in the industry are old and many-storeyed so that, despite reorganization, it is often difficult to ensure the most efficient use of new machinery. On the other hand—and several references to this have been made in the case-studies—it would be impossible to scrap existing buildings (often in older parts of the city) and to build a completely new mill or factory, and still cover costs out of existing profit margins.

A general state of technical progressiveness calls for attention to other things besides new machinery. The inability to evaluate and develop some of the work of the Research Association, which follows from the great scarcity of scientists in the industry, represents a delaying factor, and as yet little has been done to make good this deficiency. There are the few firms which already employ scientific staff, but the general attitude is still one which regards such personnel as something of a luxury—a luxury which some of the smaller firms (who are beginning to realize this need) claim that they cannot afford. The interest being shown by some firms in junior qualifications in chemistry, obtainable through attendance at the local Technical College, is a first step in the right direction. The head of the Textile Department at Dundee Technical College has spoken of the expansion in this department 'to meet the present day demands of the industry', but has also indicated that wastage in evening classes is very high.

The general change which is taking place in the industry has brought with it a realization of the need for a different type of person to fill the management roles, and in some cases such people have been selected. However, it is rarely possible to make 'a clean sweep', and in some firms it has been found that the existing managers are stumbling-blocks to the introduction of new management and other techniques. The change which has occurred has been effected without any substantial alteration in the qualifications of personnel holding management and other positions in the industry. Nevertheless it does seem that there would be benefits to the trade from a recruitment of more 'trained minds' for such roles.

Worker resistance has not been observed to be a real impediment to the undertaking of the necessary change, though there are instances where some resistance has been shown—for example, in the unwillingness to work shifts. On the whole, the reaction of the workers to schemes such as work study has been favourable, though more than one proprietor has stated that his company has had few applications of work measurement or of motion study which have been instantly and enthusiastically accepted by those concerned. In the long run, however, most of the schemes put forward have been accepted and operated with success. A feature of the industry which has probably helped forward change is the history of extremely good relations between the local textile trade unions and the jute manufacturers.

Since the war production has reached 75 per cent. of the pre-war level, although the labour force has fallen by about one-half. Such change has been due to several factors. First, the machine-makers have supplied labour-saving machinery. Though the jute industry is small, it is supplied by competent machine-makers who specialize in machinery for the jute, flax, hemp, and hard-fibre trades. As many of the problems of machinery development in the processing of these fibres are common, the machine-makers have a much wider market than is provided by the jute industry. In addition, to augment the resources of British machine-makers, overseas developments in jute machinery have been available.

Second, since the war a new situation has been facing the industry. This has been created by the labour shortage, by the availability of new machines (some of which had been proved before the war), by the existence of a measure of protection, and by the improved profit outlook as compared with that in the 1930's.

This new situation has been used as a reason for the introduction of technical and management changes. An important influence has been the change in attitude in the industry—the reasons for which are not certain, but it is clearly associated with the breakdown of insularity or 'parochialism'. For example, in the case of one small firm which has played a leading part in foreman training, the impetus to introduce management techniques new to the industry sprang from the engagement at staff level of an individual with experience in a large organization in the light engineering industry where scientific management was practised to a high degree.

Third, the advent of the Research Association in 1946 has to some extent offset the shortage of scientists and technologists in the industry, though the overall shortage does affect the extent to which use can be made of the work of the Research Association.

It is easy for a highly localized industry to be insular. However, once change has started such concentration then makes it easier for change to become widespread.

(d) The paper industry

Until the end of the eighteenth century all paper was hand made. Paper machines were devised and developed early in the nineteenth century, and by 1825 about one-half of British output was machine made. When the supply of rags for paper-making proved insufficient wood pulp and esparto were introduced. During the first half of the nineteenth century Britain made many improvements in paper-making, drying, and finishing machinery. These technical changes in raw materials and in processing were empirical, and the dependence of the industry on the rule-of-thumb methods of craftsmen remained. In these conditions the management structure was quite simple—in small firms the managing director performed the commercial and co-ordinating functions, and the mill foreman managed the technical side. In larger firms there was division of labour in the management of finance, selling, and production. The mill manager developed considerable autonomy and the 'paper-maker'—a craftsman with many years experience of paper-making—gave him technical advice.

There was little scientific understanding of the materials used or of the changes that took place in them during processing. The dependence on 'paper-makers' who had learned empirically what to do and what not to do within the established framework of materials and machines was a conservative force. Change was gradual—unless it was brought in from outside or was fortuitous. Fortuitous change was the basis of Kraft paper, which has done a great deal to increase demand for paper. Wood pulp destined for bleaching was being cooked in a Swedish mill; the time-keeping went wrong, the cooking was stopped too soon, and the pulp could not be bleached. In the hope that the whole lot might not be wasted, that it might just possibly make a cheap wrapping-paper, the obstinately brown pulp was put through the paper-making machine —and the product was found to be stronger than any paper previously known!

In the last twenty or thirty years, however, the paper industry has made many changes in methods of production that go beyond the gradual and the fortuitous. The change has not affected all firms equally, which is not surprising in an industry made up of a few giants and many small firms. Of the 180 paper-making firms in Britain, the four largest are, judged by asset size in 1953-4, among the 100 largest public companies in Britain, and they produce one-half the output of paper. Some of their large mills are nearly automatic, while in many small firms producing specialist or ordinary papers batch production and rather old-fashioned methods are still used. In a brief account of the change of paper-making from an art to a science, we are therefore forced to simplify a very complex pixture.

What factors have touched off this technical change? What explains the differing degrees of technical progressiveness?

The market for paper has been expanding as the consumption of paper increases with national income per head in industrial countries. In an expanding economy, therefore, the prospects for paper look good. During the inter-war years the industry's difficulties in meeting competition from imported papers were relieved by the imposition of the McKenna duties (1926). The growing use of paper for packaging, and in particular the production of Kraft paper from 1927 onwards, created considerable new demands. Production of paper and board other than newsprint rose from 1,395,000 tons in 1935 to 1,831,000 tons in 1939, and to 2,467,000 tons in 1954. Newsprint production fell from 857,000 tons in 1935 to 800,000 in 1939, and to 612,000 in 1954. The post-war figure is explained by currency restrictions on the purchase of pulp and control of the size of newspapers.

The change in technical methods was initiated by the larger organizations, which had developed from an amalgamation of smaller concerns during the first twenty years of this century. During this period the British industry was stimulated by the high standard of technical performance set by some American and European paper-making firms. Before the war output per man hour in paper and paper-board mills was three times higher in American than in British mills. The McKenna duties gave a barrier behind which the industry could improve its efficiency.

Improvement in output per man hour required improvements in machine speeds. High machine speeds are easier to achieve in Canada, Sweden, and the U.S.A., where pulp and paper mills are integrated. For pulp varies with the source of supply and alters in properties when dried and baled. In Britain improvements in machine speeds required improvements in machines, but also a closer control over the raw materials, and this required a scientific analysis and understanding of the raw materials.

After the First World War there was a wide growth of interest in the application of scientific work—at a time when the output of scientists from universities first became sufficient for the staffing of industrial laboratories. A few directors in the paper industry were influenced by this outlook. The employment of scientists in the industry has made possible great changes in methods. Thus, although the effects of the beating process on the fibres of the pulp are not completely understood, enough is known to enable the beating process to be brought under reasonably satisfactory scientific control. The distribution of the fibres on the paper-machine wire in the drying process are being subjected to control by electronic devices. The acidity of the pulp suspension can be recorded and controlled at different points in the process, and beta-ray apparatus is applied to measuring the weight per unit area of the paper and its thickness during manufacture. These are just a few examples of the scientific controls which are now being applied in paper manufacture.

There have also been improvements in machinery. The width of new newsprint machines, for instance, has been increased from 100 inches to the present normal of 272 inches, which is regarded as the economic optimum. Speeds of other types of machine have been increased: one new machine will produce at 1,000 feet per minute paper made now on a 350 feet-per-minute machine. Associated with greater understanding and control of the raw materials and more skilled engineering services there has also been a speeding up of old machines.

These changes did not simply result from the appointment of scientists or engineers to find out how raw materials could be controlled and machines run faster and then to pass on the information to old-style mill managers and paper-makers. The changes required also that scientists and engineers be absorbed into management—to provide a new outlook and a new balance of skills in the management complex. But this new management was not built up without tensions between the old and the new; nor has it been built up everywhere.

One large group of firms which has been through the process of creating the new form of management has found that there are three main advantages in using science or engineering graduates in management positions.

1. In paper mills it has not been possible to try out ideas except at full scale—experiments successfully completed on small slow machines can be vitiated by unforeseen difficulties arising when they are applied on large fast machines. It is thus essential to have co-operation between production and technical departments; and it is only the new type of production supervisors who can appreciate what is involved in the experiments, and who readily and helpfully co-operate in this.

2. As managers they are willing to accept changes in method, and they are able to join in objective discussions of what will be involved. On the other hand, the traditional type of production manager, who has learned from experience what to do and what to avoid without understanding why, tends to interpret a suggestion of change as a reflection on his abilities, knowledge, and experience; this is apt to put him on the defensive and to make objective discussion difficult. Such a manager can also wreck the application of a new project. We have been quoted specific examples of projects successfully applied at other factories, which 'traditional' supervisors have not wanted to see installed in their own departments; they have—no doubt unconsciously—magnified inevitable teething troubles, and have been so unable or so unready to see the necessary steps to overcome those troubles that a barrier has been created against the successful adoption of the ideas, which have had to be withdrawn.

3. The new type of manager is able to make constructive suggestions for experiments which would never have occurred to his predecessor.

An example of the effect of the differing approaches of the two types of management is provided by change in a firm recently taken over by a large group of companies. Previously the Board of the firm had little technical knowledge. They had, however, appointed a graduate scientist to control a technical department and a graduate engineer to the engineering department. The new Board appointed a paper technologist as general manager, but otherwise there were no immediate changes in the structure and personnel of the firm, though engineers from the parent firm came in to advise. There has been a marked technical awakening. For example, two machines had been run for many years at 300 feet per minute, and this was accepted as the normal (maximum) speed, although, as staff from the new parent company saw, considerable increases could be achieved without any significant alteration to equipment. To enable technical staff to adjust the pulp preparation and operatives to develop greater manual dexterity, speeds were increased by steps up to 430. After a relatively small adjustment to the design of the approach flow speeds of 500 will be possible, though the maintenance of such speed would require changes in the after-processing and despatch departments. The new management also gave greater attention to the work and recommendations of the technically trained men already in the firm. The chief chemist who remarked that 'we always felt we were banging our heads against a brick wall' now found it possible to get equipment urgently needed for his work, and found that many significant problems were now sent to him by the new management.

The assimilation of scientists into the industry has been a protracted process, but it has gone a long way in the large firms. Some of the small firms have yet to start on it; and between these extremes there is a wide variation in achievement. The problem can best be explained by considering the process of absorption in three different types of firm, which, to avoid disclosure of confidential information, have been constructed from a number of typical firms in each class.

The large firm, possibly without a conscious realization of the consequences of its action, began to employ graduate technologists by 1930 to start a scientific control section.

Until the outbreak of the war, these scientists had little responsibility. In the mills the dominant role was taken by the local mill manager, who had a well-entrenched autonomy and who tended to rely for advice on the 'paper-maker', usually a craftsman with many years' experience of paper-making, relying on his 'feel' of paper to enable him to give his manager technical advice. To these people a suggestion of technical change appeared as a reflection on their abilities, knowledge, experience; they were not receptive to new ideas. 'Top management' was generally no more co-operative. Most of the directors had experience of the sales side of the organization, but none of production, still less of the new-fangled technical sections. Several of the newly recruited scientists would have left the industry had there not been a depression and a poor market for their abilities at that time.

Q

The absorption of the scientists and engineers came about in a number of ways. Scientists in the 'technical sections' gradually built up sufficient knowledge of processes to make possible scientific controls. The opportunity to get this knowledge used was given by decisions to expand output. Such decisions necessarily take a firm out of its routine approach, and did in fact give an opportunity to get new capacity planned on a different basis. The new capacity then required men with new skills for its operation and created openings for some of the scientists and engineers in management positions. This is turn gave the scientists in the technical department a greater opportunity to get their ideas used and to get co-operation in the formulation of research problems and their subsequent trial. The successful trial led to new techniques, which for their operation required more technically trained people. Now twenty to thirty years after the start of the process, people with a technical training (or an appreciation of the technology of the industry) are in key management positions in production, the mill chemist has succeeded the 'paper-maker' as the local authority on techniques of paper-making, research into processes and new products and their development is becoming a management technique with the gradual creation of an appropriate co-ordination between the technical, production, and sales departments of the firm.

In the second 'firm' there was a change of directors just before the war, after a period of financial losses. The new managing director is a science graduate. American and Scandinavian techniques and types of paper were carefully studied, and those thought most suited to British conditions and to the capital strength of the firm were introduced. This led to a marked change in type of output. The firm in this case was small enough for the managing director to initiate and supervise the change. Initiation and supervision involved significant changes in salaried staff. A graduate chemist was appointed to institute quality control and to scour the literature for usable ideas. Engineering graduates were brought in to control and adapt new preparation and paper machines. The change to new methods of production was rapid, for the new managing director first decided what higher technical functions were needed and then provided them. Both the absorption of scientists and the technical transformation has been rapid. The problem has been kept relatively simple, however, for the firm is 'voluntarily adoptive' (p. 109). Overseas licences are used freely as a cheap substitute for organized research and development.

The third 'firm', a small specialist company, is run by full-time directors who have achieved their position through the process of family succession; they have not had any wide education or experience outside the confines of their particular firm; they have not changed their capacity and types of paper—specialized products not competitive with those of the large group; tariffs are for them a barrier behind which they can continue with traditional methods, sheltered from competition. They employ a 'chemist', but he lacks the experience and the personality needed to bring about the changes which have taken place in the large firm. The 'technologist' in this firm is a traditional craftsman, very skilful in handling paper, but with deep-rooted ideas about paper-making, and no ideas of experimenting.

In drawing attention to the importance of the new type of management, we have emphasized the importance of engineers and scientists; but it must not be thought that these technical qualifications are essential in all roles. In several case-studies there are examples of people without a formal technical education, but with considerable drive and a wide range of vision, who have inspired and encouraged their technical colleagues. Significantly, many of these non-technical leaders had education and experience outside the industry.

Our case-studies do not reveal any significant labour restrictionism, either personal or union-inspired. There have been certain minor difficulties: for example, in the case previously described, where machine-speeds were substantially increased, the change took place piecemeal over a period of three months, partly in order to allow operatives gradually to improve their dexterity, but also in order to mollify the natural psychological reaction of people who for years had accepted a slow rate as normal.

In the larger firms we have not found evidence that technical progressiveness is prevented by shortage of finance. We have, however, noticed two cases of smaller firms which were unable to raise sufficient capital to modernize equipment or to introduce a new speciality paper. A new machine used to make high-grade papers might cost $£\frac{1}{2}$ million, and the working capital needed might be more. That the larger firms are in a better position to raise sums of this size is part of the explanation of their policy of buying-up smaller firms; the other part being the possibility in some cases of getting increases in output of up to 50 per cent. without new equipment.

Despite high profit levels and the ploughing-back of a substantial proportion of available profits, the large firms have been forced to raise additional finance on the Stock Exchange. This is illustrated by an analysis of the accounts of one large group over the period 1945–55. Their total investment programme in the period amounted to some £19 million, raised as follows:

From ploughed-back profits	£6,700,000
From issue of Debentures, Loans, and Share Capital .	11,400,000
From other sources	900,000
	£19,000,000

In the same period £3,200,000 was distributed to shareholders of Ordinary Stock, and £12,000,000 was absorbed by taxation. So far, since the war, the big firms have had no great difficulty in raising the required new capital.

There is general agreement among paper-making firms which we have studied that American paper machines run considerably faster than British ones. The fastest newsprint machine in the U.K. runs at about 1,500 feet per minute, as against 2,000 in the U.S.A.; and an American paper machine makes toilet-paper at 3,000 feet per minute, the corresponding British speed being about 1,000; the paper for popular magazines is made at 1,200, corresponding British paper at about 650 feet per minute.

Various factors are said to be responsible for the difference. First, almost all the pulp used in this country is imported; as we have noted, when received at mills the characteristics of the pulp are not consistent. North American and Scandinavian firms with integrated pulp and paper mills do not have to face this problem. This affects the newsprint industry, though the specialist producers requiring small quantities of special pulps are not affected.

Second, it is said that larger American markets and greater standardization of production enable manufacturers in the U.S.A. to run continuously on one type of paper; British machines have to be more versatile, and are therefore slower. This argument should be treated with reserve, since it is clear that a number of firms produce a wider range of outputs than they would if they possessed a costing department and a widespread selling organization. We have examined changes in a number of firms taken over by large organizations. In almost all cases there has been either a change in the products produced or a reduction in the range of products. A director in one firm involved in creating greater specialization within firms in his group remarked that excepting paper for the well-known American periodicals and magazines which have a country-wide distribution, 'this argument about the size of market is not entirely valid. The American market is fragmented by geographical considerations which are just as important as the tariff considerations between countries. The West Coast of America with a population of something like 15,000,000 is economically independent from the rest of the States, and yet its paper industry is one of the most highly developed in the world. The potential market in this country is many times that of the West Coast of America in absolute figures at the present time.'

Third, there is said, by widely travelled 'paper men', to be a greater readiness in the U.S.A. to scrap obsolescent machines and to experiment with new ones. Paper machinery is expensive. A relatively small machine to make high-grade papers might cost £$\frac{1}{2}$ million; larger machines over £1 million. This is apart from plant for pulp preparation. No manufacturer would be keen to scrap it. There is often, however, an opportunity to modernize it, and those manufacturers who are parochial, or who lack the statistics on cost that enable them to judge when it is worth their while to scrap and modernize sections of the plant, often hang on to their nineteenth-century machines on a repair and maintenance basis. One important factor is that a machine with a speed or width significantly less than that of new machinery may be quite satisfactory if transferred from newsprint to magazine paper or from magazine paper to speciality paper. The opportunity for this type of transfer must have been greater in the U.S.A., where the annual production of paper and paper board increased from 2 million short tons in 1900 to the present level of 30 million tons. The British paper industry produces just over 3 million tons per year.

Fourth, machine development for this industry conforms to the pattern of design and development of expensive one-off products. That is to say, research is a background activity, generally dependent on complementary firms working on metallurgical research, problems of casting large-diameter cylinders, and so on. This research serves as background material for the designer who plans new machines. The new machine must be built at full scale without pilot-scale trials, since it is technically impossible to build models reproducing the characteristics of large fast machines. It follows that effective development depends on a collaboration between the paper-maker and the machine manufacturer. Unless both are technically progressive the new machines will not embody great improvements. The technical awakening in paper firms has come about only in the last twenty to thirty years—later than in the U.S.A. Collaboration between paper firms and machinery-makers has improved since the war with a decline of secrecy in mills. Finally, the much larger U.S.A. output makes possible the existence of several highly competitive machinery manufacturers, and the design and development effort is inevitably much greater.

In scientific development, as well as in engineering, the American industry has acquired a lead over the British, which is reflected in the number of licence agreements being made for British firms to adopt American developments. Part of these licence agreements cover special papers ('luxuries') which came first in the U.S.A. simply because of their higher level of income per head. By the time income was high enough here for a market to develop the Americans had the 'know-how' and the strategic patents. However, this does not explain the whole of the lead.

Licence agreements enable British producers to use these developments and to raise the level of performance here. This form of contact is also a stimulus to management in British industry and raises the standard of 'what is possible'. How far are these licences used to close the gap between scientific and engineering development in the two countries? The two critical factors to examine are the extent of research, and the supply of scientists and engineers.

It is difficult to get an accurate picture of the industry's expenditure on research and development, as it is often difficult to draw the line between expenditure on development and expenditure on productive equipment. Allowing a fairly wide interpretation of the term 'development', total research and development expenditure would be between $\frac{1}{4}$ and $\frac{1}{2}$ per cent. of turnover. The corresponding figure for the American industry appears to be about $\frac{3}{4}$ per cent. The absolute level of expenditure in the U.S.A. is thus at least fifteen times greater. This does not mean, however, that the Americans do fifteen times as much paper-making research. Because of the integration of pulp and paper mills in the U.S.A., their figure includes research on pulp; and the fact that (while the price of paper is much the same) the salaries of their research staff are two or three times as great as those of their British counterparts does not mean that they work correspondingly harder or more efficiently.

The Technical Section of the British Paper and Board Makers Association was formed after the First War, and has done valuable work in communicating technical knowledge; but the industry's Research Association was not formed until 1946. During the past ten years its income has increased from £25,000 to £80,000 p.a.; its research programme includes at least one project (morphological work on fibres) which has received world-wide attention; and it deals with many *ad hoc* requests by member-firms for technical information.

There appear to be no other institutions carrying out background research work for the British paper industry. By contrast, the American industry is backed by about a score of colleges and Government institutions, of which the foremost is the Institute of Paper Chemistry at Appleton, Wisconsin. This Institute, which serves the paper industry exclusively, has both educational and research functions. Many executives of the American paper industry have passed through the Institute, regard it as their *alma mater*, and take a personal interest in its research work. Moreover, the post-graduate Appleton course, with two years' research leading to a Ph.D. degree, is oriented strongly towards the requirements of the industry and also provides a flow of research work. The Institute, in addition, has a very strong research staff, which has completed some 2,000 sponsored research projects during the past twenty years.

The scarcity of scientists and technologists in Britain is beginning to have a serious, but not yet a critical, influence on the industry. The employment of qualified people has increased considerably during the past decade. Research in the paper industry is, however, a specialized function; and the man with an honours degree in science requires some two years' experience under senior research workers before he is qualified to lead a section. The only British institution giving a degree course in paper technology is the Manchester College of Technology, whose paper section has a capacity of ten entrants per year—a capacity which has often been under-used. In the U.S.A. there are at least ten colleges giving courses at or beyond degree level, including the Institute of Paper Chemistry. Apart from the effect of the shortage of graduate scientists, the industry also has difficulty in finding an adequate number of people with education to National Certificate standard in science, for control work in mill laboratories.

The paper industry is a long-established industry, but for the main part it has ceased to be traditional. Extensive changes in methods of production have entailed changes in methods of recruitment to the industry, in management methods, and in the outlook of management. The change in methods and the absorption of engineers and scientists into both management and advisory roles have taken time, and have not yet spread to all firms in the industry. This change, and the introduction of new machines, process control, and new types of papers, have been facilitated by the growing market. Close contact with developments in other countries has been of great benefit. Thus, both expanding markets and a decline of parochialism have been the basis of a growing transformation of an erstwhile craft industry.

Index

Printed in Great Britain by
Richard Clay and Company, Ltd.,
Bungay, Suffolk